Magic Trix

Museum Mayhem

Collect all the Magic Trix *books*

- ❑ The Witching Hour
- ❑ Flying High
- ❑ Birthday Wishes
- ☑ Museum Mayhem

Magic Trix

Museum Mayhem

Sara Grant

Illustrated by Erica-Jane Waters

Orion
Children's Books

First published in Great Britain in 2013
by Orion Children's Books
a division of the Orion Publishing Group Ltd
Orion House
5 Upper St Martin's Lane
London WC2H 9EA
An Hachette UK company

1 3 5 7 9 10 8 6 4 2

A catalogue record for this book is
available from the British Library.

ISBN 978 1 4440 0783 1

Printed in Great Britain by Clays Ltd, St Ives plc

For Chanelle Lloyd,
hoping all your wishes come true

Chapter One

With a flash of light, a puff of blue smoke and a soft *poof*, the tiny grey mouse transformed into a . . .

Trix rubbed her eyes. She must be dreaming. Her brain was whirling like a spinning top. The tiny grey mouse had been replaced by a real, live unicorn. Its spiral horn twinkled in the light of the magic classroom.

Trix had recently turned ten years old and discovered she was a witch. She hoped she never, ever got used to the magic of being magical. Trix stroked the unicorn's silky mane. The animal smelled sugary, like fairy cakes, and it was surrounded by a halo of light.

"Today's lesson will focus on transformations," Lulu said. Every week day, Trix and four other new witches gathered in the secret room in the Little Witching Primary School library. Lulu instructed them on how to use their new powers. The best and brightest witches would become fairy godmothers one day.

"Are transform-whatevers like magical makeovers?" Pippa asked, twisting the curl of her high ponytail around and around her finger.

"Transformations," Lulu corrected, "are *not* the same as makeovers."

Stella stepped away from the unicorn. "I'm not keen on animals, but I'm a star at makeovers." She pointed at Cara and Becka and whispered, "*Sparkle, glitter, shimmer, shine. No more ugly. It's make-over time.*"

A glimmer of light shot from her fingertip and exploded in a shower of pink glitter right over Cara and Becka. When the air cleared, Cara and Becka looked less like ten-year-old girls and more like film stars. Cara's low ponytail had twisted up into a sophisticated bun. Becka's hair was no longer

plaited but fluffed into a massive helmet of curls. Their school uniforms were replaced with long, shimmering gowns.

Trix wasn't sure Stella's makeovers were improvements. Cara and Becka were much prettier without the make-up.

"The transformations I'm talking about are to help you out of tricky situations, not prepare you for fashion magazines," Lulu said, and then whispered a spell in the unicorn's ear.

Poof!

The unicorn was once again a tiny grey mouse.

Lulu reached down so the mouse could scamper up her arm. "Thank you, Nester," Lulu said to the mouse, who curled up like an ornament on Lulu's witch's hat. "Transforming living, breathing creatures is very advanced. The practice dates back to Cinderella's fairy godmother, who turned mice into horses and pumpkins into carriages. Today we will start with something simple." She whispered a spell and pointed at the ceiling, moving her finger in a curlicue pattern which set the bangles on her wrist jingle-jangling. Fluffy white clouds appeared overhead. "We will turn rain to snow," Lulu told her witches-in-training.

Maybe it was the magic sparking in the room around her, but Trix's nose twitched and then itched. She rubbed her nose but it still felt tingly, as if she were going to sneeze. Oh, no, she couldn't be getting ill. Her family and her best friend Holly had plans to go to the Natural History Museum in London tomorrow. She couldn't wait to see all the museum's weird and wonderful creatures – especially the dinosaurs!

"With a little help from your familiars," Lulu continued, "dreary rain will become glistening snow."

Familiars raced to their witches. The lavender rat named Twitch scampered over to Pippa. Tabby the cat hopped next to Cara. Sherlock the owl perched on Becka's shoulder, while Rascal, Stella's rambunctious pug, chased his curly tail near Stella's feet. Trix's familiar, a black and white kitten named Jinx, knocked his head against Trix's leg.

"The key to transformations is to imagine your outcome. So start thinking of snow as you say this simple spell." Lulu flicked her wrist and clicked her fingers and it began to rain. Fat drops poured down all around them, bouncing on the shelves of Lulu's magical ingredients and collecting in the cauldron. *"I call upon magic – and I must insist. Change the item before me from that to this."*

The girls quickly repeated Lulu's magical spell while dodging raindrops. Jinx wiggled his whiskers, which was his way of boosting Trix's magic. The raindrops changed in mid-air to glistening white snowflakes.

Trix's nose itched and twitched. Trix covered her mouth. Creeping cats, she was going to sn . . . sn . . . sneeze.

Atchoo!

Stella scooted away from Trix. "You are so disgusting," she muttered to Trix. "Keep your germs away from me."

Pippa reached into her pink handbag and handed Trix a tissue just as her nose tingled with another sneeze.

"Th . . . th . . . thanks," Trix blurted and sneezed again.

But now the delicate crystal snowflakes had become sticky green blobs. *Splat! Splat! Splat!* The girls and their familiars were getting covered with green dots.

"Magic marbles," Lulu said, and quickly conjured a lacy parasol to shield herself. "Something's gone magically amiss."

"How perfectly revolting!" Stella exclaimed, diving behind Cara and Becka. She flipped up the trailing skirts of their lovely gowns so that she was sheltered from the goo, but her friends were slowly turning a slimy green from the ooey-gooey rain.

Trix was overwhelmed by the smell of lime. She tilted her head back and stuck out her tongue to catch one green blob and then two. "Yum!" she said, licking the green blotches off her lips. "Lime jelly, my favourite!"

Trix had a sneaking suspicion that she had somehow caused the lime-green mess, but she didn't know how. She hadn't even been thinking of jelly. She had definitely been thinking of snow. Then again, she did have a gift for creating magical messes.

"Let's try to change this back to snow," Lulu said and the girls repeated the transformation spell again.

In a flash, the green in the air and on their clothes, hair and skin became soft white snow once more.

"I'm not sure what happened," Lulu said,

closing her parasol. "But my demonstration has revealed a gap in your witchy education and it must be addressed immediately."

"I agree, miss," Stella said and smoothed her perfectly straightened hair. "It's obvious that some witches can't even perform the simplest spells." She glared right at Trix. "I think Trix definitely needs some lessons on style and—"

Trix wished she could transform Stella into a nicer person – or maybe a farm animal.

"It is obvious," Lulu interrupted Stella's list of Trix's areas for improvement, "that some of you need to brush up on your people skills." Lulu directed the pointy end of her brolly right at Stella. "If you hope to be fairy godmothers one day, you will need kind hearts and giving natures. Your assignment for this weekend is to perform as many random acts of kindness as you can." Stella groaned and Lulu glared at her. "And you are not allowed to use magic in your kind acts."

Stella groaned again. "I'd rather learn transformations," she muttered.

Trix felt as giddy as she did on Christmas Day when it was time to open presents. Tomorrow she'd have the perfect place to be randomly kind. She was travelling to London and visiting the Natural History Museum – surely there would be millions of people to help in the big city.

But Trix never could have guessed that her random acts would turn out to be more dangerous than a T-Rex.

Chapter Two

If Trix's excitement were ice cream, it would fill the Atlantic Ocean. She was on a train to London! "I want to see the dinosaurs and the Wildlife Garden and the big blue whale and the . . ." she continued to list nearly everything she'd seen on the museum website.

"I don't want to see any creepy-crawlies," Holly said as they bounced in their seats like rubber ducks on a sea of fizzy lemonade. "Can we please visit the gift shop? I love a gift shop!"

Trix's little brother Oscar popped up from the seat behind them. He must have been hiding there since they'd left Little Witching. "You two belong in a museum," he said. "You'd be in the stupid and ugly exhibition!" Oscar clutched his sides, laughing.

"Oh, go away and leave us alone," Trix muttered so their parents couldn't hear her.

Oscar hopped up on his seat and grabbed for the luggage rack above. "Look! I bet I could do six million pull-ups. Or maybe I could fit up there!" Oscar hauled himself up.

Mum and Dad were sitting a few rows ahead. Mum was reading the glossy magazine that she always kept in her massive handbag. "Oscar, stop it this instant!" she said without even glancing up.

Oscar dropped back down to the floor and swiped Trix's green, draw-string rucksack. He swung it over his head before Dad snatched it and returned it to Trix.

"Oscar, why don't you come and sit with me?" Dad said and scooted over to make room for Oscar next to him.

"Spending all day with Oscar the Horrible is worse than diving into a swimming pool of slime," Trix whispered to Holly.

"Filled with frogs," Holly added with a giggle.

"And sprinkled with toenails," Trix finished and the girls squealed in disgust.

Meow!

That had to be Jinx. Only witches could see and hear him. Lulu had cast a spell to make him invisible. Trix wasn't allowed an ordinary cat because Dad was allergic. Jinx loved a game of hide and seek – and so did Trix – but Jinx was always the one hiding and Trix the one seeking. Where could he be? She looked under the seats and then stood on tiptoes to peer in the luggage rack.

"Are you looking for Jinx?" Holly whispered. She'd only recently found out that Trix was a witch with an invisible familiar.

Trix nodded.

"Lost your brain again, weirdo?" Oscar shouted at Trix. "It's so small you'll never find it!" He laughed hysterically.

"At least I *have* a brain," Trix called back.

"I thought your witchy homework was to perform random acts of *kindness*," Holly reminded Trix.

"Not for my brother," Trix replied through gritted teeth. "He's lucky I don't perform *planned* acts of *evil*."

Meow!

Trix spotted Jinx at last. He was batting a broken red button up and down the aisle, ducking and diving around passengers' shoes.

She smiled at Jinx and all her frustration with Oscar faded away.

The train jolted to a stop at the next station. People poured into all the empty seats and spaces, like custard covering apple crumble. Trix noticed a grey-haired lady shuffling onto the crowded train as the doors thudded shut. "Oh, dearie me," the lady mumbled. A bead of sweat trickled down her brow from her mop of silvery curls.

Now was Trix's chance for kindness.

"Excuse me!" Trix yelled as she pushed through the maze of passengers. She was jostled by the train's motion and bumped by cases and handbags. She felt as if she were running uphill through an avalanche of smelly fish, but she nudged and elbowed her way through until she was face to face with the old lady.

"Hello," Trix said and smiled the sweetest smile she could muster in the hot and stinky train. "Why don't you take my seat?"

The old lady's face changed. The wrinkles that seemed to weigh her down lifted with a smile. "Thank you, dear," she said and patted Trix's cheek. Her touch was feather-light and she smelled of the expensive perfume Trix and Holly had tested last time they went shopping with Mum.

"Follow me!" Trix said and cleared a path.

The old lady sat down in the seat next to Holly. "Thank you again," the lady said. "That was very kind of you."

Zing! The most thrilling feeling rushed through Trix. She loved the way everyone was looking at her and smiling. She'd done a good deed for one person but that good feeling appeared to have spread throughout the whole train carriage.

Trix squeezed in next to Holly and pressed herself against the window as the train rumbled towards London. She watched as the leafy trees and golden fields gave way to buildings that crunched closer together and reached higher and higher with every passing mile.

The last time she'd visited London, she'd been making a secret midnight flight on her witch's broomstick. She remembered how beautiful London had looked at night with all its twinkling lights. She wondered if London would be as magical from the ground in the daylight.

As the conductor announced that the next stop was the train's final destination, Trix's nose began to itch and twitch. She could feel a sneeze gathering momentum.

The train slowed and the buildings of London came into focus. One was shaped like a gherkin, another resembled a spike of broken glass and a third looked like the billowing sail of a pirate ship.

Trix pinched her nose with one hand and covered her mouth with the other but the sneezy feeling kept growing and growing until . . .

A . . . a . . . atchoo!

"Was that you, Trix?" Mum called. "I hope you aren't getting ill."

"I'm fine," Trix replied but her attention was drawn to the strangest sight. She blinked and blinked again. One of the buildings up

ahead had an elephant's trunk, a rabbit's ears and a cat's whiskers. How did they make buildings like *that*?

Another sneeze rushed over her like a rocket. The feeling and the sneeze came in one big whoosh!

Atchoo!

She couldn't be getting ill – not today.

The train came to a stop. Trix looked back for the mixed-up animal building but she couldn't spot it anywhere. Maybe she'd imagined it – or maybe London truly was a magical place.

Chapter Three

Trix stared up at the Natural History Museum. It looked like a mix between a cathedral, a palace and an enchanted school for mythical creatures. Trix could imagine a snowy white unicorn galloping up the steps ready for its maths test. The blue and tan building stretched from one street to the next and was surrounded by a wrought-iron fence.

"Even the outside looks wonderful," Trix said as she charged up the stone steps to the rainbow-arched entrance. She felt like a princess being admitted to a ball. "What are you waiting for? There's a lot to see!" She waved to her family who were still at the museum's gate.

Holly's red curls and frilly skirt bounced as she hopped up the steps. Trix searched for Jinx, who had disappeared again. He could magically appear here and there, but he always watched over her.

"Can you believe we're here?" Trix rushed through the entrance. She stopped dead in her tracks as she entered the Central Hall. She couldn't breathe. She was face to snout with a humongous dinosaur skeleton. It nearly spanned the length of the hall which, Trix thought, looked as long as a football pitch.

"What should we do first?" Holly asked as she opened a map of the museum and held it between her outstretched arms.

"It says here that this is a diplodocus." Trix read the sign near the dinosaur skeleton.

"This huge thing was a plant-eater and lived one hundred and fifty million years ago."

Trix's brain was overwhelmed with *WOW*.

THE DIPLODOCUS WAS
A PLANT-EATER
AND LIVED ABOUT
150 MILLION
YEARS AGO!

"That's a lot of broccoli and Brussels sprouts," Holly said, glancing up from her map.

The girls studied the map's colour-coded zones. The museum was crammed with marvellous things which seemed to be from storybooks but were really real.

"Let's start with the Wildlife Garden." Trix pointed to the spot on the map.

"Hiiii-ya!" Oscar screamed as he karate-chopped the map and burst through the ripped halves. "I've already told Mum and Dad we are seeing the meteorites first!" He jerked the two pieces of map out of Holly's hands and zoomed about waving the halves like flapping wings. Holly shrugged and picked up another museum map.

"Meteorites are just stupid space rocks," Trix called after Oscar. She didn't believe meteorites were stupid, but Oscar made her so mad she couldn't agree with him.

"Look!" Oscar said and pointed to the diplodocus sign. "This dino's named after you – *dippy!*" He ran down the hall and ducked out of sight.

"Trix, have you seen your brother?" Mum asked as she and Dad caught up. Mum dropped her rucksack, which was full of snacks, plasters, changes of clothes and everything else Mum thought might be needed on a day out in London.

Trix and Holly pointed in the direction that Oscar the Horrible had taken.

They heard someone shout, “Watch out!” followed by a *crash*!

Trix and Holly exchanged a look that said they knew Oscar was already getting into trouble.

“I’ll go,” Dad said and rushed off after Oscar.

Trix felt that horrible tingly, sneezy feeling again. Before she could stop it, a sneeze erupted. She covered her mouth in the nick of time.

Suddenly lights flashed red, blue and white. All the museum visitors looked around, searching for the source of the light show.

“What has that boy done now?” Mum muttered before turning her motherly attention to Trix. “Are you poorly?” She placed her cool hand on Trix’s forehead.

Trix twisted away. “I’m fine.” She didn’t feel ill, not in the slightest. She felt excited and eager to explore the museum.

Oscar burst through an entryway marked *Museum Shop* with Dad hot on his heels. He accidentally knocked over a sweets display and lollies of every colour exploded into the air like a glass rainbow shattering into perfect sugary pieces. Oscar skidded to a stop in front of Mum. His hair was a mess and his trousers had a fresh rip at the knee.

"Mum, we've got to see rocks first and then there's a whole room of bugs . . ." On and on Oscar went, running through the museum's exhibits and – Trix was sure – making up a few things of his own. Was there really something called a giant sloth?

Oscar was tugging on the sleeve of Mum's jacket and slowly dragging her away from the dinosaur. Dad was cleaning up after the Oscar tornado. Trix knew she had to act fast or Oscar would turn a good day into a bad one.

"Dad," Trix said, standing up straight and doing her best to look at least eleven-and-a-half years old. She nudged Holly and they both started picking up the lollies Oscar had spilled. "Can Holly and I go and explore the museum on our own?"

She and Holly automatically double-crossed their fingers for extra luck. Dad *had* to let them go on their own. Oscar would be a super-duper pest all day, and they wouldn't get to enjoy anything if he was around.

"Well, I don't know," Dad said and studied Trix and Holly. But his eyes twinkled with 'maybe'.

"Trix and I are old enough to be on our own and we'll be on our best behaviour," Holly chimed in. "We could even take your phone. Then you can call us any time or we can check in with you."

"Pretty please with sugar, sprinkles and chocolate ripple fudge on the top!" Trix begged. "Holly and I have been dreaming about seeing everything at the museum and learning remarkable stuff, and Oscar . . ." Trix didn't need to finish the sentence. Oscar was crawling on the floor and barking like a dog.

Dad sighed as he looked at Oscar. "OK." He handed Trix his phone. "You need to call your mum in an hour to check in and then meet us at the dinosaur exhibition in two hours. We'll save the best for last."

Trix wrapped Dad in the biggest hug. "Thanks, Dad! You won't regret it."

Trix put Dad's phone safely in her rucksack, grabbed Holly's hand and raced away before Dad had a chance to change his mind.

Chapter Four

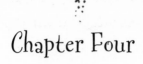

Everywhere Jinx looked there was something else equally mind-boggling. He had never been to a museum before. In a blink, he was in the tummy of a dinosaur skeleton. A second later he was staring at a display of gems from rosy pink to icy blue. And before he could say meow, he was staring up at the biggest globe he'd ever seen, which had an escalator running through it.

Trix!

He'd been so carried away with popping here and there, he'd lost sight of Trix. But it didn't matter. All he had to do was think of her and . . .

Poof!

He was at her side.

"Where have you been, you silly kitty?" Trix asked.

Jinx bowed his head and lowered his tail in apology and then brushed up against Trix. She scratched the right place behind his ear. Jinx felt his spots sparkle. That's what they always did when he was happy.

They didn't seem to be in the museum any more. He was surrounded by the buzz and hum of nature. Had they been transported from London? Jinx didn't like the hustle and bustle of the big city. There were too many wheels and feet to worry about and way too much to look at for a little cat who didn't want to miss a thing.

Jinx skipped and scampered in a crazy circle. There were trees and bushes and birds and bugs and . . .

"Do you like the museum's Wildlife Garden?" Trix asked.

Jinx nodded and nodded and nodded.

Out of the corner of his eye, Jinx saw something move. He turned in time to see a frog hop into a bed of tall reeds and a newt dart under a rock. A red and black ladybird danced in front of him and landed on the tip of his nose. It had black spots just like he did! He stared, cross-eyed, at the beautiful creature that was waving hello with its delicate wings.

"I see you've already found a friend," Trix said with a laugh.

"Is Jinx here?" Holly asked.

Jinx turned up his sparkle to maximum so that Holly could catch a glimpse of him.

"Oh!" Holly cried. "I'm not sure I'll ever get used to a magical sparkling kitten!"

Jinx was so happy that Holly could sort of see him. Trix and Holly were best friends, which meant that Holly was his best friend too!

"What should we see next?" Trix asked.

Before Jinx could decide between the bee tree and the grazing sheep, his super-sensitive ears detected the hint of a sniffle and then a whimper. He pricked up his ears. A little girl was crying. Jinx thought that was possibly the worst sound in the world and he wanted to make it stop. He dashed off and Trix and Holly followed.

There, by the pond, stood a little girl maybe half as old as Trix. Her blonde hair was braided into two plaits that trembled with each sob. Tears streamed down her rosy cheeks, dripped onto her bright pink dress and plopped onto her shiny black shoes.

"What's the matter?" Trix asked.

"I can't find my granny," the little girl said with a sniff. One of the girl's tears splatted right on

Jinx's nose. Jinx wished the girl could see him. He knew he could make her smile.

"We will help you find her," Trix promised. Another random act of kindness for Trix! Jinx was so proud. She would make a super-duper fairy godmother one day.

"What's your granny's name?" Holly asked. "If we call out to her maybe she'll find us."

The girl squinted up at Holly as if that was the silliest question she'd ever heard. "Her name is granny."

"OK," Holly said with a kind smile and Jinx could tell she was trying not to laugh.

Suddenly, Trix's nose wrinkled and her mouth opened wider and wider. The air around Jinx sizzled with magic. Was Trix going to perform a spell? She dropped her rucksack and covered her mouth as she sneezed.

Atchoo!

The sneeze ruffled Jinx's fur. That was strange.

As the rucksack hit the ground, the drawstring slipped open and out flew a dozen dragonflies.

"What are those?" the little girl cried, waving her arms to shoo the bugs away.

"Those are dragonflies," Holly explained. Jinx stood very still and one of them buzzed over and landed on his nose.

"Look," Trix pointed to the dragonfly's silvery wings and crystal blue body. "They are beautiful and they won't hurt you, I promise."

The girl looked doubtful and she leaned away. "Then why are they called DRAGON flies?"

Jinx thought that was a really good question.

"I don't know," Trix said. "But don't you wish you could fly like that?" Trix extended her arms as if she were an aeroplane and so did Holly. "Let's fly around like dragonflies and look for your granny."

Jinx liked that idea and, from the smile on the little girl's face, he could tell that she did too!

"How did those dragonflies get in your rucksack?" Holly whispered to Trix.

"I don't know how, but I bet I know who put them there," Trix replied. And then she and Holly both said in unison, "Oscar!"

But Jinx wasn't so sure. There was some funny magical business going on. He could feel it in the tingle of his whiskers.

Chapter Five

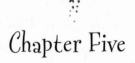

Trix, Holly, Jinx and the little girl zoomed to the information desk. With the assistance of the nice volunteers, Trix reunited the little girl with a very thankful granny. Trix beamed with the warm glow of helping others.

"What next?" Trix asked Holly as she turned the map this way and that.

"Blue Zone!" Holly said and pointed to a sign displaying a whale-shaped icon and the word *Mammals*. "The blue whale is this way!"

The girls followed the signs to the Blue Zone. Trix kept tripping over Jinx. *What is the matter with that kitty?* Trix wondered. There were so many things to inspect, but Jinx didn't even seem to notice. He just stuck right by her side.

Trix paused and crouched down to look at the duck-billed platypus. "Are you OK?" Trix whispered and gave Jinx a sneaky stroke. Jinx nodded, but his spots didn't sparkle. Trix had the strange feeling that something was wrong.

They followed the spiralling corridor past an amazing collection of animals, including a sloth, an anteater and an armadillo. Trix wouldn't have minded stopping to look but Holly kept moving forwards. Her face was flushed and her gaze was fixed straight ahead. Trix realised that Holly was a little scared. Trix had to admit that seeing all these creatures frozen in time *was* a bit creepy. With Holly and Jinx squeezing in so close, Trix found it difficult to walk in a straight line. And she was getting that tingly feeling again. This time the sneeze started at her toes and zipped through her body until it reached her nose.

A . . . a . . . atchoo!

"Are you sure you're feeling OK?" Holly asked.

Trix nodded but suddenly she wasn't so sure. She did feel a little funny.

At last they entered a massive room filled with skeletons and models of big beasts. Trix was face-to-kneecap with a giant giraffe, but that wasn't the biggest creature she could see. There was an elephant and a rhino and an even more enormous animal – a huge pink whale filled the centre of the room.

Pink?

"I thought the whale was supposed to be blue," Trix said.

"Me too," Holly replied. "Maybe the big mammal finally got some fashion sense. Pink *is* the prettiest colour."

The other museum visitors were staring wide-eyed at the whale too. That was probably what everyone did when they were faced with the largest creature on Earth.

Another sneeze sneaked up on Trix. *Atchoo!*

Gasps echoed around the room.

The big pink whale was now the big *blue* whale.

"Was that you?" Holly whispered to Trix. "Are you using your magic?"

Trix shook her head. Lulu had taught them transformations but Trix hadn't said the spell or even thought about pink or blue. "I bet it's some sort of special effect that they do with light. Red and blue make purple, right? So if they shine a red light on the . . ." – but that didn't make any sense. "Oh, I don't know. But look at this place and all these amazing creatures. The museum makes unbelievable things believable."

"Yeah, you're right," Holly said as she noticed the dolphins and prehistoric fishy skeletons suspended high above them. "If they can put a dinosaur skeleton back together then they can definitely make something change colour."

"Look at that!" Trix said and pointed to the hippo up ahead. She sneezed again and sparks burst from her fingertips. *How did I do that?* she wondered, shocked. She hadn't uttered a rhyme. She hadn't even been thinking magical thoughts! She looked around to make sure no one had noticed. Thankfully the room was nearly empty now. She clenched her hands into fists and folded her arms across her chest to make sure no more magic could accidentally escape, but how had she worked magic without meaning to?

"Trix, what's going on?" Holly whispered in her friend's ear.

Trix shrugged, unable to speak, because the hippo had just shaken its massive head, bared its mouthful of teeth, wobbled its fleshy tongue and burped!

Jinx sat at Trix's feet, staring at her with his bright yellow eyes.

"It wasn't me," Trix told Jinx right before she sneezed again.

The hippo froze with its mouth open and the creature became a model once more.

Jinx gave a loud *meow,* waved his paw and disappeared.

Trix stared in dismay at the spot where Jinx had been a second ago. How could Jinx leave her now, just when she needed him the most?

Chapter Six

Magical emergency! Jinx thought, his whiskers humming with panic. Get Lulu!

His witch was in trouble. Trix's magic was out of control, and Jinx knew the only person who could help was Lulu. He'd popped straight from the museum to the place where he'd thought Lulu might be – Magic Mansion.

The spooky old house on the top of Witching Hill was secretly the world headquarters of the Sisterhood of Magic. Most of the windows were boarded up and it looked as if it might collapse at any moment. This clever disguise ensured that no one would suspect that, inside, the mansion looked like something out of a Hollywood film.

Jinx popped directly into the grand entrance of Magic Mansion. The wooden floors gleamed in the light of a crystal chandelier and the white marble staircase swept upwards in a graceful arc. It was lined with portraits of fairy godmothers throughout the ages – including the most famous of them all, Cinderella's fairy godmother.

"What do you wish?" The room seemed to speak to Jinx. The air in front of him shimmered and a young lady materialised right before his eyes. She was older than Trix but younger than Lulu. Jinx was not a very good judge of age because it didn't matter to him. Jinx judged people on their niceness, not their age.

"My name is Twinkle Star and I'm the hostess of Magic Mansion." Her voice was like the sweetest song Jinx had ever heard. She wore a golden hooded

cape that seemed to be made out of sunshine and she carried a magic wand with a star on the top. Jinx knew immediately that on the niceness scale she was beyond measure.

"What is your wish, Jinx Jingle Jangle?" Twinkle asked.

With a flick of his tail, Jinx wrote the word 'Lulu' in the air. It was one of the only words he could spell. The word glimmered like a firework before fizzling out.

"Let me see if I can find her," Twinkle said and

waved her wand. Sparks flew from the tip and travelled throughout the mansion and back again. "I'm sorry, Jinx," Twinkle said with a sigh, "but Lulu is not at Magic Mansion. I could—"

But before she could finish her sentence, Jinx disappeared from the mansion and reappeared in the magic classroom. He raced around, searching high and low for Lulu. He even peeked behind Lulu's bookcase, which was packed with magical ingredients, and in the wardrobe stuffed with enchanted bits and bobs.

Where could Lulu be?

Jinx had one more idea for how to find her. He shut his eyes tightly, wiggled his whiskers and wished with all his might and magic for Lulu. He thought of her silvery curls and her jangling bracelets. He imagined her in the lacy black gown she wore with the matching witch's hat.

Then he felt the tingle of transportation and a cool rush of air. His fur was damp and he felt weightless. He waved his paws and realised that he was floating. He opened one eye and then the other.

He was bouncing on a white, fluffy cloud. Up ahead he spotted two figures. At first he thought they might be birds, but they were not exactly flying. They were springing into the air as if propelled from a trampoline. They somersaulted and landed with a bounce on a nearby cloud.

His spots sparkled. Lulu and Trix's Aunt Belle were cloud-hopping!

Jinx leaped into the air, whirling and twirling to get their attention.

"Jinx!" Lulu shouted. But her smile faded as she and Aunt Belle catapulted off a cloud and landed right next to him. "Magic marbles, what's the matter?" Lulu asked, knowing immediately that something was wrong.

"Is it Trix?" Aunt Belle demanded anxiously.

Jinx nodded. In a flash, he used his magical connection with Lulu and told her everything.

"Trix needs our help," Lulu explained to Aunt Belle. "There's no time to lose!"

Chapter Seven

Trix sneezed again and again.

The skeletons above rattled and Trix and Holly ducked in the nick of time as the elephant's trunk swung towards them. The museum's other visitors clapped and cheered, amazed at what they thought were the museum's special effects, but Trix was terrified. She didn't know how, but her sneezes were unleashing her powers. And a room full of the world's biggest beasts was a dangerous place for runaway magic.

"We've got to get out of here!" Trix said, hooking her arm through Holly's. Trix dragged Holly through a maze of mammals, which appeared to be momentarily coming to life as they passed.

"What are you doing?" Holly asked as she stumbled along beside Trix. "I want to stay and see the show."

"That's no show." Trix tugged Holly onwards. "Something's wrong with my magic. I think my sneezes are making all the animals come alive somehow!"

Dolphins appeared to swim through the air and Trix noticed that the wires keeping them suspended high above were starting to strain.

Holly's eyebrows arched in surprise. "You mean you can't control your magic?"

Trix nodded. She was getting that sneezy feeling again.

Now Holly ran, pulling Trix behind *her*. "We've got to get you somewhere safe."

But that wasn't going to be easy. The

corridor was lined with snapping alligators, hairy spiders, slithering snakes and too many creepy-crawlies to name.

Trix's nose began to tingle. She rubbed it hard and scrunched up her face but she couldn't stop the sneeze.

Atchoo!

As they raced through the Central Hall, one of the dinosaurs smiled at them. Trix sneezed again as they passed a special woolly mammoth exhibit. The beast's long tusks were instantly covered in purple polka dots!

"Oh, Trix!" Holly gasped as she dodged creatures that had been extinct for thousands of years. "Stop sneezing!"

Every room and passageway held another possible threat. Trix pinched her nose shut but she could feel a sneeze rattling around inside her. Her fingertips buzzed with magic.

They raced up an escalator that rose through a gigantic metal sculpture of Planet Earth. The crowd thinned as they zoomed through the exhibits. They passed a dusty old car and raced under a bright red arch. She needed to reach a place where she couldn't do herself – or anyone else – any harm.

"In here!" Holly shouted and pointed to a room marked with Japanese letters and the words *Kobe Supermarket.*

"Perfect," Trix agreed. What could go wrong in here? The bright yellow room was lined with shelves full of everyday household products. On closer inspection, Trix realised that everything was Japanese. *Why does the Natural History Museum have a Japanese supermarket exhibit?* she wondered, but she couldn't worry about that now. Her nose tingled and she couldn't keep the sneeze in any longer.

Aaatchoooooooooooooooooo!

Lights flashed and the room rocked from side to side. Holly screamed. Metal pans clanked. Shopping trollies banged together. The TV screens around the room faded to black and white static.

"Trix, make it stop, *please*!" Holly whimpered. The girls huddled close to keep from falling as the room rattled, clanked and quaked.

A little boy about Oscar's age raced in.

Trix lunged between him and the shelves to protect him from falling debris.

"Cut it out!" The boy shouted. He spread his arms and legs out wide. "I've done this ten times. Isn't it great?"

"Done what?" Trix asked as the room slowly stopped shaking.

"The earthquake room, dumbie," he said, and pointed to one of the TV screens which now showed footage of a real earthquake and gave facts about each phase of the natural disaster. "The room simulates the 1995 earthquake that happened in Kobe in Japan." With the earthquake now over, the boy exited as quickly as he had arrived.

Trix noticed the orange banners overhead that declared 'a disaster nobody could imagine'. Maybe she was wrong. Maybe she hadn't caused chaos at the museum. Trix laughed.

"What's so funny?" Holly asked.

"It wasn't me," Trix said. "It's part of the museum's special effects."

The lights blinked and the earthquake

started again. The girls clutched each other, but not in fear this time. They were falling about in a burst of uncontrollable laughter.

"What's that?" Holly asked as a glittery funnel materialised in the corner of the room.

"Maybe it's a simulated tornado," Trix said. But her laughter stopped as the whirling tornado headed straight for them. Their clothes twisted on their bodies with the force of it and their hair was whipped straight up in the air.

Trix hugged Holly and Holly hugged Trix right back as the shimmering tornado wrapped them in the biggest, most blustery hug of all.

"Creeping cats!" Trix shouted over the roar of the wind. This wasn't any special effect, this was magic!

Chapter Eight

Holly started screaming and didn't stop until the tornado had set them down on solid ground and the wind had fizzled to a gentle breeze.

"It's all right," Trix told Holly as she released her from a tight bear-hug. "Isn't it?" she asked Lulu and Aunt Belle, who were standing right in front of her.

Lulu and Aunt Belle?

Trix rubbed her eyes and looked again. What were they doing here? Then she realised that she wasn't in the Natural History Museum any more. She was standing in the middle of the magic classroom in her school library, and the expressions on Lulu and Aunt Belle's faces could have been on display at the World's Biggest Worriers Museum.

Jinx leaped into Trix's arms and she cuddled him close, but his black and white spots didn't sparkle. They didn't even twinkle. Something was definitely wrong.

"Jinx thinks there might be something a bit haywire with your magic," Lulu said as she circled Trix, looking her up and down. "Have you noticed any neon yellow bumps on your skin?"

Trix shook her head.

"Holly, has Trix's aura blinked either cyan or fuchsia?" Aunt Belle asked.

"Um, I don't think so," Holly replied, studying the air around Trix.

Lulu sniffed Trix's head. "Your hair doesn't smell like peppermint." She leaned down so she was nose-to-nose with Trix. "The whites of your eyes are still white. Stick out your tongue." Lulu took a step back as Trix

opened her mouth as wide as it would go and extended her tongue. "Hmmm," Lulu murmured.

"Wa es ee?" Trix tried to ask as Aunt Belle, Holly and Jinx inspected her tongue.

"Do those lumps look more like the sea floor of the Arctic Ocean or the sand dunes of the Sahara Desert?" Lulu asked.

Trix wiggled her tongue left and then right and went a bit cross-eyed trying to see it for herself.

"They look like normal taste buds to me," Holly said, but the look in her eyes said she was scared. And that made Trix's fear factor increase beyond spiders, snakes or even man-eating lava monsters.

"Can you use your magic to change this rock," Aunt Belle opened her hand to reveal an average, ordinary pebble, "into a bar of chocolate?"

Trix slurped her tongue back into her mouth. If there was ever a time for chocolate, this was it! Her concentration zoomed in on the rock. She thought of all the chocolate she'd ever eaten, from the two big milk chocolate eggs she ate each Easter to the Smarties she'd sneaked from the kitchen that morning before they'd left to catch the train. She whispered the transformation spell Lulu had taught her yesterday. The rock sputtered and sparked. Trix even thought she saw its colour shift from granite grey to a milk-chocolate brown, but the rock remained a rock. Her shoulders slumped.

"Maybe that was too advanced," Lulu said. She plucked the stone from Aunt Belle's hand and pinched it between her thumb and finger. "Try the disappearing spell you used in our first magic lesson."

Trix nodded.

"Remember to concentrate," Aunt Belle added.

"*Little rock, I am sincere,*" Trix said the rhyme she knew well, but it didn't trip off her tongue like it usually did. "*I want to see you disappear.*"

Trix glared at the rock, but it remained completely *visible*.

"What's wrong with me?" Trix cried, and a terrible thought entered her mind. *What if I've lost my magical abilities?* She was too scared to even say that thought out loud for fear it might come true.

"I know what we need," Aunt Belle said. She cast a spell and a chocolate bar the size of Jinx magically appeared in her hand.

"That's what I call a chocolate bar!" Holly said, breaking off a big piece for herself and an even bigger piece for Trix.

Trix raised the chocolate to her lips. She could smell its sweet fragrance, which normally made her stomach rumble and her mouth water. Chocolate always made her feel better if Oscar had been a pest or if she'd got into trouble for accidentally breaking Dad's favourite coffee mug, but she was sure chocolate wasn't going to help this time.

"What good is chocolate if I'm not a witch any more?" Trix said quietly.

"You are still one hundred per cent a witch," Lulu declared. "We just have to figure out what's going wrong with your magic."

Trix felt herself getting hotter and hotter. Maybe she did have a temperature. Something was definitely wrong if she didn't want to eat chocolate.

"And you'd be surprised what chocolate can cure," Aunt Belle said and took a big bite of the chocolate bar.

Trix held up her piece of chocolate. As she opened her mouth to take a bite, a sneeze burst out. Just a little one. She watched in horror as the chocolate melted and dripped to the floor and then turned into a purple puddle of cough syrup.

Trix shrieked. Her fingernails were flashing a rainbow array of colours like the lights on the video games at the arcade. "What's happening to me?"

"I don't know," Lulu said in her most serious voice. With a flick of her wrist and a click of her fingers, she was suddenly sitting astride her broom. "But I know who can find out."

"Who?" Trix demanded.

"Who?" Holly asked.

"Who?" Aunt Belle echoed. They sounded like a room full of owls.

"The witch doctor," Lulu said and blasted off through a glowing portal that had magically opened in the ceiling. "I'll be right back!"

Chapter Nine

Trix checked her big green watch. Lulu had been gone for five minutes, but it felt like longer – almost as long as the final minutes before the last school bell.

"Oh, no!" Holly said, grabbing Trix's wrist to double-check the time. "I almost forgot. We're supposed to call your mum right now! If we don't, she'll be worried and we'll be in big trouble." She fished around in Trix's rucksack until she found Dad's phone.

Trix slumped to the floor. Her fingernails had stopped changing colours, but now her body was covered in thin purple stripes. What did it matter if she got into trouble? She couldn't go home looking like this. Her body felt heavy with sadness.

Jinx crawled over and curled up on Trix's lap. He wiggled his whiskers like he always did when he gave Trix a magical boost. Her body felt as if she were being tickled all over, but she didn't have the energy to laugh.

"Thanks, Jinx," Trix whispered in her familiar's ear. "Whatever I've got is bigger than the both of us."

Holly thrust the phone at Trix, who shrugged it away.

Aunt Belle leaned down next to Trix. "Don't give up. That's not what we Trixibelles do." Aunt Belle and Trix shared the same first name, except Trix used the first part and Belle used the last. "Let's call your mum and then we'll try another spell."

Trix knew Aunt Belle was right. She tried to smile, but her smile wasn't working. Maybe it was another symptom.

Trix dialled her mum. "Hi, Mum!" she said. "Everything is fine," she added before Mum had the chance to ask. "We are having a . . ." She wanted to say *great time*, but the words wouldn't leave her mouth. She was not having even a slightly not-horrible time. She was having the worst day of her life.

Holly snatched the phone away. "Hi, Mrs Morgan! It's Holly!" She had turned up her enthusiasm to maximum. "The museum is fun." Holly paused. "Where are we? Where are *you*?"

Holly is so smart, Trix thought. *She's the best best friend in the world.*

"You're still at the bug exhibition," Holly was saying. "Well, we're at the top floor of the Red Zone." Which wasn't a complete lie. It was the last place they had been in the museum. "Yes, we'll meet you back at the dinosaur exhibition in one hour." Holly quickly punched the button to end the call.

"Now, let's try a simple spell," Aunt Belle said. She grabbed a red scarf from the big wardrobe at the back of the room. "Cast a spell to change this from red to blue."

Trix thought for a long while. "*Colours of the rainbow, I call on you. Change this scarf from red to blue.*" That was a good rhyme. It tripped off her tongue. That must be a good sign.

Aunt Belle, Holly, Trix and Jinx stared at the scarf. The red stayed red.

Trix glared at the scarf. It wasn't fair. She'd only just found out she was a witch. She knew she was good at helping people and she *so* wanted to be a fairy godmother one day. She couldn't believe today had started off so wonderfully. Now it felt as if her dreams were balloons and Oscar had burst them all with a pin.

And what about Jinx? If her magic never came back, what would happen to her familiar? Would he have to go and be with another witch – a *real* witch?

It was as if Jinx knew what she was thinking. His bright yellow eyes looked deep into her big brown ones. His eyes said everything he needed to say. He was Trix's familiar and nothing would ever change that. She kissed him on his furry head and his spots twinkled for a second.

"No matter what, you are my best friend and we can still help people like we did today," Holly said. "You don't need magic powers to be kind."

"I know you're right . . ." Trix started, but she couldn't finish. She felt the rush that normally came right before tears.

"It's still stinkier than the stinkiest cheese," Holly said, sitting next to Trix.

"Stinker than the stinkiest cheese wrapped in the smelliest gym socks," Aunt Belle added, sitting on the other side of Trix.

Even though her situation hadn't improved one smidge, Trix felt a bit better having Jinx on her lap and her best friend and her favourite aunt beside her. "The stinkiest cheese wrapped in the smelliest gym socks buried in a mountain of rotten eggs!" she declared.

They all groaned at the thought of such a horrible smell and smiled the tiniest smiles.

A blast of cold air blew through the magic classroom as Lulu flew back through the portal that had opened and closed in a *whoosh*. Trix, Aunt Belle and Holly jumped to their feet. Riding on the back of Lulu's broom was a tall figure, wearing a purple star-spangled coat.

"Let me introduce," Lulu said when her broom skidded to a stop in front of them, "the best witch doctor in the cosmos."

The sparkling figure stood a foot taller than Lulu. His jet-black hair was slicked away from his face. He tugged at his ruffled shirt cuffs then produced a black, old-fashioned doctor's bag from a hidden pocket in his magnificent coat. He was handsome in a scary sort of way.

"Dr A. K. Dabra at your service," he said with a sweeping bow. "Wizard extraordinaire and healer of magical maladies!"

Chapter Ten

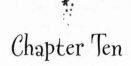

Jinx's tummy was all topsy-turvy. He danced from Trix to the strange man in the star-covered coat. He had to do something. He could see the worry in Trix's eyes and it made his whiskers droop and his tail feel limp.

Suddenly he was whisked into the air and over to Lulu. She pulled him into her arms and cradled him like a baby. Jinx could hear Lulu's heart thumping at an alarming rate, but her voice was as calm and melodious as always. "Don't worry, Jinx," Lulu said, rocking him back and forth. "Dr Dabra will take good care of our Trix. She'll soon be back to her witchy self."

Jinx wanted her to promise. She had to promise that Trix would be OK.

"I promise," Lulu said and rubbed Jinx's ears.

"Give me some room," Dr Dabra said and swirled his coat in a circle, clearing the space around him and Trix. He extended one arm over his head and grabbed a gold-tipped wand out of thin air. "There are measures for fever, pulse, heart and sound. But magical maladies appear all around!" he chanted.

He pointed his wand at Trix and a white bolt of lightning shot from the tip and circled Trix's body. Jinx covered his eyes. He couldn't watch. But he couldn't stand not knowing either. He slowly lowered his paws.

Trix was surrounded by a muddy brown halo.

"This is serious," Dr Dabra said. "A healthy witch's aura is a sparkling white or a crystal blue."

Trix's lower lip quivered. Jinx could see her bite back her fear. Trix was so brave. He squirmed in Lulu's arms. He wanted to go to Trix, to be by her side like always, but Lulu held him tightly to her chest.

"We must let Dr Dabra work his magic, Jinx," she whispered.

That's when Jinx noticed that Aunt Belle had her arms wrapped around Holly, holding her back too. Jinx looked at Holly and he knew they were thinking the same thing. They felt helpless and it hurt – maybe not as much as a vaccination or a broken bone, but standing by and watching a friend suffer was a special kind of pain.

Dr Dabra extended his arms out in front of him, palms up, little fingers touching.

Poof! A cloud of smoke enveloped his hands. When the smoke cleared, a huge book was resting on his palms.

Lulu read what was on the spine of the book to Jinx. "The Big Book of Serious Sorcerous Sickness."

The pages fluttered and the book opened.

The doctor pointed his finger at the open page. "Just as I suspected. We haven't had an outbreak of this in one hundred and sixty-seven years . . ." Dr Dabra broke off as he was interrupted by barking.

Barking?

Jinx would know that bark anywhere. He squirmed out of Lulu's arms, flipping mid-air to land on all fours, nose-to-wrinkly-nose with Rascal.

What's Rascal doing here? Jinx wondered, and then he understood, because Stella rushed into the magic classroom and sneezed the most powerful howling sneeze Jinx had ever heard. He flattened his ears to shield them from the horrible sound as the room instantly filled with thousands and thousands of butterflies.

ATCHOO!

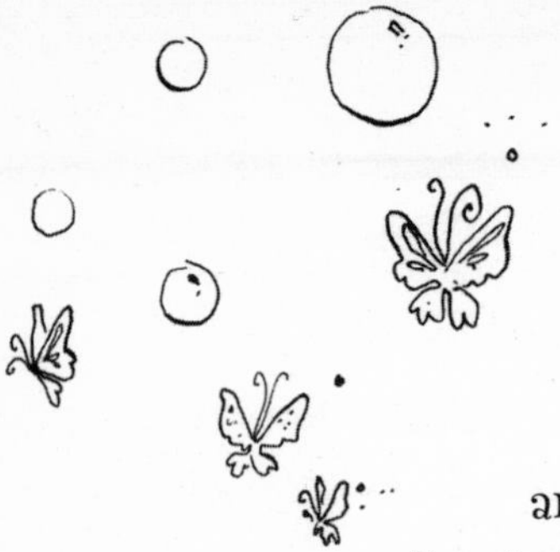

The butterflies became bouncing balls.

ATCHOO!

The balls dissolved into spaghetti that squiggled and squirmed and tangled in Jinx's fur. *He* realised the only thing he hated more than being wet was being covered in sticky spaghetti noodles.

And the only thing worse than swimming in a sea of spaghetti was the next thought that popped into his brain.

Whatever Trix had, Stella had it too!

Chapter Eleven

"Witching cough!" declared Dr A. K. Dabra after Lulu had cleared the magic classroom of spaghetti with a spell.

Trix and Stella stared at each other, wide-eyed. Stella's hair was sticking out in all directions under her witch's hat. Instead of her perfectly pressed Enchanted Grove School for Girls uniform, she wore a pink designer tracksuit.

"W-what's w-witching cough?" Trix stammered.

"Is it serious?" Stella asked and tried to flip her hair, but her hair wouldn't flip. She gasped.

"There is a cure, but it will take me a little time to find the ingredients and mix up the remedy," Dr Dabra said. "Until then, we need to quarantine you to keep the ailment from spreading."

"Quarantine?" Stella asked. "That sounds painful."

"It's not painful," Aunt Belle replied. "It just means the two of you will be put somewhere together away from everyone else."

"*Me* with *her*?" Stella screeched.

"*Me* with *her*?" Trix shrieked. Suddenly the cure for witching cough seemed more painful than the disease.

Trix and Stella bolted in different directions. The doctor raised his hands in a wide V and the girls froze mid-stride. Trix's brain screamed at her body to move but her muscles didn't listen.

Dr Dabra pointed to Trix and Stella as he chanted, "*Trix and Stella are having sickly*

trouble. Keep them safe in a protective bubble!"

Kerplop!

Trix and Stella were dropped into two big comfy beds with mounds of fluffy pillows. Being stuck in a big bubble with Stella was beyond Trix's worst nightmare. Trix touched the transparent wall. A force pushed her hand away.

"I don't know what's worse," Stella whined, placing her hat on the bedpost and smoothing her hair, "being infected with witching cough or being stuck with you. I hope I can't catch your lousy fashion sense or bad hair."

Trix looked down at her pale blue sweater with the cat on the front and her favourite checked skirt. Sure, the checks on her skirt clashed with the stripes on her skin, but she didn't look that bad. At least her curly hair was still curly. She wouldn't let Stella make her feel worse than she already did.

“This is all your fault,” Stella hissed. “I bet you gave this to me. Why do I always have to be the one to suffer?”

“Please let me out of here!” Trix begged.

“Sorry, girls,” Dr Dabra said. “Once the stripes expand to cover your bodies there’s nothing I can do, so we must act fast.”

The purple lines on Trix’s skin were getting fatter. “What do you mean, there’s nothing you can do?” Panic gurgled in Trix’s gut.

“Well, if you turn completely purple before I can administer my potion, then we will have to wait it out.”

“What?” Trix and Stella shouted in unison.

“It can take up to a month to get over witching cough,” Dr Dabra stated. “The good news is – you will fully recover.”

Trix thought she would never recover from a month trapped with Stella.

“Why don’t you girls get some rest?” Lulu said. “We will help Dr Dabra collect his ingredients.”

Dr Dabra held up a scroll and, with a flip, unrolled it. The paper stretched from one end of the magic classroom to the other. "Here's my ingredient list!"

Trix was getting very tired. Her brain felt fuzzy. Dr Dabra needed to hurry – not only because her purple stripes were getting thicker by the minute, but also because she had less than an hour before she needed to meet her parents. If she missed the meeting, she might be quarantined for a month but she'd be *grounded* for ever.

Trix heard sniffing coming from Stella's bed. She curled her body into a ball and prepared for another sneeze and more misguided magic. But then Trix heard another sniff, and another. She turned ever so slightly and peered over the pile of pillows in Stella's direction.

Stella wasn't about to sneeze. She was crying. She must be as exhausted and as scared as Trix.

This was the biggest test of Trix's fairy godmotherly skills ever. When Lulu had asked them to perform random acts of kindness, Trix had never in a million years imagined that she'd have to be nice to Stella. But she knew she had to do it.

"We're going to be OK," Trix assured Stella. "Look how hard everyone is working."

The magic classroom was a blur of activity. Everyone, including Jinx and Rascal, was collecting ingredients for Dr Dabra's remedy.

Stella looked up. One tiny Stella-perfect tear leaked from her eye.

"It could be worse," Trix said.

"How could it be worse?" Stella moaned. "I'm starting to get stripy too!"

Stella's stripes weren't purple, they were a muddy green.

"Even if the doctor can't make his medicine in time to stop the stripes, you won't be green for ever," Trix told her.

"I know," Stella cried.

"Why don't we try to be nice to each other until our skin changes back to its normal colour? Deal?" Trix asked.

Stella pursed her lips and thought for a moment. "Deal," she agreed, but then she burst into tears.

"What's the matter now?" Trix asked – and tried not to roll her eyes because a deal was a deal.

"At least you're a nice shade of purple," Stella whined. "My stripes clash with my shoes."

Stella was right. The gruesome green stripes on her skin did create an eye-wateringly bad combination with her pale pink designer tracksuit and matching shoes.

Trix crossed her fingers and lied, "I like that shade of green. I think I saw it on the cover of one of those fashion magazines."

"Really?" Stella sniffed.

Trix nodded.

"Thanks, Trix," Stella said and rolled over in her bed, away from Trix. "I know you are fibbing, but that was a very nice thing to say. You will make a great fairy godmother one day."

Trix must be really sick if Stella was complimenting her. She felt the tiniest twinge of friendship for Stella. Maybe witching cough could make friends out of enemies.

Chapter Twelve

"I must measure this ingredient out very carefully," Dr Dabra said as he held up a cone-shaped scoop. "Half a nostdram of unicorn tears." He used a solid gold eye-dropper to drip silvery goo into the measuring scoop one drop at a time.

"Nostra-what?" Holly asked.

"It's a witchy measurement," Lulu said as she walked over to the bookcase.

“Here are the petals from an Arctic poppy,” Aunt Belle said, rushing over with a handful of bright red petals.

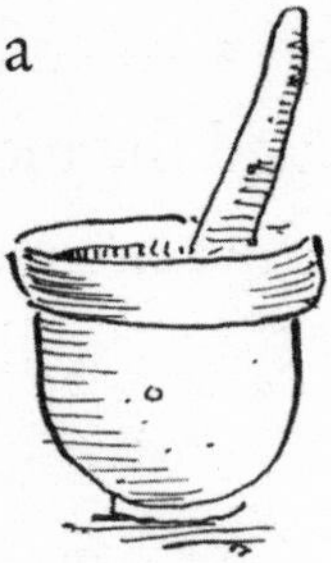

“Crush those into a fine powder with a mortar and pestle,” Dr Dabra ordered.

Lulu searched the jars on her bookcase. “I’ve got plenty of milk from a sleeping zebra,” she called to the doctor and checked the item off his long list. “And here’s sludge from the deepest sea.” She held up a jar, which sloshed with muddy water.

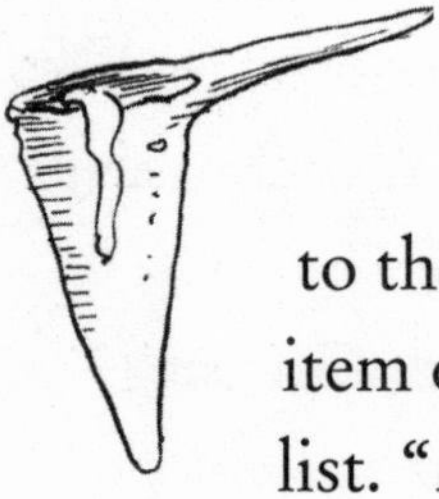

“Can you find scrapings from a walrus tooth

and crumbs from a one-hundred-year-old Christmas pudding?" Dr Dabra asked as he tipped the measured tears into the cauldron in the centre of the magic classroom.

"Ew!" Stella squealed. "I hope we don't have to drink that."

"Pinch your nose, swallow it fast and eat loads of chocolate afterwards," Trix told Stella, but her tummy was churning at the thought of scrapings, crumbs and tears. *Why can't witch medicine be made of tasty things like sweets and lemonade?*

"Do you always have to be so cheerful?" Stella groaned.

Trix knew Stella wasn't really asking her that question but she decided to answer it anyway. "Being cheerful is way better than being miserable," Trix said, wondering if Stella realised she was hinting at Stella's constantly bad mood.

Stella moaned.

"Are you feeling worse, dear?" Lulu called.

"No, miss," Stella said and buried her head under a mountain of pillows. "You are so good it makes my teeth ache," she mumbled to Trix.

"Don't you think it's easier to be nice?" Trix asked.

"I think it's exhausting!" Stella dramatically draped her arm over her pillow-covered head.

Trix was surprised by Stella's comment. She thought everyone was nice and had to try to be mean, but what if some people were mean and had to try to be nice? She hoped Stella's negativity wasn't contagious.

Meow!

Woof!

Jinx and Rascal jumped up and touched their noses to the transparent walls of the quarantine. The girls knelt in front of their familiars and pressed their palms against the invisible barrier.

"I miss Rascal already," Stella sighed. "Look at those soft furry wrinkles. I know at first I wanted a kitten," she went on, and then her voice changed to the high-pitched tone that mums sometimes use with babies, "but Rascal is perfect-werfect. Aren't you, boy?"

Rascal wagged and wagged his tail. *Woof! Woof!*

"We won't be in here for ever," Trix said, giving Jinx a wink. Jinx winked back. "We might get to miss school."

"But you'd be completely purple and I'd be green!" Stella exclaimed.

"I've never been purple before," Trix said and noticed that her stripes were getting thicker and thicker. Dr Dabra had better hurry. She might not mind being purple but she would mind not getting to go home. She wondered if she might even miss Oscar.

Holly raced over and shouted in a too-loud voice, “Only a few more ingredients to go.”

“We can hear you, silly,” Stella said. “There’s no need to shout. The wall is made of magic, not concrete.” Stella walked over and sat on her bed facing away from Trix and Holly.

“Does she have a case of the grumps as well as witching cough?” Holly whispered to Trix.

Trix tried not to laugh. “She’s upset, that’s all.” Trix leaned her body against the invisible barrier and it pinged her back into bed.

The doctor *um*-ed and *ah*-ed. Thick, blackish-brown bubbles frothed over the edge of the cauldron. The doctor scrolled through his long list of ingredients.

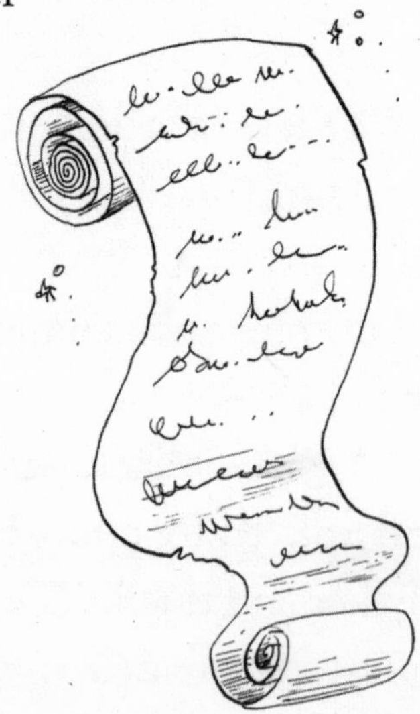

"Oh, no!" Dr Dabra cried.

Lulu, Aunt Belle and Holly rushed to his side. Jinx and Rascal scampered back and forth between the cauldron and the quarantine, unsure what to do. Trix and Stella pressed their faces against the transparent wall.

"What's the matter?" Trix asked.

"The final ingredient." The doctor removed an empty jar from Lulu's bookcase, but Trix couldn't see what was written on the label. "We need a pinch of space dust and Lulu is all out."

"That can't be!" Lulu shook the jar.

"It takes a special requisition from the Sisterhood of Magic and a note from the National Association of Space Exploration to get even a gram of space dust!" Aunt Belle said. "There's no way we'll get more dust in time."

"Argh!" Stella moaned and flung herself on the bed. "Why do bad things happen to good, glamorous people?"

Witching cough. Quarantine. And now

no remedy. That meant a whole month stuck with Stella! Trix didn't like to admit it, but her cheerfulness had dissolved like a sandcastle in a thunderstorm.

Chapter Thirteen

Now Trix's skin was purple with thin, flesh-coloured stripes, and Stella was looking greener and grimmer by the minute. The girls reclined on their beds, but Trix couldn't rest.

Think, brain, think!

"Try to keep a positive attitude," Aunt Belle said as she paced the perimeter of Trix and Stella's bubble. "We'll think of something."

The cauldron kept right on boiling and a sour smoke filled the room. Trix was beginning to wish the walls of her quarantine weren't quite so transparent.

Dr Dabra flipped through books while Lulu inspected every single jar on her bookcase. Jinx was helping Rascal, who appeared to be trying to sniff out even a speck or two of space dust. Holly was twirling curl after curl around her finger. Trix knew that's what her best friend did when she felt frustrated.

"Space. Face. Race. Lace. Case. Base." Trix found that rhyming sometimes helped to dislodge ideas. "Space dust. Must. Rust. Fust. Zust. Zest. Pest."

Wait, an idea was brewing like the potion in Lulu's cauldron . . .

Pest – that word reminded her of Oscar. And Oscar reminded her of meteorites. And meteorites reminded her of . . .

"Eureka!" Trix yelled and sat bolt upright in her bed. All eyes zoomed in on her.

"Eureka?" Stella said. "Really? What are you, one hundred years old?"

Trix didn't know why she'd said it, but it was definitely the right word for her discovery. "I know where we can get space dust," she said and bounced off the bed. "The Natural History Museum in London!"

"Her brain has turned to mush," Stella muttered and lay back down. "Is that the next phase of witching cough – downright crazy? There's only dinosaur bones and old dead stuff at that museum."

"No, Trix is right," Holly said and pulled the map out of Trix's rucksack. "Oscar said he wanted to see meteorites. Where are they?" Holly spread out the map on the floor and everyone gathered round. Jinx sat on one corner and Rascal on the other.

Trix suddenly felt a teeny tiny bit better. It was funny how hope could do that to you. She was still growing more grape-like by the minute, but inside she felt more lavender.

Lulu drew an oval in front of her as if she were tracing a mirror. She chanted, "*Open a window and show me the place.*" The air in Lulu's oval turned a watery silver. "*Natural*

History Museum. Rock from space." It sounded as if she were giving an address.

The air turned into a window. On the other side was a rock in a clear glass box.

A quarantined rock, thought Trix.

People were passing by the display and taking pictures of what looked like an average brown boulder.

"Are you sure that's the meteorite?" Stella asked. "I thought a space rock would be more sparkly, like a star."

Lulu pointed to the sign below the rock and enlarged the image. "The Cranbourne Meteorite," Trix read aloud. She couldn't believe it. This rock had fallen from the sky and landed in Australia. And even though it didn't look it, the sign said it weighed three and a half tonnes – the same as four cars – and was about one hundred and fifty million years older than Earth. And what was even better, this heavy old rock was going to save her and Stella.

"Where is it in the museum?" Lulu looked at Trix and then Holly. They both shrugged. *Shame on us for not wanting to see it because of Oscar.*

Jinx pointed his paw to the Red Zone.

"Jinx, you clever kitten," Lulu said and erased her magical window with the same motion she'd use to clean a chalk board. "All we need is a plan."

"Well, we can't go looking like this," Trix said. "And how will we get past security and inside that display case?"

Jinx bounded around the map and

scratched at the corner then jumped right into Holly's arms, spots sparkling.

"OK, Jinx!" Lulu said, patting the kitten and Holly on their heads. "Jinx and Holly to the rescue!"

"Me?" Holly said and blushed so that her skin looked only a few shades lighter than Trix's.

"Here's the plan!" Lulu wrapped Holly and Jinx in a hug and whispered in their ears. Girl and kitten nodded.

"You mean my future rests in the hands of a kitten and a plain old ordinary human?" Stella groaned.

"No," Trix replied. "Your future rests in the hands of the world's most brilliant familiar and the best friend in the entire galaxy!"

And with a flick of Lulu's bangle-filled wrist and a click of her oh-so-magical fingers, Holly and Jinx vanished.

Chapter Fourteen

Jinx's claws tip-tapped with excitement against the tiled floor. *He* and Holly were hiding behind the display case that contained the meteorite. The room was full of funny mismatched items – a big square rock, pots and pans and a pallet of fizzy drinks cans. The walls were covered with colourful pictures and illustrations and lots and lots of words that Jinx couldn't read.

Holly was going to stand guard and distract

anyone who came along while Jinx completed his super-important mission.

"Are you ready?" Holly asked and checked her watch. "We have five minutes before Lulu will transport us back."

Jinx shook his head, but not because he wasn't ready to save Trix and, he supposed, Stella – even if she was mean sometimes. He shook his head because Lulu had given him the most fantastic gift he had ever received – a bright white collar with beautiful glittering gems. He loved the collar, but it felt strange around his neck and he was still getting used to it.

Being beautiful was not the collar's only purpose. It also allowed Holly to see where he was. It had a special star-shaped scoop for collecting the space dust and it acted as what Lulu called a 'transmitter'. That was a new word, and Jinx knew it meant that the collar gave out a signal so that Lulu could easily find him with her magic.

Jinx and Holly peeked out of their hiding place. The room was nearly empty.

"Now," Holly whispered and Jinx magically popped into the glass box that contained the meteorite.

The space rock smelled funny – like dirt, metal and musty old attics. The display lights heated up the space. He didn't like the feeling of being trapped and on display. He wondered if it was what goldfish felt like in aquariums. It must be what Trix was feeling being quarantined – but it was much worse for Trix because she was stuck with Stella.

Focus, Jinx! he scolded himself. His thoughts were like bouncing balls sometimes. He'd catch one and think about it for a while and then be distracted by another. He mostly loved that about his brain. He could curl up on Trix's comfy bed for hours and let one thought boing into another and bing into another and on and on . . .

Tap! Tap! Tap!

Holly was tapping on the display glass and pointing to her watch.

Yes, it is time for Super Jinx to get busy, Jinx thought. He extended his front claws and admired their needle-fine points. They were the perfect tool for the job. He scratched and scratched at the rock. He was probably the only cat with a three-tonne space rock for a scratching post. The rock was hard, but little by little meteorite flakes gathered on the floor of the cabinet in front of Jinx.

ATCHOO!

Jinx dived behind the rock. That was Holly's signal that someone was coming. Jinx peeked from behind the rock and watched a pack of young kids press their noses against the glass.

"Hey, what's that?" A little girl pointed at Jinx, who was invisible to non-witches except for his collar.

"Oh, that's nothing," Holly said. "It's just a monitoring device for the exhibit." Her face was getting redder and redder by the minute as if she were a meteor burning through the Earth's atmosphere. "Move along. The exhibition will be clo— OH!" Holly ducked behind the display.

What is wrong with her? Jinx wondered.

"Drat and double drat!" Holly muttered.

Then Jinx saw what was making Holly act so strangely.

Mum, Dad and Oscar were heading this way. Oscar looked like an octopus, with his legs scrambling this way and that and his hands grabbing for anything he spotted.

With a wiggle of his whiskers, the space dust swirled in the air and deposited itself in the tiny star scoop on Jinx's collar.

"There it is!" Oscar shouted and pointed right at the meteorite and Jinx. "We finally found it."

Just as Oscar lunged his grubby little fingers in Jinx's direction, Jinx magicked himself next to Holly and then the air around them sizzled and fizzled and pop, pop, POPPED!

The moment his paws touched the floor of the

magic classroom, Jinx sprang up again. As he arched over the cauldron, he dumped the space dust into the bubbling goo. He landed with a tumble and a roll. Lulu, Aunt Belle, Holly and Stella applauded, Rascal barked his thanks and Trix cheered the loudest of all.

Jinx raced over to get as close as he could to Trix. He loved to be near her. She made him feel as if he were the best and brightest familiar in the universe. He rubbed up against the invisible quarantine barrier. Trix was almost completely purple now, and the whites of her eyes had turned a watery orange. She smiled weakly at him.

"Thanks," she whispered and reached out as if to touch him.

Dr Dabra gave the cauldron one final stir. The contents glowed and swirled around the room in thick ribbons of shimmering light. The whole room seemed to vibrate as the ribbons wrapped themselves around Trix and Stella, then, with a whoosh, the ribbons disappeared.

Jinx looked at Trix.

Trix looked at Jinx.

Their wide eyes asked the same question: did the remedy work?

Chapter Fifteen

Trix thought she felt different. Lulu, Aunt Belle, Holly, Jinx and Rascal stood in a line outside the invisible barrier.

She desperately wanted to be on the outside with them looking in. She hoped her magic was working again. She focused on a spot behind the others and wished and hoped and prayed before she said her spell. Then, with all her magical might, she tried to move from here to there.

Nothing happened.

Trix's eyes flooded with tears. The remedy had come too late! But she would not cry – not when everyone had worked so hard to make her better.

"Let me try," Stella said and stepped to the centre of the quarantined area. "*Sparkle, glitter, shimmer, shine. Once again let us look fine.*" A glimmer of light shot from Stella's fingertip as she first pointed to herself and then to Trix.

A cold shiver snaked over Trix's body.

Everyone clapped! Trix knew that must be good news. She looked down at herself. Not only was her skin back to its normal colour, but also her hair was perfectly curled and her sweater was transformed into a silky purple blouse with a sequined cat on the front! Stella was wearing a frilly green dress with ruffles.

"No need to thank me," Stella said. "Purple really is your colour."

Creeping cats! If Stella was being nice to her, then she must be getting worse.

"Try your magic again," Stella said without a trace of mean or nasty in her voice.

Trix thought for a moment and then said slowly and clearly, *"Shimmer, glimmer, I've got nothing to lose. Stella and I need matching shoes!"*

Trix pointed to Stella's feet and then her own. Sparks of light fizzled at her fingertips.

And then the most spectacular thing happened – sparkly purple trainers appeared on their feet.

"My magic is back!" Trix cheered.

The walls of the quarantine dissolved. Jinx leaped into her arms and suddenly Trix and Stella were wrapped in the biggest group hug ever.

"What a wonderful team!" Lulu said

with one final squeeze. "And, Stella, congratulations on your acts of kindness towards Trix."

"I *was* particularly nice," Stella said as she smoothed her once-again perfectly straightened hair. "I mean, Trix, really, purple shoes with a green dress . . ." The rest of Stella's sentence, as well as Stella herself, faded away.

"I sent her home," Lulu explained.

Trix and Holly laughed. Trix knew one more minute and Stella would have blown her nice act with mean words.

One more minute! Trix thought and checked her watch. That's exactly the amount of time they had left to meet Mum and Dad. She didn't want to be in any more trouble today.

As if reading her mind, Lulu and Aunt Belle waved goodbye and, with a synchronised double flick of their wrists and click of their fingers, they returned Trix's clothes to normal and sent the girls and Jinx back to the dinosaur exhibition.

"Sorry we're late," Mum said as she and Dad raced to greet them. "Did you girls have a good time?"

Trix and Holly shared a smile. "You could say it was *magical*," Trix said.

Roooooaaaarrrr!

A dinosaur on the platform ahead of them swivelled its head and roared again.

Holly screamed. Trix panicked. Maybe she was still ill. She hadn't even sneezed and yet that dinosaur had come to life. Dread oozed over Trix like hot chocolate sauce over a sundae.

"Let's get out of here," Trix said. She had to save her family from her runaway magic.

"Not before I push every single one of these buttons!" Oscar yelled, jumping out from behind the dinosaur and racing through the exhibition, punching every button he saw. Dinosaurs of all shapes and sizes began to twitch and roar.

This time it wasn't Trix's magic, it was the museum's!

Trix and Holly started to giggle, and soon they were laughing so hard that they were gasping for breath.

Trix was cured and the world was back to normal. Well, as normal as it ever was when you were a witch!

The adventures continue in

Magic Trix

SECRETS AND SPIES

✶

Available January 2014

DON'T MISS IT!

The adventures began in . . .

When Trix turns ten she finds out that she's a witch! It's the best birthday present ever and Trix can't wait to start casting spells.

But learning witchcraft isn't easy, and nobody non-magical must know!

Can Trix keep the secret and use her magic to help her best friend, Holly?

Join Trix and Jinx in another magical adventure . . .

There's a big surprise in store for witch-in-training, Trix Morgan, but first she must learn to fly her own broomstick – with a little help from her magic kitten, Jinx.

There are lots of thrills and spills – will Trix ever get the hang of flying? And can she help Pippa overcome mean-girl Stella's nasty tricks?

Don't miss . . .

Parties and potions. Secrets and surprises!

Witch-in-training, Trix Morgan, is planning a surprise birthday party for her best friend, Holly. But nothing goes according to plan especially when mean-girl Stella adds a secret ingredient to Trix's magic potion . . .

CRESCENT MOON RISING

CRESCENT MOON RISING

THE ISLAMIC TRANSFORMATION OF AMERICA

PAUL L. WILLIAMS

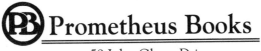

Prometheus Books
59 John Glenn Drive
Amherst, New York 14228–2119

Published 2013 by Prometheus Books

Cover design by Grace M. Conti-Zilsberger

Inquiries should be addressed to
Prometheus Books
59 John Glenn Drive
Amherst, New York 14228–2119
VOICE: 716–691–0133 • FAX: 716–691–0137
WWW.PROMETHEUSBOOKS.COM

17 16 15 14 13 • 5 4 3 2 1

Library of Congress Cataloging-in-Publication Data

Williams, Paul L., 1944–
Crescent moon rising : the islamic transformation of america / by Paul L. Williams.
p. cm.
Includes bibliographical references and index.
ISBN 978-1-61614-636-8 (pbk. : alk. paper)
ISBN 978-1-61614-637-5 (ebook)
1. Islam—United States. 2. Muslims—United States. I. Title.

BP67.U6W55 2013
297.0973—dc23

2012036326

Printed in the United States of America on acid-free paper

For Katie at the start of her new life

CONTENTS

ACKNOWLEDGMENTS

This work would have never appeared on a bookshelf without the constant support of my wonderful wife, Pat. It took five years to write, including visits to several of the "hotbeds" of radical Islam and spawning grounds of homegrown terror, including Islamberg, Red House, Dar al-Hijrah, Masjid al-Farooq, Masjid al-Taqwa, and the Gulen fortress within the heart of the Pocono Mountains. I was accompanied on these trips by intrepid companions, including Patrick Walsh, Bill Krayer, and Michael Rash. Others, including Judith Schmitt, Judy Forti, Patti May, Pitts Evans, Frank Salvato, and Dr. Hugh Cort, provided the financial, technical, and spiritual support so crucial for the investigations. I would be remiss if I neglected to express my gratitude to Barbara Johnson, my terrific agent; Mary Riggall, my good and faithful assistant; and the crew at Prometheus Books, including Steven L. Mitchell, my editor, and Jill Maxick, my publicist.

"Therefore I tell you that the kingdom of God will be taken away from you and given to a people who will produce its fruit. Anyone who falls on this stone will be broken to pieces; anyone on whom it falls will be crushed."

Matthew 21: 43–44

CHAPTER 1

THE SEA OF CHANGE

"The past is a foreign country; they do things differently there."

So begins *The Go-Between*, L. P. Hartley's classic novel.

For proof of this claim, let's journey back to 1975. The leading bestselling books of this year are *Sylvia Porter's Money Book*, E. L. Doctorow's *Ragtime*, Theodore H. White's *Breach of Faith*, and Leo Rosten's *Religions of America: Ferment and Faith in an Age of Crisis.*

The Rosten work of 672 pages represents an exhaustive compilation of statistical information on every major and minor body of believers in the country. Chapters are devoted to such Protestant denominations as the Disciples of Christ, the Seventh-Day Adventists, the Unitarian Universalists, the Jehovah's Witnesses, Presbyterianism, Lutheranism, the Baptist Movement, and every branch manifestation of Methodism. The thick volume contains abundant data concerning the three forms of Judaism (Orthodox, Conservative, and Reform); lengthy discussions about the liturgical and doctrinal differences between Greek Orthodoxy and Roman Catholicism; and authoritative explanations of the basic tenets of Mormons, Quakers, Christian Scientists, Jehovah's Witnesses, and Seventh-Day Adventists. It even presents facts and figures concerning the 5 percent of Americans who claim to be either agnostic or atheist.

In his preface, Rosten writes that this "New Guide and Almanac" represents "a massive compendium, more complete and far-ranging" than any book in print of "the statistics, public opinion polls, and basic documents which characterize religion in the United States."[1]

NO MENTION OF MUSLIMS

But the book contains no discussion of Islam as a religious factor in America. This is not an oversight. In 1975, Sunni, Shiite, and Sufi Muslims in America were statistically insignificant, numbering fewer than one thousand.

Rosten, however, does devote three pages of his text to an excursus on the Nation of Islam, noting that these so-called Black Muslims practice a form of Islam that bears no semblance to the seventh-century pronouncements of the prophet Mohammed. He writes that the Nation of Islam was founded in 1930 by W. D. Fard, who "disappeared quite mysteriously in 1934."[2] He maintains that black Muslims regard Fard "as Allah, himself, in human form" and preach a dogma in which all whites are denounced as "devils."[3] At the end of this brief discussion, Rosen dismisses the Nation of Islam as a fringe group—a sociological aberration of black culture—with a total membership of 6,000–6,500 that is destined for sociological extinction.[4]

In 1975, American sociologists continue to insist that membership within the three great bodies of Western religion (Protestantism, Catholicism, and Judaism) remain the main means of self-identification within American society. In *Protestant, Catholic, Jew,* Will Herberg first articulated this finding by writing:

> Not to be a Catholic, a Protestant, or a Jew today is, for increasing numbers of American people, not to have a *name*. . . . To have a name and an identity, one must belong somewhere; and more and more one "belongs" in America by belonging to a religious community, which tells one *what* one is. The army sergeant who, when confronted with some theologically precise recruit (probably a high-church Episcopalian) who insisted he was neither Catholic, nor Protestant, nor Jewish, exclaimed in exasperation, "Well, if you're not Catholic, or Protestant, or Hebrew, what in blazes *are* you?" gave voice to the prevailing view of contemporary America. Unless one is either a Protestant, or a Catholic, or a Jew, one is

> "nothing"; to be "something," to have a name, one must identify oneself to oneself, and be identified by others, as belonging to one or another of the three great religious communities in which the American people are divided.[5]

Americans continue to identify themselves by their Judeo-Christian roots. For this reason, people of different faiths (Buddhists, Hindus, and Muslims) are not viewed as *real* Americans. "An eccentric American who adopts Buddhism," Herberg writes, "may identify himself to himself and find his stance in life in terms of his exotic cult, although it is more than likely that a Yankee turned Buddhist would still be regarded as a 'Protestant,' albeit admittedly a queer one."[6] Herberg's analysis, first stated in 1955, is reaffirmed in 1975 by a cover story of the *U.S. News & World Report.*

In 1975, America is a place that is not inhabited by Pakistanis, Somalis, Palestinians, Iranians, Iraqis, Saudis, Afghanis, Chechens, ethnic Albanians, and Islamic Indonesians. Americans can walk through crowded airports without encountering a woman in a burqa or a student in a shalwar kameez. Words such as *jihad, imam, Sunni,* and *Shiite* are only understood by students of comparative religion. Many major cities contain no Islamic bookstores or clothing shops featuring designer Muslim headdresses. And vendors selling halal foods cannot be found within the confines of New York City.

VANISHED RECOGNITION

By 2000, the religious landscape throughout America and the Western world had undergone a monumental transformation, although few scholars and statisticians took note of the fact. September 11, 2001, was not the day that changed everything. It was rather the day that revealed how much already had changed. The real shock came not only from the devastation but also the demographics. The world for many Americans became a place suddenly unrecognizable. They came to realize that Catholic churches throughout France had become mosques; that the most common name for baby boys in Belgium, Amsterdam, and Malmo, Sweden, was Mohammed (Mohammed came to run a close second to Jack in the United Kingdom); and that 40 percent of Rotterdam had become Islamic. There were over 60 million Muslims in Western Europe and, according to pollsters, the vast majority of them—over 70 percent—favored the imposition of *sharia* (Islamic law) on the general populace.[7]

But Europe was Europe. And what transpired among the French, the Germans, the Swedes, the Spaniards, and the Brits seemed far removed from what took place in the land of Paul Revere, Johnny Appleseed, Teddy Roosevelt, and John Wayne—or so it seemed.

The ultimate shock came with the gradual revelation that Islam had permeated nearly every aspect of American life; the full extent of the permeation remained the X factor. But this much came to light. In 1990, fewer than six hundred mosques existed in the United States.[8] By 2012 that number had climbed to 2,106.[9]

Although the 2,106 figure came from reliable sources, the count was seriously flawed, since it failed to include the masjids that have sprouted up in low-rent storefronts, abandoned warehouses, private residences, college dormitories, and the back rooms of Islamic business establishments. Despite this fact, the number showed that nearly 8.5 percent of America's 330,000 houses of worship were now mosques.

A 2008 study by Cornell University estimated that the number of Muslims in America had climbed to 7 million from 1.6 million in 1995.[10] A *U.S. News & World Report* survey, which was conducted at the same time in 1995, placed the figure at 5 million.[11] The real number remained anyone's guess, since the US Census Bureau neglects to collect data on religious identification.

In 2008, the Pew Research Center estimated the Islamic population of the United States to be 2.35 million. But Pew researchers admit that their survey was not thorough, since it neglected to take into account immigrant and poor black Muslims.[12] What's more, researchers contacted only Americans with telephone landlines and failed to take into account the fact that nearly 50 percent of US residents ages 18–35 and nearly 100 percent of illegal immigrants communicate exclusively by cell phones.[13] Muslim organizations, such as the Council on American-Islamic Relations (CAIR), supported the Cornell University estimate of 7 million—based on mosque attendance.[14]

The Islamic boom was evidenced by reports of the new mosques and halal restaurants that had sprouted up within every major American city. By 2010, according to one report, Washington, DC, boasted 7 mosques and 134 halal restaurants; San Francisco, 24 mosques and 176 halal restaurants; Houston, 15 and 50; Chicago, 27 and 61; Cleveland, 15 and 11; Boston, 19 and 60; Knoxville, 32 and 6; St. Louis, 21 and 8; Lansing, 27 and 6; Toledo, 17 and 5; Buffalo, 9 and 11; Dallas, 21 and 13; Grand Rapids, 19 and 7; New Orleans, 6 and 3; Nashville, 11 and 10; Columbia, 12 and 2; Detroit, 3 and 89; Atlanta, 9 and 22; Peoria, 5 and 1; Lincoln, 25 and 2; and Shreveport, Louisiana, 21 and 1. There are 14 new mosques in Hattiesburg, Mississippi, and 25 in Anchorage, Alaska.[15]

Many of the Islamic houses of worship were massive structures that attracted thousands of believers to Friday afternoon prayer service (*Jummah*). These large mosques included the Islamic Center of America in Dearborn, Michigan; the Islamic Center of Washington, DC; the ADAMS Center in Sterling, Virginia; the al-Farooq Masjid in Atlanta; the Islamic Society of New York; Dar al-Hijrah in Falls Church, Virginia; the Tucson Islamic Center; and the King Fahad Mosque in Los Angeles.[16] Even the smallest mosques—including the Mother Mosque of America in Cedar Rapids, Iowa—could easily contain several hundred members and visitors for a single service. Much of the funding for the new mosques came from wealthy Saudi princes who sought to further the Islamic transformation of America.[17]

By 2010, the median mosque in America drew a crowd of three hundred worshippers to its Friday service,[18] while the average Christian church mustered a meager Sunday gathering of seventy-five.[19]

ONLY THE DEAD KNOW BROOKLYN

To come to terms with the social, political, economic, and religious impact of Islam on the US landscape, you need only pay a visit to Brooklyn—the borough of New York City once known as "the all-American neighborhood." Such a visit will make you aware not only of the radical Islamic transformation of US cities but also of the woeful inadequacies of religious statistics, especially those that pertain to mosques and the number of Muslims now residing within major metropolitan areas throughout the country.

Brooklyn conjures up magical images in the American imagination —the Brooklyn Bridge, Coney Island, Fulton's Ferry, brownstone townhouses, and the Dodgers. It was home to William "Boss" Tweed, Currier and Ives, Margaret Sanger, Louis Tiffany, Al Capone, Gil Hodges, "Pee Wee" Reese, Leonard Bernstein, Barbra Streisand, and Ralph and Alice Kramdon of *The Honeymooners*. Brooklyn gave birth to hot dogs, roller coasters, soda pop, and more breweries than any other city in the country. One out of every seven Americans can trace his or her family roots to the streets of this borough.[20]

Yet Brooklyn is no longer quintessentially American. The breweries are closed, Ebbets Field is a memory, and the hot dog stands have disappeared. Gone, too, is the navy yard that built such legendary warships as the *Monitor*, the *Arizona*, and the *New Mexico*. Gone is the *Daily Eagle*, where Walt Whitman once toiled as an editor. They have vanished with the Jewish delis, the Irish bars, and the nightclubs that were made famous by John Travolta in *Saturday Night Fever*. Brooklyn is transmogrifying into a place that is antithetical to American sensibilities. It has become a thriving haven of Islam.

Returning to Brooklyn after a hiatus of twenty years, Sarah Honig of the *Jerusalem Post* was shocked by the changes that had occurred in her old neighborhood:

> When I climbed up the grimy station stairs and surveyed the street, I suspected that some supernatural time-and-space warp had trans-

> ported me to Islamabad. This couldn't be Brooklyn. Women strode attired in hijabs and male passersby sported all manner of Muslim headgear and long flowing tunics. . . . Pakistani and Bangladeshi groceries lined the main shopping drag, and everywhere stickers boldly beckoned: "Discover Jesus in the Koran."[21]

Throughout Brooklyn, one can now hear the call of the muezzin five times a day from rooftop speakers: *Allahu akbar. Ashhadu an la ilaha illa-Llah.* Cab drivers pull their hacks to the side of the road and perform ritual ablutions. Shopkeepers roll out their prayer rugs toward the holy city. And life within the borough—which was once known as the "city of churches"—comes to a standstill.

The massive migration of Muslims to this borough of New York, coupled with the widespread conversion to Islam of African Americans throughout Bedford-Stuyvesant and other Brooklyn neighborhoods, has been hailed as a salubrious development by many Brooklynites. The Muslim newcomers have been credited by Brooklyn borough president Marty Markowitz with closing crack houses and driving drug dealers from the crime-infested streets. "I see more and more Muslims taking part in social life. The future is looking good," Markowitz says.[22]

Eric Bullen recalls that Al's Men Shop, his store on Fulton Street, was one of the few functioning businesses on what had become a block of vacant storefronts. "It used to be so bad at times that people didn't want to even be seen out here too late. You could guarantee that, had they come through once it started to get dark, they were going to get mugged," he recalls. The Muslims, he says, were instrumental in changing things.[23]

Community affairs officer Steven Ruffin says that the imams of Brooklyn mosques, including Masjid al-Taqwa, have established unprecedented community cooperation with the police by creating civil patrols to police many of the borough's trouble spots.[24]

ENEMY TERRITORY

Yet others view the Islamic transformation of the borough as something threatening and sinister. Many Jews and Christians throughout Brooklyn now display American flags and an assortment of patriotic/jingoistic banners in their front yards. These displays, for the most part, are acts of defiance. "We're besieged," one resident told the *Jerusalem Post*. "Making a statement is all we can do. They aren't delighted to see the flag wave. This is enemy territory."[25]

Even Markowitz and others supportive of the newcomers reluctantly note that the vast majority of Muslim newcomers display an unwillingness to assimilate.[26] They continue to wear Islamic attire, maintain halal diets, and rigidly comply with *sharia* (Islamic law). Most equate Americanism with hedonism. They shun fast-food restaurants, any food containing alcohol (including chocolate), and American cars.[27] Few Muslim women walk the streets without a head covering; some wear full burqas that conceal their bodies and niqabs that conceal their faces, leaving only mesh-covered slits for their eyes. The assimilation process in Brooklyn appears to be working in reverse, since the new male converts to Islam, almost all of whom are African American, now wear skull caps and long, white tunics (*shalwar kameezes*), while their wives walk several feet behind them in black burqas or abaya gowns. They dye their beards with henna, refrain from eating pork and drinking alcoholic beverages, and greet each other in Arabic (*As-Salāmu `Alaykum*).

Polygamy, among the newcomers and converts, is commonplace, and khat—the favorite narcotic of North African Muslims—is now cut up and sold on street corners, in halal grocery shops, and in places like the Blue Province Restaurant.[28] In crowded flats and makeshift clinics along Atlantic Avenue, young Muslim girls—some as young as two—are subjected to the practice of female genital mutilation. Dubbed "female circumcision," this practice consists of the removal of the clitoris without the benefit of anesthesia or surgical instruments. Broken bottles or tin can lids occasionally serve as scalpels.[29] Recent statistics show that forty-one thousand Somali and other North African Muslims in Brooklyn and the other boroughs of New York City have been subjugated to this ordeal.[30]

While the overwhelming majority of Muslims in Brooklyn are moderate in belief, at least 7 percent are extremely radical and support violent attacks against all nonbelievers, including the attacks of 9/11.[31] By 1989, the first North American cell of al-Kifah, an organization that would eventually morph into al-Qaeda, was implanted by Abdullah Azzam within Brooklyn's Masjid al-Farooq on Atlantic Avenue, a six-story converted factory trimmed in orange and gold. Members of this mosque came to play key roles in the assassination of Rabbi Meir Kahane, the 1993 bombing of the World Trade Center, and the planning of 9/11.[32] By 2002, they managed to raise over $20 million for Osama bin Laden and millions more for other terrorist groups.[33] The mosque purportedly continues to serve as an arsenal, stocked with rifles, shotguns, 9 mm and .357 caliber handguns, and AK-47 assault weapons. Yet it remains off-limits to law enforcement officials, since it is registered as a "house of worship."[34]

Brooklyn has given birth to Dar ul-Islam, the nation's most notorious Islamic street gang; Jamaat ul-Fuqra, a Muslim group that has been responsible for thirty terror attacks on American soil; and the Albanian Mafia, which now represents the country's "leading crime outfit."[35]

NEARING CRITICAL MASS

What has taken place in Brooklyn has occurred in major cities throughout the country—most notably, Detroit and Minneapolis—and even in quaint towns and villages, such as Lodi, California; Lewiston, Maine; Hancock, New York; and Commerce, Georgia.

If Islam continues to grow at its present rate, critical mass will be achieved by 2020 and the eventual Muslim transformation of America will become a statistical possibility. This is not to say that sharia will be the law of the land, but it is to affirm that the religion of the prophet will be a force that cannot be denied by our elected officials. Demands will be met; concessions, granted.

This development should bolster the stance of many Christian conservatives. The Muslim newcomers and converts will be intolerant of same-sex marriage, abortion on demand, pornography, adultery, gay rights, and premarital sex. They will address the problems of drugs and crime in a manner that the present moral majority has been incapable of adopting. The land will change and become, to a large extent, unrecognizable.

How did this phenomenon come to pass?

How did thousands of mosques sprout up throughout America—almost overnight—like magical mushrooms?

How did the crescent moon come to eclipse the star of David in the land that was founded as the New Zion?

The answer, to a large degree, resides in the legacies of a flamboyant con artist, a self-proclaimed prophet with an IQ of 70 and a mental age of 10.6, a petty crook, and a US senator.

CHAPTER 2
MUSLIM AMERICA
THE MYTHICAL PAST

Addressing the Muslim world from a podium at Cairo University on June 4, 2009, President Barack Obama informed his listeners that Islam "has always been part of American heritage and tradition."[1] Similarly, the first American president of Muslim heritage hosted an iftar on August 10, 2011, in which he said: "Like so many faiths, Islam has always been part of our American family, and Muslim Americans have long contributed to the strength and character of our country, in all walks of life."[2] Mr. Obama was not the only occupant of the Oval Office to make such claims about the role of Islam in US history. On January 20, 2005, in the course of his second inaugural address, former president George W. Bush maintained that Islam represented a major factor in the development of American heritage and culture and that "our national life [is sustained] by the truths of Sinai, the Sermon on the Mount, the words of the Koran."[3]

ESTEVANICO UNEARTHED

But there were no Muslims among the passengers on the *Mayflower* or the settlers at Jamestown. Several Islamic apologists contend, however, that a Muslim named Estevanico (a Spanish diminutive for "Stephen") explored Arizona and New Mexico during the early decades of the sixteenth century. Estevanico (or Esteban), we are told, was a Berber from North Africa who was sold into slavery to Andes Dorantes de Carranaca, a Spanish nobleman. He accompanied Dorantes on an expedition to the New World led by Panfilode Narvaez. Eventually, as the story goes, Estevanico was captured by a tribe of Native Americans who came to worship him as a god. Although the accounts of this mysterious figure are presented as facts in twenty-first-century textbooks, they are undermined by historical records that show that Estevanico was a devout Roman Catholic.[4]

THE MYTH OF THE MORISCOS

Despite popular folklore, few Muslims numbered among the 12 million black Africans shipped to the New World from the seventeenth to the nineteenth centuries. The Muslims, in fact, were not the slaves but the slave traders. Senegalese educator Amadou-Mahtar M'Bow has written that in 1587 a shipload of Moriscos (Spanish Moors) landed in a coastal area of South Carolina. The Moors, he contends, migrated to the mountains of eastern Tennessee and western North Carolina, where they bred with Native Americans to give rise to the Melungeon communities.[5] This theory is supported by N. Brent Kennedy, who maintains that the Melungeons are "a blend of the Powhatans, the Lumbees, and the Santa Elena colonists, with a strong Moorish/Turkish element."[6]

Unfortunately, there is not a scintilla of archival or archaeological evidence to support this claim. The basis of the theory comes from the argument that "Melungeon" is a name that derives from the Arabic *melun jinn*, meaning "cursed soul." Most etymologists refute this by saying that the word comes from the French *mPlange*, meaning "mixture." The French colonists in southwestern Virginia in the late 1700s, according to this explanation, referred to the crossbreed of people in these settlements with the plural of *mPlange* or *mPlangeon*, which eventually became corrupted to "Melungeon."[7]

This is not to say that no Muslim slaves were transported to the colonies. Two such slaves—Ayuiba Suleiman Diallo and Omar ibn Said—were brought to America in 1731, but both were returned to Africa in 1734.[8]

LOST IN THE WOODS

Edward E. Curtis makes the spurious claim that a mosque was established on Kent Island, Maryland, sometime between 1731 and 1733. The *Washington Post* reporter contends that Muslim slave and Islamic scholar Job Ben Solomon, a cattle driver, would regularly steal away to the woods there for his prayers—in spite of a white boy who threw dirt on him as he made his prostrations.[9] This story stems from an account by Thomas Bluett, a lawyer who encountered Job while traveling through Maryland.[10] Job, who may have been the first Muslim to land in America, spent only two years as a slave in the tobacco fields of Maryland before obtaining his freedom and gaining employment by the Royal African Company in Gambia.[11] There remains no reliable sources for Curtis's claim that Job built a mosque or made an effort to establish an Islamic community in the New World.

CLAIMS BY NAMES

Muslims appeared to have been conspicuously absent from the ranks of George Washington's army during the Revolutionary War and to have played no role in the creation of the American republic—save for the fact that the new country's first declaration of war was against the forces of Islam in the form of the Barbary pirates.[12] The only argument to refute this claim comes from an Islamic website that maintains that such veterans of the War of Independence as Bampett Muhamed, Francis Saba, Joseph Saba, and Joseph Benhaley must have been Muslims, since their names signify Islamic roots. The real name of Joseph Benhaley, according to the website, very well may have been Yusuf Ben Ali.[13]

This curious argument was set forth as historical fact in a *Washington Post* piece by Johari Abdul, the imam of Dar al-Hijrah in Falls Church, Virginia.[14]

THOMAS JEFFERSON'S QURAN

Pro-Islamic revisionists of American history present Thomas Jefferson, the country's third president, as a Muslim sympathizer because he owned a copy of the first English edition of the Quran.[15] In 2007, Keith Ellison, the first Muslim to be elected to the US House of Representatives, received permission to use Jefferson's Quran as the sacred text upon which he swore his oath of allegiance to the Constitution at his inaugural ceremony.

But Jefferson's purchase of the work reflected neither his admiration of the Prophet Mohammed nor his esteem of the Muslim holy book. It rather reflected his interest in natural law and the fact that the Quran was referenced in Frieherr von Pufendorf's *Of the Law of Nature and Nations*, the standard text on this subject in 1765. Von Pufendorf cited the Islamic text in his discussions of marriage, adultery, the prohibition of gambling, and the validity of warfare.[16]

Jefferson's interest in Islam was peaked again in 1785 when the Muslim Barbary pirates demanded $80,000 from the United States as tribute. Jefferson and John Adams met 'Abd al-Rahman al-Ajar, the personal representative of the pasha of Tripoli, to come to terms with the pirates in order to ward off terrorist attacks on American ships. The two founding fathers reported to Congress the following response of al-Ajar to their questions concerning the basis of the attacks on defenseless ships: "The Ambassador answered us that it was founded on the laws of the prophet, that it was written in their Koran, that all Nations who should not have acknowledged their [the Muslims'] authority were sinners, that it was their right and duty to make war upon whoever they could find and to make Slaves of all they could take as prisoners, and that every Mussulman who should be slain in battle was sure to go to Paradise."[17]

BEN FRANKLIN AND BEN ALI

The absence of Muslims in colonial America was noted by Benjamin Franklin, who wrote concerning the establishment of a nondenominational society in Philadelphia that "even if the Mufti of Constantinople were to send a missionary to preach Mohammedanism to us, he would find a pulpit at his service."[18]

Bilali (Ben Ali) Muhammad, we are told by Sheila Masaji, editor of the *American Muslim*, was a Fula Muslim from Timbo Futa-Jallon (present day Guinea-Conakry), who arrived at Sapelo Island, off the coast of Georgia, in 1803. While enslaved, this fanciful figure reportedly became the religious leader and imam for a slave community of eighty Muslim men, who served to protect their master's property during the War of 1812. Ben Ali, according to Ms. Masaji, fasted during the month of Ramadan, wore a fez and kaftan, observed the Muslim feasts, and daily performed the five obligatory Islamic prayers.[19] This is all well and good save for the fact that the sole source of this information comes from Cornelia Walker Bailey, an African American woman who resides on Sopelo Island and professes to be the great-great-great-great-granddaughter of Ben Ali, whose esteemed name became corrupted into Bailey.[20]

MOHEGANS AS MOHAMMADANS

In a herculean effort to materialize at least one Muslim living in America before the Civil War, Muslims in America, an Islamic website, points to the name of Mahomet, the great-grandson of Uncas, the founder of the Mohegan tribe, on a gravestone in Norwich,

Connecticut.[21] The name of this Native American, they argue, resembles that of the prophet. Therefore, he must have been a convert to Islam. In a similar example of straining at gnats, the compilers of *The Collections and Stories of American Muslims*, a nonprofit organization, claim that Peter Salem, a former slave who fought at the Battle of Bunker Hill, must have been a Muslim, since "Salem" bears an etymological resemblance to "Salaam," the Arabic word for peace.[22] For additional proof, the compilers turn to folklore, such as the story of Old Tom, a slave at a plantation in Georgia who allegedly uttered, "Allah is God and Mohammed his Prophet" on his death bed, and the apocryphal tale of "Old Lizzy," a slave from Edgefield County who reportedly said, "Christ built His first church in Mecca."[23]

THE CURIOUS CASE OF "HI JOLLY"

The only historically verifiable Mohammedan, as Muslims were then called, to live in this country before 1860 was a curious character known as "Hi Jolly," whose real name may have been Hajj Ali. This affable drover was brought here in 1856 to assist in the creation of the US Army Camel Corps. The War Department, at the time, believed that camels could be of great use in the exploration of the southwestern territories that had been ceded to the United States at the close of the Mexican-American War. The experiment failed, and "Hi Jolly" went on to California to prospect for gold. Granted citizenship in 1880, he married Gertrude Serna of Tucson, converted to Christianity, and fathered two children.[24] In 1935, the State of Arizona commemorated the exploits of "Hi Jolly" by erecting a stone pyramid, topped with a bronze camel, on his grave in the town of Quartzsite.[25]

NEITHER BLUE NOR GREY

There is no record of any Muslim among the blue and grey armies of the Civil War, despite the incredible claim by the *Encyclopedia of Muslim American History* that 292 Islamic American soldiers took part in the struggle.[26] Islamic apologists, however, are correct in stating that Nicholas Said (also known as Muhammad Ali ibn Said) enlisted in the Fifty-Fifth Massachusetts Colored Regiment in the United States Army and rose to the rank of sergeant. But Said in his autobiography writes: "Reader, do not misunderstand me, I was a Mohammedan; I am now, in belief, a Christian and a Swedenborgian."[27] The same apologists set forth the argument that Max Hassan, a black Union soldier, was a Muslim on the sole basis that he bore an Islamic-sounding name. Such quaggy argumentation is accepted in the politically correct climate of contemporary America as historical verification.

GREAT MIGRATIONS WITHOUT MUSLIMS

The great migrations that lasted from 1865 to 1915 brought 35 million people to the New World: 4.5 million from Ireland, 4 million from Great Britain, 6 million from central Europe, 2 million from the Scandinavian countries, 5 million from Italy, 8 million from eastern Europe, and 3 million from the Balkans. But the number of Muslims who came here from the Islamic world remained statistically nil.[28] The few hundred who made their way to these shores came from the rural areas of what was then called Greater Syria (currently Syria, Jordan, Lebanon, and the Palestinian territories)—a territory under the rule of the Ottoman Empire.[29]

Regarding the absence of Muslims in the country at this time, Roger Daniels in *Coming to America: A History of Immigration and Ethnicity in American Life*, writes:

> It is hard to be a Muslim in a non-Muslim society. Although Muslims, like Jews, have no priesthood and can pray almost anywhere, the imam and the mosque have become as central to Muslim worship as the rabbi and the synagogue have become to the Jewish, [Alixa] Naff illustrates this by talking about one of the few early Muslim settlements, near Ross, North Dakota, established around the turn of the century. There was no mosque until the 1920s, and prayer and ritual were conducted in private homes. The small community, which received no reinforcement, soon lost the use of Arabic. Many adopted Christian names, married non-Muslims, and others moved away. The ethnically conscious community shrank, and the mosque was abandoned by 1948. Only two other mosques are known to have been built anywhere in the United States before the 1930s.[30]

THE MISSING MUSLIM SOLDIERS

In 2009, the American Civil Liberties Union (ACLU) objected to the Argonne cross that stood at the Veterans of Foreign Wars' Death Valley post to honor the American soldiers who died in combat during World War I. Peter Eliasberg, a managing ACLU attorney, said that the cross fails to commemorate the thousands of veterans, including Muslims, who served in the Great War and were not Christians.[31] But conscription and enlistment records show that few, if any, Muslims served in the US military during World War I.

The same holds true for World War II. In 2006, Gordon England, deputy secretary of the US Department of Defense, was singled out to speak of the Muslim American soldiers who served during World War II. The deputy secretary could only come up with the name of Sergeant Abdul-Hakim, who fought on the beaches of Normandy with the army's amphibious engineers.[32]

PROHIBITED FROM ENTERING

In 1965, aside from the temples of the Nation of Islam (an African American religion sect that bore no similarity to the teachings of the Prophet Mohammed), the only mosques in the United States were in Cedar Rapids, Iowa; Dearborn, Michigan; and Washington, DC (which opened in 1957)—and all three boasted fewer than a hundred members. Four other cities contained miniature mosques with fewer than fifty members.[33] Small wonder, therefore, that Islam in America failed to merit the attention of religious demographers, such as Leo Rosten and Will Herberg, let alone a line of ink in the two volumes of Sydney E. Ahlstorm's *A Religious History of the American People*, which appeared in 1972.

What accounts for the absence of Muslims from the millions of immigrants who came to these shores in the century between 1865 and 1965?

The answer resides with the restrictive immigration legislation that remained in effect to safeguard the racial and religious balance of America. The Naturalization Act of 1790 stipulated that "any alien, being a free white person, may be admitted to become a citizen of the United States." The Chinese Exclusion Act of 1882 prohibited Chinese families from immigrating to the United States. With their strange language, customs, and dress, the Chinese were considered incapable of assimilation. The ban on the Chinese would persist until Chang Kai-shek became a US ally during World War II.[34] The Immigration Act of 1891 reorganized the states bordering Mexico (Arizona, New Mexico, and a large part of Texas) into the Mexican Border District to stem the flow of immigrants into the United States. This act also contained a list of "undesirables" who should be prevented from entering the country. The list included (in an apparent reference to Islam) "polygamists," along with diseased persons, convicts, paupers, idiots, and the insane. The Immigration Acts of 1903 and 1907 expanded the category of "undesirables" to include political radicals, people with physical and mental defects, and children unaccompanied by their parents.

By 1924, the US Congress closed the floodgates to the country and limited the annual flow of immigrants to 2 percent of the population of each nationality present in the country in 1890. The reliance of this legislation on the ethnic composition of the country before the turn of the century guaranteed that the majority of new arrivals would be from northern Europe. Since few Italians and eastern Europeans lived in the United States in 1890, the quotas for these nationalities became fixed at marginal rates and the number of new immigrants from "undesirable" regions greatly reduced. The following chart shows the effects of this legislation:

Immigration Statistics, 1920–1926

Year	Total Entering US	Country of Origin		
		Great Britain	Eastern Europe	Italy
1920	430,001	38,471	3,913	95,145
1921	805,228	51,142	32,793	222,260
1922	309,556	25,153	12,244	40,319
1923	522,919	45,759	16,082	46,674
1924	706,896	59,490	13,173	56,246
1925	294,314	27,172	1,566	6,203
1926	304,488	25,528	1,596	8,253

It is hard to conceive of an act of Congress that could be more culturally biased, and yet it received nearly unchallenged bipartisan support. The *New York Times* editorialized: "It is both natural and wise that the American race wishes to preserve its unity and does not wish to see its present blend greatly changed [because it] prefers immigrants who will be easily absorbed and . . . it strenuously objects to the formation of alien colonies here [and not because it] adheres to silly notions of 'superior' and 'inferior' races."[35]

As a result of the 1924 act, immigration fell sharply. By the 1930s, it declined to fifty thousand a year. During World War II, it was halted, though four hundred thousand displaced persons were brought to the United States following the war.[36]

THE QUOTAS UPHELD

In 1952, the McCarran-Walter Immigration Act affirmed the national-origins quota system of 1924 and limited total annual immigration to one-sixth of one percent of the population of the continental United States in 1920, or 175,455. The act exempted spouses and children of US citizens and people born in the Western Hemisphere from the quota. The new legislation angered President Harry Truman, whose veto had been overridden by both houses of Congress: "The idea behind the discrimatory policy was, to put it boldly, that Americans with English or Irish names were better people and better citizens than Americans with Italian or Greek or Polish names. . . . Such a concept is utterly unworthy of our traditions and our ideals."[37] Mr. Truman's concern centered on the thousands of residents from eastern and southern Europe who wished to migrate to America, not the millions of Muslims who lived in Central Asia, Africa, and the Middle East. And neither Truman nor any other prominent liberal Democrat took issue with the quota limit of 156,700 per year, a limit that had been lowered by the Immigration and Nationality Act of 1952. "There is a legitimate argument for some limitation upon immigration," wrote Senator John F. Kennedy in 1958.[38]

THE AHMADIYYA MISSIONARIES

Few Muslims were found in the United States before 1965 because they were prohibited from coming here, and neither the claims of politicians nor the writings of historical revisionists can serve to subrogate this fact. To make matters worse, only the heretical Ahmadiyya movement—condemned by both Sunnis and Shiites—managed to gain a tenuous foothold in this country. Mirza Ghulam Ahmad, the Indian Muslim who founded the movement in 1888, claimed to be not only the Mahdi, whose coming Muslims have long expected, but also the tenth incarnation of the Hindu god Vishnu.[39]

He also taught that Jesus survived the crucifixion, journeyed to Asia, and continued preaching until he reached the age of 136.

The first Ahmadi missionary to arrive here was Mufti Muhammad Saddiq in 1920. Hoping to reap a conversion bonanza among black Americans, Saddiq addressed meetings of Marcus Garvey's Universal Negro Improvement Association (UNIA) and established the headquarters of his mission in Chicago, where he started publication of the periodical *Moslem Sunrise.*[40] In the first issue, Saddiq wrote:

> The spread of El-Islam cannot help but benefit the UNIA, for they are desperately engaged in preparing for That Day—that day that we of the Universal are also preparing for. Great Britain, France, and Spain—in fact all the white powers—fear Mohammedanism. None of them can afford to offend El Islam. With millions of Moslems in India, China, Arabia, Persia, Afghanistan, and Turkey, Negroes would find valuable allies.[41]

Within a year, Saddiq managed to attract several hundred followers—including dozens of "sheiks," who were responsible for conducting weekly meetings, collecting dues, and granting their converts new names. "Change your name and you won't be a Negro anymore" became the movement's slogan.[42] Since the "sheiks" lacked any knowledge of Islam, they drew upon their personal experience and "Negro folklore" to concoct their doctrines.

In 1934, Muhammad Yussef Khan became the new "headman" of the movement. Billing himself as an educator, psychologist, metaphysician, and divine medium, Khan offered correpondence courses without "needless theory" for the meager fee of twenty-five dollars. In an ad for a course, Khan wrote: "Islam will tone down your nervous excitement . . . improve temperament . . . [and] teach you how to have the thrill of influencing and controlling people in your personal relations."[43] In addition, he sold prayers for twenty-five cents apiece, magical charms, turbans, and "dust from a Prophet's tomb."[44] By 1934, the enterprising Khan had amassed enough loot for retirement in his native India and had appointed "Professor Ashraf," one of his understudies, to serve as his successor.

The fleeced Ahmadi flock chased Ashraf from the community, seized what was left of Khan's possessions, and redressed their grievances to the Ahmadiyya khalifa at his headquarters in India. The khalifa responded by sending Sufu Bengalee, another missionary, to Chicago. Bengalee, a scholar who wrote a credible biography of the Prophet Mohammed, attempted to impart the actual teachings of Mirza Ghulam Ahmad to the few remaining members of the movement. These teachings included obedience to the Five Pillars of Islam, including the recitation of shahada. Through Bengalee's efforts, the movement spread to Indianapolis, Kansas City, Cleveland, Columbus, and Youngstown. In 1950, the American Fazl Mosque was established within the first floor of a brick two-story home in Washington, DC. By 2010, the Amadi sect in the United States could boast of more than twelve thousand adherents, thanks to the migration of thousands of persecuted members from Pakistan, Bangladesh, and other Islamic countries, where they are reviled as "kafirs" and "apostates."[45]

Despite claims to the contrary, the story of Islam in America does not begin with the Ahmadiyya missionaries. Their influence on the religious landscape of the United States was miniscule, and the sect only managed to survive because of the elimination of the eventual quota system. But their numbers to this day remain small and rather insigificant. Neither does the story begin with the importation of hundreds of Muslim slaves nor with the establishment of a mythical Islamic colony off the coast of Georgia.

Rather, it begins in 1910 on a street corner in Newark, New Jersey, with the appearance of a flamboyant flim-flam artist who called himself Noble Drew Ali.

CHAPTER 3
THE FIRST AMERICAN MUSLIM

Wearing a black bolero jacket, yellow balloon pants, and a red fez, Noble Drew Ali (formerly Timothy Drew) popped up on a street corner in Newark and announced that he was the long-awaited reincarnation of the founder of an ancient religious cult, who had disappeared during the reign of the great Pharaoh Cheops.[1] He proceeded to tell a small crowd of African Americans that they were members of the lost race of Moabites, who had been driven from the Land of Canaan by Joshua and forced to settle in northwest and southwest Africa, where, in time, they became castigated as "negroes" and "blacks." He sold them new identity cards and copies of a pamphlet called *The Circle of Seven Koran,* which was purportedly a clandestine version of the holy book of Islam. Business was brisk, and Noble Drew Ali managed to amass a small army of followers—all of whom assumed new identities and exotic dress.

THE SECRETS OF THE CIRCLE SEVEN

The Circle contains almost no mention of Prophet Mohammed and not a single verse (let alone a surah) from the original Quran. Rather, it consists of lengthy passages from *The Aquarian Gospel,* a work, first published in 1908, which claimed to tell "the true story of Jesus," including his lost eighteen years, and contains material lifted from the Rosicrucian text *Unto Thee, I Grant*, homespun homilies on a wide variety of subjects, and a hefty helping of Masonic lore.

The central figure in this work is Jesus, who is depicted not as a Jew, but as a black man of "the true blood of the ancient Moabites and the inhabitants of Africa." His mission is not to lay down his life for the sins of the world, but rather to "redeem His people" [the black race] from "the pale skin nations of Europe."[2] The author, who assumes Muslims lived in ancient Egypt during the Middle Kingdom, also maintains that Europe existed as a distinct continent in the first century.

The peripatetic Christ of *The Circle* spends much of his adult life wandering from Crete to China and mouthing ungrammatical platitudes: "Man is the Breath made flesh, so truth and falsehood art conjoined in him, and they strive, and naught goes down and man as truth abides."[3] When Jesus finally returns to his native Palestine, he is put to death by conniving Jews who "borrowed their faith from the idol worshippers of other lands" and believed that a scapegoat must be slaughtered every year as a sacrifice for the sins of the people.[4]

The resurrected Jesus sets out on a world tour. He makes appearances in Greece, Crete, and Rome (where he walked on the Tiber). He pays a visit to India before venturing on to Persia, where he has dinner with the three wise men who had made the trek to Bethlehem at the time of his birth.

DREW'S DIVINE COMMISSION

Drew told his listeners that he had undergone months of advanced training in the truths of Moorish Science from the high priest and "adept" members of the Ancient Mystery System before making his way to Mecca to meet Sultan Abdul Aziz Ibu Saad, the so-called head of the Islamic world. This esteemed figure allegedly bestowed upon Drew the power to preach "the old time gospel of Islam" to one of the lost tribes of Moabites, namely, the Negroes in America.[5]

Upon his return to America, the newly appointed prophet of

Islam claimed that he was summoned by Woodrow Wilson to the Oval Office, where he discovered the ancient flag of his Moorish ancestors within a secret vault. Drew said that, following his meeting with Wilson, he came upon black separatist Marcus Garvey, who recognized him as the savior of the black race and pledged to serve as his John the Baptist.[6]

"Getting to the truth about Timothy Drew ain't easy," black historian James "Chimsey" Williams observes. "You got to have the eye of a barnyard hen. A barnyard hen can peck kernels of corn from mounds of cow manure. You need that knack in order to remove the fact from the fiction in the accounts of Drew's life."[7]

By employing this unique methodology, it is possible to establish the following few kernels of truth about Timothy Drew's life before 1910, the year in which he appeared on a street corner in Newark as Noble Drew Ali, the divinely appointed prophet of Allah:

(1) He worked for several years as a train expressman;
(2) he held membership in the Pullman porters' union;
(3) he was a member in good standing of the Ancient Egyptian Order of Nobles of the Mystic Shrine of North and South America, a Masonic organization that would loom large in the formation of the Moorish Science Temple.[8]

AMERICA'S FIRST MOSQUE

By 1913, Noble Drew Ali opened what is reportedly the first mosque in America—the Holy Moabite Temple of the Science of the World, also known as the Canaanite Temple. "The Moors were living up and down the Mississippi River before the European man came to them," Drew told his flock. "The bananas were large and the grapes were four-in-hand. It took two men with hand sticks to carry a bunch of grapes."[9]

No one within the Moorish Science Movement came to realize that the Prophet Mohammed viewed the black race with contempt and referred to Negroes as "raisin heads" several times in the Hadith (1:662; 9:256).[10]

GIRDLES AND SNAKE OIL

The male members of the temple were required to wear an official red fez (available for three dollars), a girdle (priced at thirty cents) and a robe (at the cost of five dollars).[11] Women were obliged to cover their hair at all public gatherings and to augment their headpieces with a blue and oval Moorish pin, featuring the number 7 in a circle. All members were encouraged to add "Bey" or "El" to their names in order to signify their Moorish descent on their membership cards (renewable yearly for one dollar). The cards read as follows:

> *This is your nationality and identification card for the Moorish Science Temple of America, and Birthright for the Moorish Americans, etc. We honor all the Divine Prophets, Jesus, Mohammed, Buddha and Confucius. May the blessings of the God our Father Allah be upon you that carry this card. I do hereby declare that you are a Moslem under the Divine Laws of the Holy Koran of Mecca.*
>
> *Noble Drew Ali*[12]

The reception of such membership cards, Drew maintained, represented relinquishment of US citizenship. "By being born here doesn't make you a citizen," Drew told his disciples. This claim resulted in the refusal of many temple members to comply with the Selective Service Act of 1917.

The mandatory wearing of red fezes, the lofty titles of "Noble" and "Sheikh," the secret handshake, and the symbol of the "All-Seeing-Eye" displayed the roots of Drew's movement in the Masonic Shrine. More Masonic influence was evident by the establishment of "initiation" and "adept" chambers within the temple and of several orders—the Fatimid Order, the Order of Jerusalem, and the Order of the Paraclete—through which the members could progress and by which they could achieve such lofty titles as deacon, exilarch, and papessa. All members were obliged to attend Friday worship services and to make payment of the monthly dues of two dollars for men and one dollar for women. And they were encouraged to purchase Noble Drew's magical elixirs—Old Moorish Healing Oil, Moorish Blood Purifier Bath Compound, and Moorish Herbal Tea for Human Ailments—for a nominal fee.[13] "My remedies," Drew proclaimed, "will cure you of anything you weren't born with."[14]

SUNDAY SCHOOL LESSON

Besides *The Circle of Seven Koran*, Drew gave his followers several manuals containing questions and answers that had to be memorized. One catechetical lesson was as follows:

Q. Who is Noble Drew Ali?
A. He is Allah's Prophet.
Q. Why did Allah send Jesus to earth?
A. To save the Israelities from the iron hand of oppression of the pale-skin nations of Europe who were governing a portion of Palestine at that time.
Q. Who were Adam and Eve?
A. They are the mother and the father of the human family—Asiatics and Moslems.
Q. Where did they go?
A. They went to Asia.
Q. What is the modern name given to their children?
A. Asiatics.[15]

THE NEW MECCA

The Newark temple became so successful that Drew opened branch temples in Harlem, Brooklyn, Philadelphia, Pittsburgh, Cleveland,

Toledo, Flint, Detroit, Indianapolis, Milwaukee, Kansas City, Norfolk, and Louisville.[16] In 1925, Drew relocated to Chicago, where he established the central shrine of the movement on Indiana Avenue. "Chicago, Illinois is going to be our new Mecca," he said.[17]

By 1926, when the Moorish Science Temple became a legal corporation, the movement had garnered more than thirty-two thousand adherents. Within the next three years, a host of other temples—thirty-six in all—were established throughout the country. The temples were governed by Grand Sheikhs and "Grand Sheikhesses" who had been appointed by Noble Drew. One such "Grand Sheikhess" turned out to be Pearl Jones Ali, the aunt of one of Noble Drew's wives.[18]

By 1929, the Chicago branch of the Moorish Science Temple boasted twelve thousand members, and the the Detroit branch had ten thousand members. The movement operated grocery stores, clothing shops, and the *Moorish Voice*, a national newspaper.

A devout Shiite, Sunni, or Sufi Muslim from the Middle East who happened to stumble into one of Drew's Moorish Temples on a Friday night would have thought that all Bedlam or Parnassus had been let out. The temple members, with their red fezes, yellow pantaloons, and curled slippers, knew nothing of the Five Pillars of Islam. They prayed standing upright with two fingers lifted on one hand and five on the other. They were ignorant of the exordium and even the basmalah. They claimed that the Prophet Mohammed was a black man, even though various hadiths spoke of the whiteness of the Prophet's skin. They fancied that the holy city of Islam was Morocco, not Mecca. They upheld shocking shirks, such as their insistence that Noble Drew was the divinely ordained prophet of Allah—a heresy in Islam, which teaches that the age of the prophets had ended with the death of Mohammed. They presented themselves as "angelic gods," even though the words of the *shahadah—Ashhadu an la ilaha illa Llah* ("I testify that there is no God but Allah")—represented the basis of Muslim belief. And they sang Christian hymns.

FAME, FORTUNE, AND POLYGAMY

Such matters appeared to be of little concern to Drew and his followers in October 1928, when the first national convention of the Moorish Science Temple took place in Chicago. By this time, Drew's movement boasted more than one hundred thousand followers, and his annual salary was listed at $36,000, a fortune at the time.[19] Drew received additional stipends for his living expenses, including the mortgage payment for his luxurious trappings on Chicago's South Side and the salaries for his chauffeur, maid, butler, and other domestic attendants. He kept several wives, a host of concubines, and fathered at least twenty children.[20] When he tired of one wife, he would quietly "divorce" her and "marry another."[21] He also kept four women at the same time and paid for each to live in separate homes.

Along with Father Divine, Daddy Grace, and Prophet Jones, Timothy Drew, at the age of forty-two, had emerged as one of the wealthiest and most influential black religious figures in America. "If you have money and don't give it to me to uplift our people," Drew assured his followers at the convention, "I am going to get it anyhow."[22]

With the millions pouring into the organization's coffers, members of Drew's inner circle began to vie for a piece of the action. Drew tried to placate them with promises of future rewards. "I have two wives," he said. "One day you will be able to have two, or as many as you can afford."[23]

MURDER AND MADNESS

But such words of assurance could not dispel the storm clouds that were brewing. On March 12, 1929, Claude Greene Bey, Drew's personal chaffeur, staged a coup d'état by pronouncing himself the grand sheikh, removing all files and furniture from Drew's headquarters and setting up a rival temple at the Unity House on the North Side of Chicago, where he began to call for the assassination of all whites and all Moors who objected to his leadership. Drew imported some thugs, including Ira Johnson Bey, from Pittsburgh to quell the rebellion. Three days later, Greene was shot and stabbed to death in the alleyway behind Unity House.[24]

Drew, while hosting a party to celebrate Greene's demise, was arrested as an accessory to homicide. From his prison cell, he penned the following message to his flock:

> To the Heads of All Temples, Islam: I, your Prophet, do hereby and now write you a letter as a warning and appeal to your good judgement for the present and the future. Though I am now in custody for you and the cause, it is all right and it is well for all who still believe in me and my Father-God Allah. I have redeemed all of you and you shall be saved, all of you, even with me. I go to bat Monday, May 20, before the Grand Jury. If you are with me, be there. Hold on and keep the faith, and great shall be your reward. Remember my laws and love ye one another. Prefer not a stranger to your brother. Love and truth and Peace I leave all. Peace from Your Prophet, Noble Drew Ali.[25]

ENTER MASTER FARD

While released on bail and awaiting trial, Drew Ali hastily promoted David Ford-el, also known as Master Fard Muhammad, as the acting head of the movement on July 20, 1929. It was not a prudent move. Fard was a criminal with fifty-eight aliases. He had served three years in San Quentin before gaining release on May 27, 1929, and purchasing a one-way ticket to Chicago, where he joined the Moorish Science Temple.[26]

Fard gained ascendency in the movement by assuring Drew and the other temple members that he was an Islamic scholar, had been born and bred in Mecca, and could convince the Muslim world that *The Circle of Seven Koran* represented the true teachings of Allah. Drew and Fard became inseparable, and Drew overnight elevated his new charge to the rank of grand sheikh with an annual salary of $25,000—far more than the amount paid to other Moorish officials. When members of

Drew's inner circle balked at the appointment, Drew chided them by saying: "There are going to be new Moors that are going to come in with their eyes wide open, seeing and knowing, that are going to take you old Moors, seat you in the back, and carry out my law."[27]

One month later, Noble Drew Ali was found dead at his home. The cause of his death has never been determined. Several of his followers speculated that he died as a result of injuries sustained in beatings from the police; others insisted that he had been murdered by his rivals. Neither an autopsy nor a full-scale police investigation was ever conducted.

THE POWER STRUGGLE

A struggle for the leadership of the Moorish Science Movement now got underway. Master Fard stepped forward to say that he had not only been duly appointed to the position of supreme grand sheikh but that he also now represented the living reincarnation of Noble Drew Ali. Charles Kirman-Bey, one of Greene's closest associates, refuted this by insisting that Fard had not been in the movement long enough to assume leadership. What's more, Kirman maintained that he himself had been duly named to serve as Drew's successor and that he could provide proof of this claim by referring to Noble Drew Ali's personal will, which just happened to be in his possession.[28]

Yet another claim to Drew's throne came from Ira Johnson Bey, the Pittsburgh thug who had been brought to Chicago to deal with the matter of Greene. Johnson claimed that Kirman was mentally unfit to serve as Drew's successor and that Master Fard was a fraud because Drew's resurrected spirit had, in fact, entered *his* body, making him the rightful leader of the American Moors.

A fourth faction materialized in the form of John Givens El, Noble Drew's personal chaffeur, who claimed to be the heir to Drew's mantel because he, too, had come to possess the *real* resurrected spirit of the dead prophet.

Things came to a boil on September 25, 1929, when Johnson and his thugs collared Givens and beat him to a bloody pulp. They next kidnapped Kirman from Greene's temple at the Unity House and held him prisoner at Johnson's apartment. When police attempted to rescue Kirman, a shoot-out ensued. One policeman and two Moors were killed. Sixty-three members of the Moorish Temple, including Johnson, were subsequently taken into custody. Johnson was committed to the state hospital for the criminally insane, where he subsequently died.

Upon recovery from the beating, Givens attempted to break into the residence of Drew's attorney in order to locate the prophet's personal papers. He, too, was sent to a mental asylum, but he gained release several years later. In 1941, he was heading a Chicago Moorish Temple on East Fortieth Street and still proclaiming himself as the supreme grand sheikh of all Moorish American Science temples.[29]

The future of Islam in America now rested with Fard Muhammad, the acting grand sheikh, who had packed up his bags and headed off for Detroit, where the story of Islam's intital appearance in America would become considerably more macabre.

Though ignored by scholars and students of religion, few have altered America's religious landscape to a greater extent than Timothy Drew. He convinced many within the black community that Islam represents their native religion and that Christianity remains the oppressive religion of the white man. At present, 90 percent of the American converts to Islam are African American; 60 percent of these African Americans converted to Islam while serving time in prison.[30] Many of the temples that Drew established are now Wahhabi mosques that incite anti-American sentiment among the poor and disenfranchised residents of the nation's inner cities.

CHAPTER 4

THE MYSTERY OF MASTER FARD

No one knows the true identity of Wallace D. Fard (Fred Dodd, Wallace Max Ford, or David Ford) or his nation of origin. Several FBI officials say that he was Polynesian; some maintain that he was a Russian Jew; others believe that he was a mulatto from Jamaica; and a few insist that he was born and raised in Bolton, England. Fard told his followers that he hailed from the holy city of Mecca and that his light-skinned appearance was "pre-ordained" by Allah so that he could more easily mix with white people. "I know you think I'm white," he told them, "but I'm not. I'm an Asiatic black man. I have come to America to save my long lost uncle [the African in America]."[1] When pressed further about his identity, he replied: "I am W. D. Fard and I came from the Holy City of Mecca. More about myself I will not tell you yet, for the time has not yet come. I am your brother. You have not yet seen me in my royal robes."[2]

Fard entered the annals of history on May 14, 1926, when he was found guilty of violating the California Poison Act for attempting to sell heroin and cocaine to undercover police officers. He was sentenced to a term of four years of hard time at the San Quentin State Penitentiary.[3] Prison records show that Fard stood at five feet six, weighed 127 pounds, and possessed a high forehead, with balding hair, and a large black mole on the right side of his stomach. They further attest to one physical feature that set him apart from all the other prisoners. Fard's eyes were "maroon," serving to give him the appearance of an emissary from the netherworld. In addition to the strange color of Fard's eyes, the prison records classify him as a "psychopath."[4]

When released on July 4, 1930, Fard hopped a freight train for Chicago, where he joined the Moorish Science Movement. Within a matter of months, he ascended the various orders to become an "exilarch" and Timothy Drew's closest associate.

After Drew's murder, Fard headed to Detroit, where he went from door to door throughout the newly burgeoning black community peddling silk dry goods and proselytizing the faith of Moorish Science. "I come from your homeland," he told the black housewives. "There, your people are princes, and there fine silk are what princes wear."[5] The line worked like a charm from the Arabian Nights. In no time at all, Fard amassed a considerable following, a comfortable nest egg of savings, and enough extra cash to establish the Allah Temple of Islam on the second floor of a clothing shop on Hastings Street.[6]

MODERN MUSLIM MATH

At the temple, Fard began producing hundreds of pamphlets that contained his unique spin on Moorish doctrine. One pamphlet contains thirty-four mind-boggling problems that must be addressed by all those who seek to join the temple. A sample follows: "A lion, in a cage, walks back and forth sixty feet per minute, seeking a way out of the cage. It took him nearly four centuries to find the door. Now, with modern equipment, he is walking three thousand feet per minute and he has three thousand miles by two thousand miles to go yet. How long will it take him to cover this territory of said three thousand miles by two thousand miles? He also has seventeen million keys, which he turns at the rate of sixteen and seventeen one-hundredths per minute. How long will it take him to turn the whole seventeen million? The above figures do not include rusty locks."

A cult member provided a partial solution to this problem by disclosing to agents of the Federal Bureau of Investigation that the lion in the cage represents the "original man," or Asiatic, who has been held in bondage for four centuries within a trap fabricated by the "Caucasian devil." The 17 million keys stand for the number of Asiatics who have been kept in bondage within the "wilderness of North America." The "modern equipment" is the teachings of Islam, which affords "original man" the means of achieving emancipation. The rusty locks represent the recalcitrant "originals" who have not yet accepted Islam.[7]

RULES OF THE TEMPLE

Another pamphlet authored by Master Fard sets forth the rules (one for each letter of the alphabet) for temple members:

a. All persons entering the Temple must be searched—products of the Caucasian Devil's art must not be taken into the Temple, such as, weapons, mirrors, fingernail files, cosmetics, cigarettes, medicine, etc.
b. All men leaving the Temple for the washroom must be searched upon their return to the Temple.
c. All men sit in a body in the front section of the Temple.
d. All women sit in the rear section.
e. All men use the right aisle of the Temple.
f. All women use the left aisle.
g. All men salute each other when passing.
h. Outside the Temple the women salute each other with a kiss on the side of the face.
i. All Moslems must greet each other with the Moslem greeting, "As Salaam Alaikum."
j. Moslems eat only one meal a day: orange juice or cocoa in the morning and a big meal at 4:00 o'clock.
k. The eating of pork is forbidden.
l. Tobacco is forbidden.

m. Alcohol is forbidden.
n. Moslems fast 18 days per year: Ministers and Officials fast 2 or 3 days per week: A Mohammed's family fasts seven days: A Prophet fasts twenty-three days.
o. A Moslem must not cross his legs while seated in the Temple.
p. A ninety-day suspension is given for sleeping during service.
q. A Moslem mother must wear full-length dresses to cover her feet.
r. A Moslem woman must wear low heel shoes.
s. A Moslem woman's hat must cover her hair.
t. A Moslem girl must wear dresses below her knees.
u. A Moslem woman must not use cosmetics.
v. A Moslem woman must not use hair preparations.
w. A follower must attend religious training sessions from 3 to 9 months in order to master the teachings and become a Moslem.
x. No Caucasian must enter the Temple.
y. 150 lbs. is the "righteous" weight for Moslem men.
z. A Moslem woman's place is in the home. A girl must be accompanied on the streets by her father or brother.[8]

In other writings and speeches, Fard presented himself as the reincarnation of Noble Drew, the long-awaited Mahdi of the Muslims, the Messiah of the Jews, and the anthropomorphic Allah. "In truth, I am the Supreme Ruler of the universe," he announced to police officials in 1933.[9] To this day, the belief that Master Fard, the ex-con from San Quentin, was Allah in the flesh remains a cardinal tenet of the Nation of Islam.

MUSLIMS FROM THE MOON

Gradually, Fard abandoned the teachings of *The Circle of Seven Koran* and fabricated his own theology and cosmology. The universe, he maintained, came into existence 78 trillion years ago when Allah created himself out of a single black atom, which materialized from nothing.[10] Trillions of years passed before another atom (also black) sprouted from the great darkness. This atom—the "atom of life"—attached itself to the divine atom, and, voila, Allah could now think. Endowed with this ability, Allah created the universe and planet Earth, which was originally the Moon. He also created the original man from the black mud of the Moon in his own image and likeness.

On planet Earth, the black race—the "original men"—settled in East Asia—a geographical area that, Fard believed, incorporated not only China and Japan but also India and the Middle East. From this original settlement, twelve tribes arose. One tribe of "Asiatics" moved on to northern Africa to create the ancient Egyptian civilization; a second tribe settled in Arabia and built the holy city of Mecca—a place that Fard always depicted as a virtual Garden of Eden.[11]

THE LOST TRIBE OF SHABAZZ

Fifty thousand years ago, a black scientist named Shabazz became bored with the idyllic life on the Nile and moved his tribe to the jungles of central Africa so that they would become better able to deal with the rigors of life in any setting. Over the course of thousands of years, the members of this tribe underwent phenotypical changes. Their hair became coiled and kinky; their thin lips swelled; and their noses became broader. These Asiatics, indeed, became more rugged physically, but at a price: they lost the cultural legacy of their forefathers.[12]

But the mistake of Shabazz in leading his people into darkest Africa paled in comparison with the evil exploits of another black scientist. Eight thousand four hundred years ago, Dr. Yakub, also known as "the big head scientist," set about to create a white race—a race bleached of any vestige of goodness—in order to gain control over his fellow Moors. When they learned of Dr. Yakub's plans, the Moors exiled him to the island of Patmos in the Aegean Sea.[13]

THE MAD SCIENTIST'S REVENGE

But the evil Dr. Yakub remained bound and determined, and, after six hundred years of trial and error, he succeeded in bringing the white devils into existence. He granted them a mandate to reign over the black race for six millennia—a time that had come to an end with the appearance of Master Fard in Detroit.[14]

The black folk in America, Fard maintained, were members of the tribe of Shabazz, who had been abducted from Africa by white slave traders during the fifteenth and sixteenth centuries. Fard proclaimed that part of his mission was to bring about the return of the tribe to their original home in Mecca.[15] "The Moslems have the wisdom," Fard assured his flock. "We're not afraid of the devil, this so-called white man. We talk right up to them. They're afraid of you if you've got the Truth. Just tell 'em, 'White man, you're a devil. You were grafted from the original black man.' He'll say, 'Yes, you're right.' He'll admit it 'cause you got the power. Just say, 'You're a beast, you've got one-third animal blood.' He won't deny it, 'cause it's true. When they were driven from the Holy City of Mecca they lived in the Caves of Europe and mingled with the beasts."[16]

The end of the world, according to Fard, will occur when a spaceship, known as the "Great Mother-plane," releases its fifteen hundred flying saucers equipped with special bombs. The Mother-plane, which measures a half mile by a half mile, hovers four miles above Earth and can be seen twice a week. When released, the special bombs will burrow one mile into Earth and ignite fires that will consume the planet. The white race will be destroyed and 144,000 Moors will be spared by the mercy of Allah. Fard freely admitted that he obtained the number 144,000 by listening to the broadcasts of Joseph Rutherford, president of the Jehovah Witnesses.[17]

THE TEMPLE AND "TRICKNOLOGY"

Three services a week—Wednesday and Friday at 7:00 p.m. and Sunday at 2:00 p.m.—were scheduled at the Allah Temple. All Muslims were expected to attend. Within a matter of months, the services became so crowded that additional times were added. By the end of 1931, the movement had become so vast that Fard rented another facility, on Melbing Street, and hired a staff of assistant ministers. At the end of one gathering, Elijah Poole, a Baptist sharecropper from Georgia, approached Fard and said: "I know who you are, you're God himself." To which Fard replied: "That's right, but don't tell it now! It is not time for it to be known."[18]

Thousands of black men with new Muslim names now appeared in the streets of Detroit with red fezes and black waistcoats. Black women, wearing silk scarves as headdresses, refused to send their children to public school for fear their sons and daughters would fall prey to the "tricknology" of white devils.[19] Black children were instead expected to drop out of public school and enroll in the University School of Islam, where they were confronted with Fard's bewildering mathematical problems and bizarre astrological projections.

In 1932, Detroit police officers raided the two Allah Temples and arrested several members of his cult, including Elijah Poole (Elijah Muhammad), for "contributing to the delinquency of minors."[20] The arrest prompted a large band of Moslems to storm the city lock-up in order to cause the release of the "teachers." The situation deteriorated rapidly until a judge intervened and ordered the prisoners' release.

THE "VOODOO MURDER"

On Thanksgiving Day 1932, Robert Harris, who had been renamed Robert Karriem, set up a makeshift altar from empty crates in a backroom of his house on Dubas Street. He strapped James T. Smith, one of Harris's boarders, to the altar and, in the presence of his wife "Queen" Bertha and twelve witnesses from the Allah Temple of Islam, plunged a silver dagger into the screaming victim at the stroke of noon. He narrowly missed Smith's heart. Smith fell from the table to the floor. Harris then smashed Smith's skull with the "rod of iron," a modified automobile axle.[21] Smith was stunned but still alive. Harris then proceeded to stab Smith in the chest again and again. Blood from severed arteries spurted throughout the room and soaked the caramel-colored carpet.[22] When it was finally certain that Smith was dead, the witnesses left the house in a daze. But the screams from the victim had attracted a flock of neighbors. The police were summoned, and officers stepped into a scene of unspeakable carnage.

Taken into custody, Harris told Detroit police officers that he had conducted the sacrifice in accordance with the teachings of Master Fard and cited the telling passage from "Secret Rituals of the Most-Found Nation of Islam." The next day, at his arraignment, Harris, wearing a fez, which he refused to remove, confessed to the crime with this statement: "The ninth hour of the twentieth day had come Sunday. It was predestined 1,500 years ago that at that hour I must make a human sacrifice to my gods. It must not be a member of the Order of Islam, but some stranger—the first person I met after leaving my home. It was crucifixion time. That's why I killed him."

Harris went on to say that he had made plans to kill Detroit's Mayor Murphy, two judges, and Miss Gladys Smith, a social worker; to cut off the head of his wife; and to dismember their two children, Ruby, nine years old, and Araby, twelve.[23]

THE VOODOO KING

The so-called voodoo murder created a media sensation and led to a raid on the Allah Temple of Islam, where Detroit detectives confiscated ritual books containing Fard's directive that it was the duty of every believing Muslim to offer "four Caucasian devils" as sacrifice in order to return to Mecca.[24] When questioned by the detectives, temple members refused to speak, maintaining that the penalty for divulging any secret of their religion was death.[25]

On November 23, Fard was arrested as "chief of the Voodoos" at the Fraymore Hotel on Jefferson Avenue.[26] At police headquarters, he "evaded questions cleverly," and, "with the complacent smile of the Oriental fakir," said that he was "the supreme being on earth."[27] Twelve other temple officials were taken into custody. These arrests caused hundreds of Moors, in full temple regalia, to descend upon police headquarters to demand the release of their "Savior." The action did little save to create the new headline: "500 Join March to Ask Voodoo King's Freedom."[28]

THE EXILE OF ALLAH

On November 27, Harris and Fard were transferred to the psychopathic ward of Detroit's Receiving Hospital. While Harris was deemed criminally insane, Fard was pronounced to be of sound mind and fit for trial. Facing a life sentence in prison as an accessory to murder, Fard confessed that his teachings were "strictly a racket" and that he was "getting all the money out of it he could."[29] He agreed to leave Detroit in order to receive immunity and boarded a train bound for Chicago on December 7.

In Chicago, Fard went about business as usual—selling silk goods from Mecca to black housewives and spreading the doctrine of Moors from the Moon. He managed to escape from the uproar of the "voodoo killing" by changing the name of his movement from the Allah Temple of Islam to the Nation of Islam.

The idea of establishing such a separate nation within the United States was not without precedent. In 1913, the Supreme Court had found that 561 Native American tribes could rightfully form their own governments on reservation land; enforce their own laws, civil and criminal; establish their own standards for membership; license and regulate their own activities; and zone and exclude people from their territories. What was good for the red man, Fard reasoned, was good for the black.

"We are a nation within a nation," Fard told his Chicago congregants. As a nation, they unfurled their own flag—a white star with a crescent on a red field—to symbolize "freedom, justice, and equality." The first letters of these words were emblazoned in the corners of the banner along with the letter *I* for *Islam.*[30]

And what better city could be found to establish a Nation of Islam than Chicago? In 1933, Chicago had one of the largest urban communities of African Americans in the country, second only to New York. And the Windy City offered opportunities for black folk that could not be found elsewhere. In 1928, the people of Chicago elected Oscar DePriest, an alderman, as the first black congressman since 1901. The public schools had become fully integrated without widespread public protest. What's more, blacks had obtained enough economic mobility to move into middle-class neighborhoods on the city's South Side.[31]

Within three months of his arrival in Chicago, Fard established the first Temple of the Nation of Islam on Linwood Street and a second temple on South Stony Island to accommodate the groundswell of converts.

THE FAREWELL VISITS

Despite his agreement with the police authorities, Fard made several clandestine trips to Detroit in order to come up with a strategy for the survival of the temples he was forced to abandon. He changed their names from the Allah Temples of Islam to the Temples of the Nation of Islam and placed them under the control of Elijah Poole, now Elijah Muhammad.

During one of his "farewell" visits to Detroit, in 1934, Fard proclaimed the "good news" that the impending war between blacks and whites was about to begin. "The white man will be destroyed this year," he said.[32] He assured his followers that the unidentified flying object recently sighted in Canada was really the Mother-plane that was ready to release its fleet of flying saucers. The Mother-plane, he said, had been built in Japan by "our Asiatic brothers," who longed for the elimination of all Caucasians from planet Earth.[33]

To prepare for the coming racial conflict, Fard created a paramilitary unit, called the Fruit of Islam, that all male members of his sect were obliged to join. These units drilled nightly in the temples with swords and wooden rifles and on weekends with actual firearms. The recruits were taught self-defense, including karate, and the ministers within each temple were assigned military ranks.[34]

Although Fard's prediction failed to take place, his announcement of a holy war proved to be of profound significance. Sixty-six years before the first bombing of the World Trade Center by Islamic radicals from a black congregation in Brooklyn, a Muslim preacher was proclaiming jihad to African Americans in Detroit and Chicago. The failure of law enforcement officials to come to terms with the threat of radical Islam that emerged from the black community was apparent from the get-go. The first act of violent jihad in the Western Hemisphere was about to occur while America remained in the grip of the Great Depression.

And then something astonishing happened. In June 1934 Fard disappeared from planet Earth without a trace.[35] For the next forty years, the FBI would engage in a massive manhunt to determine his fate or his whereabouts. Several of his followers said that he returned to Mecca; others, that he had gone to the Moon. One source claimed that he had boarded a ship for Australia; another, that he had booked a flight for Europe. Stories also arose that he had been slain by his followers as a sacrificial offering, under the direction of Elijah Poole, and had been buried in an unmarked grave.[36]

CHAPTER 5
THE RISE OF THE NATION OF ISLAM

Elijah Poole, now known as Elijah Muhammad, assumed leadership of the Nation of Islam (NOI) in the wake of Fard's disappearance. Born in 1894, Poole left school while in the fourth grade to work in the cotton fields around Sandersville, Georgia. Throughout his life, he remained inarticulate and illiterate, with little of the charm, charisma, and gift for the con that characterized Timothy Drew and W. D. Fard. His prison records show that he suffered from severe psychosis, possessed an IQ between 70 and 79, and displayed a mental age of 10.6 years.[1] Yet Poole, as Elijah Muhammad, would come to convince millions of African Americans that Islam represented the religion of the black race and that Mecca remained their true spiritual home. Few religious leaders of the twentieth century would come to have a greater impact on future generations.

THE MESSENGER'S WIT AND WISDOM

In order to impress his fellow members of the NOI, Poole set forth the following "actual facts" of physical science, history, and religion in the movement's official catechism:

1. Weight of the Planet Earth is 66 sex [*sic*] trillion tons.
2. Mussa (Moses) tried to civilize the Nordic Beast 4,000 years ago in the caves of Europe (year 11,000).

3. Jesus' justice came 2,000 years later. Jesus was a half original man, born in the month of September NOT in the month of December. Jesus was a prophet. Nimrod was born in the month of December, 25th day.
4. All prophets are black—never before in history has there ever been a white or Caucasian prophet.
5. Jesus' body is guarded by 10,000 Muslims by day and 10,000 by night. Jesus' body lies in the Temple of Omar in Jerusalem.
6. Remember the Crusades? The white devil tried unsuccessfully to take the body of our brother Jesus by laying siege to Jerusalem.
7. The root of Civilization is at the Holy City, Mecca. Mecca is in the far east and from Mecca comes all wisdom. All good things had their beginning in Mecca.
8. Allah means "peace," and reversed it means Halla, "joy." Have you not heard Christians cry HALLALUJAH while supposedly happy from the religion of a skunk.
9. English originated in 1382.
10. Christianity originated in 1522.

Poole insisted that the allotted time for the "white devils" to rule the world had come to an end and that the "War of Armageddon," in which the black race would cast over its shackles and overcome the white oppressors, was about to dawn in the streets of Detroit.[2]

POOLE'S SECRET SCHOOL

The dawn came sooner than expected. In January 1934, Detroit truant officers became aware that most of the high school dropouts within the Paradise Valley section of the city were affiliated with Fard's "voodoo cult" and that their parents had signed "Mohammedan" names on the public school enrollment forms. Under the prevailing school law, the removal of juveniles from public school without authorization from the school district represented child neglect.[3] Over the next three months, the truant officers observed forty African American children entering the Hastings Street Temple of the Nation of Islam day after day with schoolbooks. They reported their finding to Attorney George Schudlich, the city's chief prosecutor.

Alarmed by the news that the "voodoo cult" had not disbanded despite the agreement with Master Fard, Schudlich obtained a court order to close the school and, on April 13, summoned the police to conduct a raid on the temple. The officers discovered that more than four hundred "Moslem children" were enrolled at University School of Islam "campuses" throughout the Motor City. Each campus was lodged within a storefront temple. Of the teachers who were interrogated, not one was deemed "equipped to teach school"—even on the "most rudimentary" level. Some were completely illiterate. The curriculum at the campuses consisted of such subjects as "General Knowledge of the Spook Being Displayed for 6,000 Years," "Prophecy," and "General Knowledge of the Spook Civilization."[4]

TRAINED TO KILL

The discovery of the unlicensed schools produced more lurid headlines about the cult. One read: "Voodoo Cult Revived in the City: Negro Children Found in Islam School." In their reports, Schudlich and his aides confirmed that they witnessed "forty-six children" undergoing "military drill" at the Hastings Street Temple. "One of the children," the prosecutor said, "has informed me that the American flag means nothing to Moslems. The only flag they are taught to respect is the flag of Islam. Such practices might be considered as anarchism and syndicalism." He added that interviews with other children led him to conclude that they were being trained to kill.[5]

Several NOI officials, including Poole and his brothers James and John, were taken into custody, arraigned on charges of contributing to the delinquency of minors, and released on their own recognizance.[6]

At the hearing on April 18, 1935, Sally Ally, a seventeen-year-old student at the University of Islam, was called as the state's first witness. She underwent the following questioning by Attorney Schudlich:

> Q. What are you taught at the University of Islam about white people?
> A. I was taught that, if I cut the heads off four devils, I would win a trip to Mecca and a button with Allah's picture on it.
> Q. Who is Allah?
> A. W. D. Fard.
> Q. And when was the last time you saw Allah?
> A. About two months ago.
> Q. What else are you taught about Caucasians?
> A. That Caucasians would be put off the planet in 1934 and destroyed.
> Q. How destroyed?
> A. By poison gas and fighting.[7]

During his closing argument, Schudlich maintained that the children at the schools were being trained not only to decapitate white people, but also to kill blacks who refused to take part in the holy war. He reminded Judge Arthur Gordon, who presided over the hearing, that there already had been at least one victim of the "voodoo cult rituals" and that other murders were bound to occur unless Poole was placed behind bars and the cult outlawed for the common good.

The chief prosecutor's argument was forceful and profound. But Judge Gordon had received death threats from Poole's henchmen, and he was faced with a large number of angry Muslims in the courtroom. At the same time, he couldn't overlook the real threat that the Nation of Islam posed for the general populace. For this reason, he opted for a compromise. He found Poole guilty as charged but placed him on six months probation, with the stipulation that he close all the campuses of the University of Islam and oversee the reenrollment of all four hundred students in Detroit's public school system.[8]

THE REARING OF RACIAL JIHAD

Judge Gordon's verdict served only to embolden the NOI. To protest the closing of the schools, Poole assembled five hundred of his followers—many of them armed with sticks, bricks, knives, and straight razors—for a march on the Canfield Police Station, a few blocks from the Hastings Street Temple. When the marchers arrived at the station, they were met by a cordon of police officers. A shoving match ensued in which several Muslims were hit with nightsticks. When the police tried to pull Poole from the group in order to take him into custody, one of the Muslims yelled, "Get the coppers!"

All hell broke loose. A Muslim grabbed a bucket of paint from a man who was painting the rails at the entrance of the station. He spilled the paint over the face and head of one officer and then clubbed another with the empty bucket. Another temple member slashed a policeman's face with a straight razor. Still another cop was stabbed in the right temple by a Muslim with a pocket knife. More policemen arrived at the scene. When the riot was finally quelled, thirteen officers required medical treatment and forty-two Muslims, including Poole, were cuffed and placed in holding cells.[9]

The first incident of jihad had occurred on US soil. It emerged from the bizarre teachings of Timothy Drew and fantastic claims of Wallace Fard. It was spearheaded by Elijah Poole. And the motivating factor was not religion, but race. Few American historians took note of this incident, but foreign observers, including agents of Emperor Hirohito of Japan and scholars of orthodox Islam from the Middle East, were duly impressed by the deep-seated rage that burned within the bellies of thousands of African Americans against their native land.

Such foreign observers were equally astonished by the judicial outcome of this occurrence. Despite the attacks with straight razors and pocketknives on the police, Elijah Poole and his followers walked free and clear from the courtroom on April 21.[10] The judge dismissed all charges, fearing that more eruptions of violence would occur if he sentenced the rioters to a prolonged stay in the state penitentiary.

THE JAPANESE ALLIANCE

In the wake of the riot, Poole became associated with Satohata Takahashi, a prominent Japanese militant who had moved to the United States in 1930 to promote the aims of the *Kokuryukai* or Black Dragon Society (BDS).[11] The BDS had been a guiding force behind Japan's invasion of Korea in 1910 and the Japanese conquest of Mongolia in 1931. The organization possessed global aims that surpassed those of Hitler's National Socialist Party. It became intent on establishing a Fifth Column in the United States in preparation for a full-scale Japanese invasion.

Takahashi and his BDS associates believed they could accomplish this aim with the help of the Nation of Islam and other black organizations that championed racial revolution. On May 19, 1934, Takahashi announced the solidarity of the black and yellow races in the struggle against the white world to a gathering of the Bethel A.M.E. Church in downtown Detroit:

> I come here to promote international unity between the dark people of Japan and the dark people of America to lead them to a better and fuller life. What Japan has done in the past seventy years, the Negroes, too, can do in accepting Japan's guiding principles. The white man will give you little. If you obtain anything, it will be done through conquest. You must fight.[12]

His words were music to the ears of the members of the Nation of Islam. Here was a Japanese official giving credence to the teachings of Timothy Drew, Wallace Fard, and Elijah Poole: that blacks were Asiatics and not Africans; that the era of the white man was over; and that the long-awaited Armageddon—the great battle between blacks and whites—was just around the corner.

With the Japanese agents as Poole's allies and benefactors, money flowed into the NOI's coffers as never before. And with the money came a host of new converts, especially in the wake of an incident that occurred on February 24, 1935.

While riding a streetcar, Rosetta Hassan, an NOI member, became embroiled in an argument with Athenasia Christopolous, a Greek immigrant who had made a remark about Hassan's manner of Islamic dress. Mrs. Hasan responded by punching Miss Christopolous in the face and breaking the Greek woman's glasses. The police were called, and Hassan was charged with assault.

AMERICAN JIHAD'S FIRST FATALITY

At the hearing on March 6, Mrs. Hassan showed up in court with a posse of sixty temple members. The arbitrator, fearful of the crowd, ruled in favor of Mrs. Hassan. The Muslims broke out with cheers and headed for the rear door—the door to the judge's chambers. When the baliff cried out, "You people turn around and use the other exit," the NOI members reacted with violence. King Shah, the leader of the posse, knocked to the floor Joseph Palczynski, the seventy-three-year-old police captain, while other NOI members proceeded to kick and punch him until he lost consciousness. A police officer in attendance responded by shooting King Shah in the shoulder. The Muslims retaliated by shooting the baliff in the chest. Amid the mayhem, Allah Shah, another leader of the gang, was shot in the foot. By the time order was restored, the courtroom was riddled with bulletholes and Captain Palczynski lay dead in a pool of blood.[13]

One hundred fifty policemen took forty-three Muslims into custody on charges of aggravated assault and battery. King Shah and Allah Shah were charged with the shooting of the baliff and the murder of the police captain. Radical Islam had claimed its first fatality on American soil, but few of the Christians and Jews in Detroit seemed concerned or outraged. At the pretrial hearing, Muncipal Court Judge Edward Scheffler, fearful of another riot, dropped all charges against the Muslim defendants, even the Shah brothers.[14]

Detroit had now witnessed the voodoo murder, the illegal enrollment of four hundred children in a malevolent madrassah, a series of bloody riots in which police officers were clubbed and stabbed, and the killing of a police captain. Yet few cries of outrage emerged from the Christian and Jewish communities, not even over the rulings of the city's magistrates and judges. The situation was allowed to fester, and the crescent moon continued its ascent over the New World.

MUSLIM CORNPONE

By 1935, the Nation of Islam manifested some similarities to orthodox Islam. It upheld a halal diet, maintained a modest dress code, observed the holy month of Ramadan and certain prayer rituals, and accepted Abraham, Moses, and Jesus as prophets. But the dissimilarities remained enormous and insurmountable. Traditional Islam worshipped Allah as immortal, incorporeal, eternal, and omniscent. The NOI presented Allah as mortal, corporeal, and temporal—a divine being who underwent several incarnations. Traditional Islam held that all people were created by Allah "from mud moulded into clay" (Quran 15: 26–29). The NOI insisted that white people were "grafted" into devils through the process of bleaching. Traditional Islam viewed Mohammed as the last prophet of Allah, but the NOI reserved this title for Poole.

Regarding eschatology, traditional Islam upheld that the Last Judgment would occur in the wake of the final conflict between the *dar ul-Islam* (the House of Believers) and the *dar ul-Harb* (the House of Unbelievers). Within the NOI, the epic battle would take place not between believers and nonbelievers, but rather between blacks and whites. This struggle would terminate not in the establishment of a universal caliphate, but rather with the arrival of the Motherplane to transport the blacks back to Mecca.

There were other differences. Within traditional Islam, the *ulema* (a group of scholars) interpret doctrine and guide the worship of the *umma* (the body of believers) with the assistance of *imams* (prayer leaders). Within the NOI, Poole ruled in a dictatorial manner and with an iron fist. In a traditional mosque, unlike the NOI temples, there are no altars, sanctuaries, or chairs; no ministers to mediate between Muslims and Allah; and no music or dancing.

Inadverently, Poole was clearing the urban wilderness for the arrival of genuine Islamic imams; and the racially charged Nation of Islam, despite the messenger's inepitude, was becoming more than a blip on America's religious landscape.

POOLE TAKES A POWDER

But in the wake of Judge Scheffler's ruling, Poole, filled with euphoria, began to make announcements that almost broke the movement's newfound momentum to a grinding halt. He proclaimed that the Japanese had completed the construction of the Mother-plane and that "the end of the world" would occur before the end of the year. "This is the last of the devil," he said. "He will have no more power."[15] Because the time was short, Poole encouraged his followers to surrender all their worldly possessions to the NOI and to refrain from reading any newspaper save the *Final Call*, the movement's weekly publication.

Poole was not known as farsighted. The year 1935 came and went. Yet the white race had not been vanquished, and no Mother-plane, let alone a slew of flying saucers, had appeared in the skies over Detroit. The messenger attempted to explain the delay by saying that Fard (Allah) had decided to give the white man a "one-year extension."[16]

An extension of a year seemed understandable. But by 1937, the white devils were still strolling the streets, and not a single flying saucer was in sight. Poole had placed himself in a proverbial pickle. There was a growing belief among his followers that he was a fraud. Moreover, he was living high off the hog in a spacious fifteen-room dwelling, while they remained in flop houses and rundown tenement buildings. To make matters worse, in preparation of their deliverance, they had disposed of all their earthly goods—their living-room furniture, their dining-room tables and chairs, their silverware and utensils, even their pots and pans. Poole had received these items, sold them as salvage to local junk dealers, and pocketed the cash. It was small wonder, therefore, that a sizeable number of NOI adherents were now prepared to tar and feather him.[17]

Poole packed his bags, bid farewell to his wife and children, and headed off for Washington, DC.

VOODOO REDUX

Before his departure, Poole had decreed that it was the duty of every Muslim to convert all the members of his household. He threatened to excommunicate all those who failed to accomplish this objective within the span of a year. In addition, Poole upheld Fard's teaching that believers were expected to sacrifice four unbelievers in order to board the Mother-plane for the magical journey to Mecca.[18]

On January 16, 1937, Tata Pasha, an assistant minister at a satellite temple in Detroit, ordered Verlen McQueen, an NOI member, either to convert his wife Rebecca and his eleven-year-old daughter Dorothy or to sacrifice them as offerings to Allah. McQueen pled with them to sign their names to the "Lamb's Book of Life" and enroll in the movement. When they refused, he began to boil a ten-gallon pot of water and to transform the kitchen table into a make-shift altar. Rebecca, noting the preparations, called the police. Hauled into custody, McQueen admitted that he was planning to kill and cook his family members because they were "unholy." He was arrested on charges of attempted murder, and Rebecca and Dorothy were placed in a protection program so that they would be safe from the clutches of other NOI affiliates.[19]

The adverse publicity from the incident caused hundreds of African Americans to rethink their commitment to the NOI. By February 1937, over five hundred families yanked their membership from the Detroit and Chicago temples and reassumed their "slave names." The movement, it seemed, was about to go bust.

ENTER GULAM BOGANS

In Washington, DC, Poole rented a room as Charles Evans, proclaimed the doctrine of the Nation of Islam as Muhammad Rasoull, and collected welfare as Gulam Bogans. He continued to receive bountiful financial support from Satohata Takahashi and the Japanese militants, who printed flyers and pamphlets that were distributed throughout the inner city. "Japan's new policy," Takahashi proclaimed in one pamphlet, "is to establish a new epoch in world history by leading the darker majority of mankind to a new life funded on international justice."[20] He urged the inner-city blacks to support Poole's new NOI temple, a storefront building on U Street. In exchange for such support, Takahashi pledged that blacks would receive a single-family detached house in Hawaii and lifetime employment by the Japanese government as soon as America was defeated in the coming war.[21] Lured by this promise, hundreds of the 180,000 blacks within the nation's capital made their way to the makeshift temple, where they purchased fezes and headscarves and received new identity cards.

POOLE GOES TO PRISON

In 1940, Congress passed the Selective Training and Service Act of 1940, which required all men between the ages of twenty-one and thirty to register for the draft. Poole ordered his followers to ignore the law and to challenge induction on moral and religious grounds. In May 1941, the act was extended to include all men between the ages of eighteen and forty-four. To make matters worse, the law now permitted individuals with fourth-grade scholastic abilities, such as Poole, to serve in the armed forces.

This amendment prompted Poole, at forty-four years of age, to go on a crash diet in order to reduce his weight to below the 112-pounds minimum requirement for military service. Failing to achieve this goal, he neglected to show up for his preinduction physical. A warrant for Poole's arrest was issued on February 16, 1942. The prophet was taken into custody several months later and placed in a detention facility.

On July 23, Poole's wife Claire traveled from Detroit to post the $5,000 bail and secure his release, pending trial. Still fearful of induction, Poole opted to go on the lam. On September 20, he was located at his mother's house in Chicago, where he was hiding under a bed and wrapped in a carpet. Two months later, the messenger of Allah was sentenced as Gulam Bogans to five years at the federal corrections institute in Milan, Michigan, for violation of the Selective Service Act.

At the prison, Poole was subjected to a battery of psychological tests that displayed his low IQ and his mental age of 10.6 years.[22] He was diagnosed as suffering from dementia praecox and acute schizophrenia. He was placed on medium security status and assigned to work as a janitor in the administration building.[23]

BACK IN BUSINESS

Poole was released from prison on October 7, 1947—his fiftieth birthday. By this time, the Nation of Islam had dwindled to fewer than two hundred members. Temple no. 1 in Detroit had fallen from five hundred members in 1937 to only thirty-five, twenty-one of whom were women and children. Temple no. 2 in Chicago attracted a skeletal crew, while Temple no. 3 in Milwaukee and Temple no. 4 in Washington, DC, had closed. These temples were far from architectural marvels with spiraling minarets and large golden domes. They were dusty old storefronts in the poorest sections of the cities. The meeting halls consisted of folding chairs before a podium and painted blackboards depicting black men hanging from trees and crescent moons.[24]

But Poole, thanks to his Japanese friends, had managed to squirrel away a substantial nest egg. He had also managed to recruit scores of African Americans within the federal prison system to his movement. Along with these disciples, the NOI leader returned to the rundown temple in Detroit not with a message of a coming spaceship and free homes in Hawaii, but rather with talk of "Blackstone Nation," which would be created from the acquisition of four to five Southern states. Poole felt that this goal could be accomplished through Dr. Ralph Bunche, the undersecretary of the newly created United Nations (UN).

Bunche, who had won the Nobel Peace Prize, was an African American who had been instrumental in the separation of Palestine into separate Jewish and Arab states. If the UN could create a homeland for the wandering tribes of Israel, why not a separate nation for the lost-found Tribe of Shabaaz? If Bunche was willing to relocate hundreds of thousands of Palestinians, why not millions of white Southerners? This appeal, Poole believed, was in accord with the National Association for the Advancement of Colored People's petition to the UN for consideration of the economic plight of African Americans that had been filed on October 23, 1947.[25]

Several hundred blacks eventually trickled back to the temple—enough to allow the movement to regain its footing in Detroit and to revitalize its deserted temple in Chicago. In addition to the promise of free land and a home in "Blackstone Nation," Poole also offered his followers employment opportunities. By 1948, he had used a portion of his savings to purchase a 140-acre farm in White Cloud, Michigan, and to open a string of businesses in Chicago and Detroit, including grocery stores for faux halal food, a dry-cleaning plant, a beauty shop, an Islamic restaurant featuring Muslim black-bean pie, and a bakery on South Wentworth Avenue.

HIGH OFF THE HALAL HOG

Insight into Poole's financial condition at this time could be judged by his nineteen-room mansion on Woodlawn Avenue, his taste for dining in the city's finest restaurants, his family's fleet of new Cadillacs®, and his harem of concubines and eleven illegitimate children—all of whom he kept in separate dwellings and supported with weekly stipends from his seemingly bottomless treasure chest.

The size of the movement can be judged by the annual national convention of the NOI in 1952—an event that attracted fewer than two hundred participants. At the gathering, Poole introduced Malcolm Little, a former pimp, petty crook, and homosexual prostitute, who had just been released from the Norfolk Prison Colony in Massachusetts, where he had served an eight-year stint for grand larceny.[26] Poole presented him as the prototype of the "Biblical Job" and gave him the new name of Malcolm X. "The Muslim's X," Malcolm later explained, "symbolized the true African name that he could never know."[27]

CHAPTER 6
MALCOLM X
THE CALL TO MECCA

Malcolm Little, the "new Biblical Job," had dropped out of junior high school in 1940 and had been ruled mentally disqualified for military service in 1943. At Norfolk, the prison psychiatrist ruled that he suffered from "pre-psychotic paranoid schizophrenia" and represented a threat to society. In short, he was an ideal soul mate for Elijah Poole and the perfect candidate to spread the NOI doctrine of racial upheaval throughout postwar America.[1]

Malcolm, a charismatic speaker, was sent on "fishing expeditions" in Boston, Philadelphia, and New York. The purpose of the expeditions was to attract enough members to establish new temples. Malcolm believed that black people would go anywhere to hear "good preaching."[2] And he knew that he could outpreach the staid and somber pastors of mainline Christianity with his message of how the "white man had kidnapped, robbed, and raped the black race."[3] He and his associates began to hold services at 2:00 p.m. on Sundays—when the Christian services were over and the people had been "conditioned" for the bait. These outings were so successful that the NOI's new firebrand was dispatched to Atlanta, Hartford, Los Angeles, Baltimore, Richmond, Atlantic City, Camden, and Springfield, Massachusetts. At all of these locations, he met with tremendous success.

THE X FACTOR

By 1960, membership in the NOI, thanks to Malcolm, had more than tripled, and more than one hundred temples, now called mosques, popped up at various locations throughout the country. Several, including the mosque in Richmond, were Christian churches where the gospel became replaced with the doctrine of racial hatred and the cross on the steeple became reshaped into a crescent moon. Some of the ministers were former Protestant clerics, including David X of the Richmond Mosque; one—Louis X (soon to be known as Louis Farrakhan)—was a popular singer, known as "the Charmer," who penned the movement's hymn "White Man's Heaven Is Black Man's Hell."

In meeting after meeting, Malcolm held that Christianity represented the false religion of the white man, with precepts that must be denounced by all African Americans. Jesus, he argued, was a black prophet who preached for twenty years in the streets of Jerusalem. He was killed, and his body remains there—guarded by Muslims. "He is dead," Malcolm proclaimed, "and cannot come back to save the black man."[4] Instead of decrying this message as heresy, Christian clerics throughout the country welcomed Malcolm into their pulpits, and regular meetings of the NOI were held at the Tabernacle Baptist Church in Chicago, the King Solomon Baptist Church in Detroit, the Mount Sinai Baptist Church in Pittsburgh, and the First Baptist and Cory Methodist Churches in Cleveland. Even more mind-boggling is the fact that the annual gatherings of the NOI were held at the Metropolitan Baptist Church at Forty-First and South Parkway in Chicago, where Poole (Elijah Muhammad), crowned with a jewel-studded fez valued at $150,000, held forth as the "Savior of the black race."[5]

Throughout this time, Malcolm, Poole, and the other NOI officials remained blissfully unaware that the Prophet Mohammed held the black race in contempt and referred to his black slaves as "raisin heads" (Hadith 1:662; 9:259). The white racism inherent within the core of Islam is further evidenced by these passages from the Quran and the Hadith:

> Narrated Anas bin Malik: Allah's Apostle said, "You should listen to and obey, your ruler even if he was an Ethiopian (black) slave whose head looks like a raisin." (Sahih Bukhari, vol. 9, book 89, no. 256)
>
> Muhammad warned that dreams of black women meant disease was forthcoming. (Hadith 9:162,163)
>
> Muslims are told that Africans "annoy the Prophet" (Ishaq 243) and have hearts "grosser than a donkey" (Surah 9:61) and that blacks should be left to die if injured and should be denied intercession and entrance to heaven. (Bukhari, vol. 4, book 52, no. 137)

Malcolm further assumed that the bizarre doctrine of Elijah Poole represented the thought of mainstream Islam throughout the world. In a speech to the Harvard Law School Forum in 1960, he said: "We here in America, who are under the Divine Leadership of the Honorable Elijah Muhammad, are an integral part of the vast world of Islam that stretches from the China Seas to the sunny shores of Africa."[6]

GIFTS FROM GAMAL

The NOI's additional momentum came from Arab dignitaries, including President Gamal Nasser of Egypt. A committed Communist, Nasser sought to foster racial unrest throughout the United States with the intent of weakening the democratic process. This contention was upheld by Thurgood Marshall, the top attorney of the NAACP Legal Defense and Education Fund, who described the NOI as an organization "run by a bunch of thugs from prisons and jails, and financed, I am sure, by Nasser or some other Arab group."[7] Malcolm traveled to Cairo to meet with Anwar el Sadat and other Muslim leaders who pledged to assist in the construction of mosques throughout the country. Poole also made the trek to Egypt, where he met with Nasser, who reportedly offered to build for him a seventy-five room palace.[8]

How much financial support poured into Poole's coffers from such sources still remains a matter of conjecture. But FBI officials became deeply alarmed by the ties between Poole and the Arabs. A confidential 1959 report from the agent in charge of the New York field office to Director J. Edgar Hoover reads as follows: "There is intense cooperation between representatives of Arab nations in the United States and this Muslim movement. They have been on the platforms of Elijah [Poole] in any number of instances. The heads of the Arab students in the United States have cooperated with them. . . . In terms of personnel; in terms of appearance on their platform; in terms of encouraging what they [Poole and company] have to say, I am prepared to say that this cooperation does exist and for which reason I suggest that the movement is more dangerous than many of us appreciate."[9]

STRANGE BEDFELLOWS: BAD FRUIT

But the weirdness of the group became increasingly weirder. To oppose integration and to uphold miscegnation, Poole formed an alliance with George Lincoln Rockwell of the American Nazi Party. Rockwell, in full Nazi regalia, attended a gathering of eight thousand members of the NOI at the Uline Arena in Chicago on June 25, 1961. On this occasion, Malcolm delivered an oration titled "Separation or Death." Rockwell liked what he heard and placed twenty dollars in the collection plate.[10]

By the time of Rockwell's visit, members of the NOI, thanks to the publication of a book by C. E. Lincoln,[11] became known as Black Muslims, and the Fruit of Islam, the paramilitary arm of the NOI, evolved into a terror squad that served to ensure conformity among the rank and file. Those who tried to leave the movement were hunted down by Poole's goons, who brandished straight razors and rubber hoses. The same fate befell those who failed to pay their tithes and membership dues. Malcolm later admitted that he had been a witness to such tactics.[12]

In 1964, Clarence "Pudding" 13 X and a group of other Fruit of

Islam thugs, broke away from the NOI to form the "Five Percenters." The name derived from the group's insistence that they were the chosen five percent of humanity to manifest "the true nature of the black man who is God or Allah."[13] From their origin in Harlem, the Five Percenters formed gangs within the five boroughs of New York and within the New York prison system. The headquarters of the splinter group was set up on the corner of Adam Clayton Powell Boulevard and 126th Street. The site was called the "Allah School in Mecca"—Mecca being Harlem. Funding for the headquarters came from John Lindsay, New York's mayor, who believed the Five Percenters could be used to stem urban violence. His belief was misplaced, and Pudding himself was eventually gunned down in gang warfare on June 12, 1969.[14]

POOLE HITS PAYDIRT

By 1963, Poole, as Elijah Muhammad, had become as rich as Cressus. In addition to his mansion and farm, he purchased two additional personal residences in Arizona and employed a staff of house servants and attendants. His wife and daughters were adorned with furs and jewels, and he kept a harem (compliments of his followers) of five concubines. In addition to their tithes and offerings, all members were required to cough up annual payments of $125 to cover Poole's living expenses; men were expected to purchase forty-four copies of each edition of *Muhammad Speaks*, the movement's biweekly newspaper; and women were required to purchase their ankle-length robes and headpieces from a store owned by one of Poole's legitimate daughters. The excess revenue was whisked away to Swiss bank accounts.[15] No financial records were kept and no audits were conducted by the IRS.

INCEST AND INDISCRETION

But there were cracks in the temple that soon would become fissures. Poole could no longer conceal his adulterous relationships, since several of his mistresses threatened to file paternity suits. Word of Poole's indiscretions, his eighteen illegitimate children, incestuous behavior, and financial irregularities was leaked to Malcolm and other NOI ministers.[16] The allegations seemed preposterous. Poole was small (five feet five), frail (weighing less than 140 pounds), and sickly. He suffered from acute bronchial asthma, diabetes mellitus, and arteriosclerotic heart disease.[17] The guy could scarcely breathe, let alone walk. But when Malcolm confronted the NOI leader with the rumors, Poole readily admitted his failings. "I'm David," he said. "When you read about how David took another man's wife. I'm that David. You read about Noah, who got drunk—that's me. You read about Lot, who went and laid with his own daughters. I have to fulfill all of these things."[18]

MALCOLM BREAKS RANK

Malcolm was aware of Poole's hypocrisy and corruption but continued to serve as the minister of Temple no. 7 in Harlem. He might have remained one of Poole's faithful lackeys, save for the assassination of President John F. Kennedy on November 22, 1963. When questioned about the event in Dallas, Malcolm labelled the assassination as a case of "the chickens coming home to roost."[19] Poole, who had become increasingly annoyed by his disciple's celebrity, responded to Malcolm's ill-timed statement by silencing him for ninety days.

Being disciplined by a rogue and a charlatan was difficult to swallow. Malcolm realized that the silencing was an excuse to keep him out of the limelight before eliminating him from the movement. And he knew that Poole, with his Fruit of Islam thugs, was capable of violence. This awareness became crystallized into fear when he began to receive death threats from officials and members of his temple.

On March 8, 1964, Malcolm left the NOI to establish Muslim Mosque, Inc. (MMI) and the Organization of Afro-American Unity, two groups for Muslims who wished to disassociate themselves from Poole and his movement. This creation drove Poole beyond the edge of sanity. "This hypocrite is going to get blasted off the face of the earth," he intoned on a tape that was cut for airing at all the NOI temples.[20] The day after Poole issued this unmistakable order to kill Malcolm, the FBI's Domestic Intelligence Division sent the following communiqué to all US intelligence offices:

> Muslim Mosques, Inc. (MMI), is a black nationalist group formed by Malcolm X Little, former New York Nation of Islam (NOI) leader who has been attempting to discredit Elijah Muhammad, head of NOI.
>
> Attached reports formation of group by Malcolm X Little called "Organization of Afro-American Unity," which has announced purpose of sponsoring a reform program aimed at getting racial problems before United Nations. We have been following this development very closely. Dissemination is being made to [Justice] Department, State, Secret Service, and Military agencies.[21]

It was time for Malcolm to get out of town and head for Mecca and his long-awaited hajj.

MALCOLM'S MECCA EPIPHANY

Malcolm's trip to Mecca served as a spiritual awakening. He became aware that real Muslims do not believe that they came from the Moon and that white people were created by Dr. "Big-Head" Yakub. They made no mention of a Mother-plane or of the lost tribe of Shabazz. What's more, most of the folks walking around the Kaaba were white—maybe not lily-white, but certainly Caucasian. Malcolm was shocked to the quick. He wrote to his friends at the MMI:

> America needs to understand Islam, because this is the one religion that erases from society the race problem. Throughout my travels in the Muslim world, I have met, talked to, and even eaten with people who in America would have been considered "white"—but the "white" attitude was removed from their minds by the religion of Islam. I have never before seen sincere and true brotherhood practiced by all colors together, irrespective of color.[22]

The Muslims, too, were amazed to encounter an American who actually claimed to be a Muslim. He represented a religious oddity of such magnitude that Saudi Arabia's Prince Faisal opted to make him a guest of the state.[23] "The Muslim from America," Malcolm wrote, "excited everywhere the most intense curiosity and interest."[24] At the House of Saud, "America's angriest Negro"[25] performed the rituals of Umrah as an "orthodox" Sunni Muslim and assumed the new name of El Hajj Malik El-Shabazz.

As a Sunni convert, Malcolm was embraced by the Arab world. Kwame Nkrumah of Guana offered him a cabinet post. Similar offers were made by Ben Bella of Algeria and Egyptian president Nasser. Saudi Arabia presented him with twenty-five scholarships for American Muslims interested in studying Islam and becoming imams.[26] The Saudis also promised to construct a multimillion-dollar mosque in Los Angeles for the new convert.

THE TV APPEARANCE

Upon his return to America, Malcolm made an appearance on the *Irv Kupincet Show* as El Hajj Malik El-Shabazz. During the course of the program, which was aired on January 30, 1965, Malcolm spoke of his epiphany in Mecca and said, "What Elijah Muhammad is teaching is diametrically opposed to the principles of Islam and the Muslim world itself. The religious officials at Mecca . . . and those at the top authority on Islam theology totally reject Elijah Muhammad as being . . . Islam." Adding that there were so few Islamic scholars and mosques in the United States, Malcolm proclaimed that it was easy for "any phony or faker to come along with a concocted, distorted product of his own making and say that this is Islam."[27]

PRESCRIBED PUNISHMENT

Poole and the members of the NOI inner circle were fit to be tied. In the December 4 issue of *Muhammad Speaks,* Louis "the Charmer" Farrakhan, who now occupied Malcolm's position at Temple no. 7, wrote, "If any Muslim backs a fool like Malcolm in building a mosque, he would be a fool himself. . . . Only those who wish to be led to hell, or to their doom, will follow Malcolm. The die is set, and Malcolm shall not escape. . . . Such a man as Malcolm is worthy of death."[28]

The Charmer's words served as a directive. In the early hours of February 14, Malcolm's house in Queens was firebombed as he and his family slept.[29] A week later, Malcolm was gunned down while addressing a crowd of four hundred people at the Audubon Ballroom near Harlem. He was pronounced dead on arrival at Presbyterian Hospital. The autopsy revealed that he had been hit fifteen times with 9 mm caliber bullets and shotgun pellets, with five exit wounds. Nine bullets and pellets were retrieved from the body.[30]

ALLAH ENTERS AMERICA

The sad status of orthodox Sunni Islam in the United States is verified by the attempts to have Malcolm buried from a traditional mosque. No such mosque could be located in New York City or its environs. Malcolm's family was equally hard-pressed to find an orthodox imam who could prepare the black leader's body for burial. This caused a delay in the internment that represented a violation of the Islamic law that the sun should not set twice on a believer's body. Ahmed Hassoun, a Sudanese sheikh, was flown to New York to wash the body with special holy oil and to wrap Malcolm's remains in the seven white linen shrouds, known as the *kafan*.[31] Six days after his death, the funeral was held at the Faith Temple Church of God in Christ. The irony of the setting seemed lost on the hundreds of people in attendance.

But this situation of Islam in America was soon to be reversed. In the past, Arab leaders, such as Nasser, had supported the NOI for political reasons, with the hope of creating civil unrest that would serve to undermine US foreign and domestic policy, but now they realized that millions of African Americans could be converted to orthodox Islam from Christianity without much effort. Many, like Malcolm, despised Judeo-Christianity as the "white man's religion" and Jesus as "the white man's God." They had come to believe, thanks to Drew, Fard, and Poole, that Islam was "the black man's religion" and that Mecca was their spiritual home. What's more, as a result of Malcolm's conversion, Islam had gained a firm footing on American soil for the first time in history. Hundreds of his followers had converted by his example. The converts included Poole's son, Akbar, who volunteered to assist in the implantation of orthodox Sunni mosques at strategic locations throughout the United States.[32]

MALCOLM'S LEGACY

Two years after Malcolm's death, the members of the MMI, with generous gifts from Arab Muslims, established the Mosque of International Brotherhood on 113th Street in Harlem. The storefront establishment was located next to a neon-lit laundromat. Shaykh Allama al-Hajj Ahmad Tawfiq, one of Malcolm's closest friends, became the founding imam. In accordance with the agreement that Malcolm had effected with the Saudis, Shaykh Allama and other members of the MMI had been trained in radical Wahhabi doctrine at the al-Azhar University in Cairo. Soon a host of other orthodox mosques popped up throughout the five boroughs of New York—

almost all had been funded by Saudis, and almost all of the imams had been trained at the al-Azhar University.

In 1988, the dome of the first mosque ever built in New York rose like a half-moon above a construction site on Third Avenue. The $12 million structure was built with funds from the emir of Kuwait and the king of Morocco. Building the Islamic Cultural Center was not without problems. Aly S. Dodran, the architect for the project, was dismissed by the indignant Sunni trustees when they learned that he had paid a fee to a Jewish concern for technical assistance.

Within thirty-five years of Malcolm's death, hundreds of orthodox Sunni mosques were thriving within every borough of the city. Malcolm, however, does not deserve sole credit for the proliferation of orthodox mosques in New York City and throughout the country. This development could not have occurred without the legislative changes that were championed by Senator Ted Kennedy of Massachusetts.

CHAPTER 7
THE OPENING OF THE FLOODGATES

"This bill we sign today is not a revolutionary bill. It does not affect the lives of millions. It will not restructure the shape of our daily lives." So said President Lyndon Johnson at the signing of the Hart-Celler Act—a ceremony that took place within the shadow of the Statue of Liberty. The quota system that governed the United States throughout much of its history was viewed as an outgrowth of a system of racism and discrimination that had to be eliminated for the greater good of the country. "This [quota] system," Mr. Johnson maintained, "violates the basic principle of American democracy—the principle that values and rewards each man on the basis of his merit as a man. It has been un-American in the highest sense, because it has been untrue to the faith that brought thousands to these shores even before we were a country."[1]

At the time of the signing, immigration reform was not a pressing concern of the American people. A 1965 Harris poll showed that the public strongly opposed any change to the existing immigration law by a two-to-one margin (58 percent to 24 percent).[2] Nevertheless, as civil rights laws loosened the grip of racial discrimination, the national origins system, which favored Irish, German, and British immigration at the expense of southern and eastern European, as well as Asian and Latin American immigration, became viewed as the equivalent of Jim Crow, a reflection of ethnic superiority that contradicted "America's ideal of the equality of all men without regard to race, color, creed, or national origin," as Senator Hiram Fong (R-HI) proclaimed at the commencement of the Senate hearings for the new immigration legislation.[3]

NEW MORAL DILEMMA

The push for the end of quotas reflected the new moral self-consciousness of the Cold War. How could the United States exert world leadership, asked Congressman Emanuel Celler (D-NY), one of the bill's cosponsors, if our current immigration system was "a gratuitous insult to many nations?"[4] The new legislation, according to its Republican and Democratic advocates, was part of the evolutionary trend in federal politics toward a new age of equality and toleration. Rep. Philip Burton (D-CA) upheld this belief by saying: "Just as we sought to eliminate discrimination in our land through the Civil Rights Act, today we seek by phasing out the national origins quota system to eliminate discrimination in immigration to this nation composed of the descendants of immigrants."[5] Similarly, Rep. Robert Sweeney (D-OH) said, "I would consider the amendments to the Immigration and Nationality Act to be as important as the landmark legislation of this Congress relating to the Civil Rights Act. The central purpose of the administration's immigration bill is to once again undo discrimination and to revise the standards by which we choose potential Americans in order to be fairer to them and which will certainly be more beneficial to us."[6]

Under the old system, admission largely depended upon an immigrant's country of birth. Seventy percent of all immigrant slots were allotted to natives of just three countries—the United Kingdom, Ireland, and Germany—and went mostly unused, while there were long waiting lists for the small number of visas available to those born in Italy, Greece, Poland, Portugal, and elsewhere in eastern and southern Europe. The new system eliminated the various nationality criteria, supposedly putting people of all nations on an equal footing for immigration to the United

States. It substituted a system based primarily on family reunification and needed skills.[7]

A SIMPLE SYMBOLIC ACT

The new legislation was supposed to serve as a symbolic act—an extension of civil rights sentiments—that would not produce a huge and sustained increase in the number of newcomers from third-world countries, let alone serve as a vehicle for globalizing immigration. Senate immigration subcommittee chairman Edward Kennedy (D-MA), who served to shepherd the bill through the Senate, offered this reassurance to his fellow legislators:

> First, our cities will not be flooded with a million immigrants annually. Under the proposed bill, the present level of immigration remains substantially the same. . . . Secondly, the ethnic mix of this country will not be upset. . . . Contrary to the charges in some quarters, [the bill] will not inundate America with immigrants from any one country or area, or the most populated and deprived nations of Africa and Asia. . . . In the final analysis, the ethnic pattern of immigration under the proposed measure is not expected to change as sharply as the critics seem to think. . . . The bill will not flood our cities with immigrants. It will not upset the ethnic mix of our society. It will not relax the standards of admission. It will not cause American workers to lose their jobs.[8]

Echoing this claim, the new attorney general, Nicholas Katzenbach, testified:

> This bill is not designed to increase or accelerate the numbers of newcomers permitted to come to America. Indeed, this measure provides for an increase of only a small fraction in permissible immigration.[9]

THE WARNINGS IGNORED

Opponents of the bill, most of them conservatives still in disarray from the Goldwater rout in 1964, argued that the Hart-Celler Bill would vastly increase the number of immigrants coming into the country and that the bulk of those immigrants would be coming from third-world nations, representing a threat to the country's existing demographic profile. Myra C. Hacker, vice president of the New Jersey Coalition of Patriotic Societies, warned of granting entree to "an indeterminately enormous number of aliens from underprivileged lands."[10] Whatever may be America's benevolent intent toward many people, Ms. Hacker maintained, the bill "fails to give due consideration to the economic needs, the cultural traditions, and the public sentiment of the citizens of the United States." She also said that the proposed legislation had "hidden mathematics" about which the public was not being informed.[11]

In the Senate, another opponent, Sam Ervin (D-NC), said that it was impossible not to discriminate and that it was therefore alright to favor "groups who historically had the greatest influence in building the nation."[12] To put all the earth's peoples on the same basis as prospective immigrants to the United States, Ervin argued, "was to discriminate against the people who had first settled and shaped the country." Ervin found an ally in Senator Robert Byrd (D-WV) who said our current (1965) system is "just and wise," since "additional population" from western European countries is "more easily and readily assimilated into the American population." Byrd added: "Why should the United States be the only advanced nation in the world today to develop a guilt complex concerning its immigration policies?"[13]

The House of Representatives voted 326 to 69 (82.5 percent) in favor of the act, while the Senate passed the bill by a vote of 76 to 18. The floodgates to the New World finally had been pried open. Only Malcolm X had foreseen this enormous development in legislation, for he had written:

> As the Christian Crusade once went East, now the Islamic Crusade is going West. With the East—Asia—closed to Christianity, with Africa rapidly becoming converted to Islam, with Europe rapidly becoming un-Christian, generally today it is accepted that the "Christian" civilization of America—which is propping up the white race around the world—is Christianity's remaining strongest bastion.
>
> Well, if this is so—if the so called "Christianity" now being practiced in America displays the best that the world Christianity has to offer—no one in his right mind should need any much greater proof that very close at hand is the end of Christianity.
>
> Are you aware that some Protestant theologians, in their writings, are using the phrase "post-Christian" era—and they mean now?[14]

THE MUSLIMS ARRIVE

In 1965 and 1966, 6,490 Arab Muslims immigrated to the United States, compared to the period between 1962 and 1964 when 4,683 Arabs arrived (mostly Christian) under family reunification programs.[15] But word gradually trickled down that America was now open to the Islamic world. The first sizeable number of Muslim immigrants began to arrive here from Palestine in 1969. They were uprooted from the Palestinian territories as a result of the Six-Day War in which the Israelis defeated the collective armies of Egypt, Jordan, and Syria by a series of surprise and devastating air strikes. Following the war, Israel gained control of the West Bank and East Jerusalem from Jordan, the Golan Heights from Syria, and the Gaza Strip and the Sinai Peninsula from Egypt. Approximately 150,000 Muslims—a quarter of the population—went into exile from the West Bank; 170,000 fled the Golan Heights; and 70,000 emigrated from Gaza and Sinai.[16] Eventually, 72,564 of the Palestinian refugees, along with 13,529 Egyptians, rolled up their prayer rugs and came to settle in such US cities as Chicago, Detroit, Cleveland, San Francisco, Houston, Jacksonville, and New York.[17] In addition, upheavals in

Yemen, which gained its independence from Great Britain in 1967, resulted in the arrival of an additional 3,477 Muslims.

A study of Palestinian Arab immigrants from Israel, the West Bank, and Gaza, published in 1994, used the 1980 census to look at socioeconomic characteristics. Among the 90 percent of Palestinian American men and 40 percent of women who were in the labor force, 40 percent and 31 percent, respectively, had either professional, technical, or managerial positions. There were also large numbers in sales: 26 percent of men and 23 percent of women. The self-employment rate for men was a significant 36 percent (only 13 percent for women), compared to 11 percent for nonimmigrant men. Of the self-employed, 64 percent were in retail trade, with half owning grocery stores. In terms of income, the mean for Palestinian families in 1979 was $25,400, with 24 percent earning over $35,000 and 20 percent earning less than $10,000.[18] By 1990, according to several analysts, the Palestinian American community of Muslims stood at 180,000.[19] But other researchers believe that the actual number of Palestinian newcomers was considerably higher. They base this contention on the fact that the Palestinians who came here were technically stateless. Many held passports from Egypt, Israel, Lebanon, and Jordan. Others entered with immigration documents from Kuwait, Saudi Arabia, the United Arab Emirates, Bahrain, Oman, and Qatar, where they had worked prior to the 1991 Persian Gulf War.[20]

THE OLD PROBLEM

The same problems that faced the Muslim newcomers had confronted the last great influx of European immigrants who arrived here during the first decade and a half of the twentieth century. During that time, more than 35 million people made their way to the New World, making America the most culturally and linguistically diverse nation on earth: 4.5 million came from Ireland, 4 million from Great Britain, 6 million from central Europe, 2 million from the Scandinavian countries, 5 million from Italy, 8 million from eastern Europe, and 3 million from the Balkans.

The European immigrants, who came before the Great War, lived together in clusters, creating the great ethnic neighborhoods within America's inner cities; published their own newspapers in their own language; and established ethnic clubs and organizations. They were naturally preoccupied with economic problems—making the transition from work on the land in "the old country" to labor in the factories, mills, and mines of their new home. But their "big concern," as Will Herberg writes in *Protestant, Catholic, Jew,* was in the transplanting of their churches: "Back home, the church (or synagogue) had been, for most of them, the meaningful center of life, the repository of the sacred symbols of community existence. As soon as they touched land in the New World, they set themselves to re-establishing it."[21]

This need for cultural and religious continuity became the "big concern" of the first wave of Muslim immigrants that arrived in the wake of Celler-Hart. The immigrants established mosques in storefronts along Atlantic Avenue in Brooklyn, in abandoned retail outlets in Bedford-Stuyvesant, and in former churches, which they transformed into mosques by capping with domes (as evidenced by the Islamic Center in Youngstown, Ohio).[22] Since most of these newcomers were Palestinian, Palestinian organizations sprouted up from the asphalt of inner cities, including the Institute for Palestine Studies, the Bethlehem Association, the Palestine Aid Society, and the United Holy Land Fund.

AND THE NEW PROBLEM

Along with these groups, cells of the Palestinian Islamic Jihad (PIJ), an offshoot of the Muslim Brotherhood, which has been labeled a "foreign terror organization" by the US Department of State, appeared with several newly transplanted masjids and in the form of such Islamic "charities" as the Islamic Fund for Palestine, the

Elehessen Society, and the Muslim Women's Society. The PIJ also popped up on such college campuses as the University of Arkansas and the University of South Florida.[23] One such cell appeared in the form of the Holy Land Foundation for Relief and Development, with headquarters in Richardson, Texas. By 2000, this charity was receiving $13 million in annual donations.[24] A substantial proportion of these funds were purportedly funneled to the PIJ for the elimination of Israel through violent jihad.[25]

After the outbreak of the Palestinian Intifada in 1987, a number of the PIJ cells transformed into pockets of Hamas, another duly designated "foreign terror organization," which seeks the destruction of Israel and the creation of a Palestinian state from Israel and Israeli-held territories. Hamas (the Islamic Resistance Movement) launched its campaign of violence in 1989, first against Israeli soldiers and suspected Palestinian collaborators, and then against Israeli civilians.[26] In the wake of the Oslo agreement, Hamas leaders intensified their rhetoric and vowed to derail the peace process through violent attacks. Drive-by shootings, fire bombings, and stabbings increased. Suicide missions began in April 1994, when a Hamas suicide bomber rammed an explosives-laden car into a bus in Afula, killing eight and wounding fifty others.[27]

THE YEMEN YIELD

Yemeni communities sprouted up in Brooklyn, New York; Alexandria, Virginia; Chicago, Illinois; Oakland, California; and Fresno, California. However, most of the Yemenis—over fifteen thousand—came to settle in Michigan, particularly in Detroit and the south side of Dearborn (Salina area). The first generation of Yemeni Americans was overwhelmingly Islamic and possessed little more than a rudimentary education. Some served as farm laborers; others found jobs in manufacturing plants, including General Motors, Chrysler, and the Ford Motor Company.

A survey of Arab Americans in the Detroit area after 9/11 found that Yemenis had the largest families, the lowest rate of business ownership (3 percent compared to 20 percent for other Arab groups), and the highest rate of employment in "trades" as opposed to services, administration, professional, or sales (43 percent in trades compared to 7 to 17 percent for other Arabs groups).[28] Anthropologist Loukia K. Sarroub, in her study of Yemeni culture through the perspective of six high-school-age girls, noted that the Yeminis inhabited "a ghetto-like enclave of Dearborn," where "this community continued to live much as they did in Yemen"[29]

DEEP IN THE HEART OF DEARBORN

At the Dix Mosque, which forms the heart of the Yemini community in Southend Dearborn, the muezzin's call to prayer over amp-shattering loudspeakers is answered by the appearance of hundreds of bearded men in *gallabiyyas,* white, ankle-length tunics, and white skullcaps who leave their houses and walk to prayer. All of the dwelling places—some wood-frame, others brick—within a few miles of the mosque are inhabited by Yemeni Muslims.[30] At the mosque and nearby restaurants, according to Geneive Abdo, a recognized authority on Islamic political movements, outsiders—including Muslims from Pakistan, Egypt, and Somalia—are not welcome. Ms. Abdo explains:

> The unique situation of Yemeni immigrants and their strong attachment to the ways of the Old Country have shaped every aspect of life at the Dix mosque. Yemeni arrivals are overwhelmingly young men who arrive with little or no education or job skills. Few intend to settle in America permanently, and many keep wives and families back home, visiting periodically and sending funds whenever possible. With no personal investment in a Western future, the Yemenis are strongly resistant to compromise with contemporary American life. They often struggle to make a living wage, with some estimates

putting the median household income in the Southend at $20,125, less than half the average among Muslims. Approximately one-third of the population has never learned English and many first generation immigrant women are illiterate. Any concession to a new identity, say that of Muslim American or even Yemeni American, is often fiercely resisted.[31]

CHAPTER 8

BEFORE THE FLOOD

There had been a trickle before the flood. In 1946, Congress established the Fulbright Program, which sought to "increase understanding between the people of the United States and the people of the world by means of educational and cultural exchange."[1] In keeping with this legislation, the Immigration and Nationality Act of 1952 (McCarran-Walter Bill) permitted foreign students to enter the United States in order to study at approved institutions with F-1 visas. From 1946 to 1965, higher education became the only pathway for wealthy Muslims to migrate to the United States, and the number of Muslim students on American campuses increased from 2,709 to 13,664.[2]

The Muslim students hailed from such Arab countries as the United Arab Emirates, Iraq, and Saudi Arabia. One of the first students to arrive was the Egyptian scholar Sayyid Qutb, who spent the better half of 1949 in Greeley, Colorado, studying curriculum at Colorado State Teachers College, now the University of Northern Colorado. What he saw prompted him to condemn America as a soulless, materialistic place that should be shunned by all believing Muslims. Upon his return to Egypt, Qutb became one of the leading members of the Egyptian Muslim Brotherhood, the first and largest mass Islamist group. After the Brotherhood fell out with the ruling Arab nationalists in Egypt and an attempt was made on the life of president Gamal Nasser, Qutb, the nationalists' leader, was imprisoned. Ten years later, accused of another plot against the government, he was hanged. He taught that Muslims are not merely obliged to wage jihad in defense of Islamic lands, but must wage offensive jihad in order to liberate the world from secular governments.[3] His writings would later become the theoretical basis for many radical Islamic groups—including al-Qaeda.[4]

Along with Qutb, one of the first Muslims to arrive with a student visa was Ismail Raji al-Faruqi, the son of wealthy Palestinians. Al-Faruqi enrolled at Indiana University's Graduate School, where he obtained a master's degree in philosophy in 1949 and a doctorate in 1952. In 1968, he became a professor of religion at Temple University. Eventually, al-Faruqi came to believe that the transformation of the United States of America into the United States of Islam could become a reality because of the great waves of Muslim immigrants that had begun to inundate our shores and the liberalized immigration laws of 1965. "Nothing could be greater," al-Faruqi wrote in an essay, "than this youthful, vigorous, and rich continent [of North America] turning from its evil past and marching forward under the banner of *Allahu Akbar.*"[5] He went on to list five reasons why the newly arrived Muslim immigrants in America should become religious activists:

1. Activism will assuage any guilt for settling in the land of the *kafirs,* because God was leading them to become da'iyya (missionaries).
2. They will see America through Islamic eyes and realize that its culture is inferior.
3. They will experience a feeling of personal worth since they will be performing the will of Allah.
4. The Islamic vision would provide the immigrants with necessary criteria for making American society conform to the will of Allah.
5. They will come to experience a level of attachment to the United States since they are transforming it into an Islamic nation. Immigrants, however, must constantly remain focused on their homeland, so that Allah will permit them to return there and not be assimilated into the American way of life.[6]

Shortly before he was murdered in 1986 by a member of the Muslim Student Association, al-Faruqi wrote: "If you look upon this [the arrival of Muslim immigrants in the United States] as an event in world history, you will see that Allah has prepared the course of history to welcome you in the West. By bringing you here, Allah has carved out a vocation for you, a new mission, and this mission is to save the West."[7]

THE MUSLIM STUDENT ASSOCIATION

Many of the Muslims who arrived with student visas eventually obtained professional, academic, and industrial employment and, thanks to the Hart-Celler Act, never returned to their homelands. Three such Arab students—Ahmed Totanji, Jamal Barzinji, and Hisham al Talib—formed the Muslim Student Association (MSA) at the University of Illinois, Urbana-Champaign, in 1963. Other Arab individuals who served as early cofounders of the MSA were Mahboob Khan and Malika Khan.[8] Soon after its founding, the MSA boasted ten affiliate chapters. Within a year, it listed thirty-eight chapters and gained a representative on the board of the Federation of Islamic Organizations of the United States and Canada.[9]

A RADICAL FOUNDATION

There was a difference between the MSA and other international student organizations. Its members espoused the radical doctrines of Qutb and Mawlana Mawdudi, the founder of Islamism, and saw themselves as participants in the creation of a New Islamic World Order. Mawdudi sought the destruction of all secular governments and the elimination of the rights of unbelievers living within the Muslim world.[10] He wrote: "Islam requires the earth—not just a portion, but the whole planet . . . because the entire mankind should benefit from the ideology and welfare program [of Islam]. . . . Towards this end, Islam wishes to press into service all forces which can bring about a revolution and a composite term for the use of all these forces is 'Jihad'. . . . the objective of the Islamic 'jihād' is to eliminate the rule of an un-Islamic system and establish in its stead an Islamic system of state rule."[11] America, the proverbial melting pot, was viewed by the MSA as the crucible in which people of varying cultures and ethnic backgrounds could be blended to create *Homo Islamicus*, the man of the future.[12] For this reason, they viewed their work in the New World as nothing less than historic by announcing: "Our ancestors have already created a history that one refers to with pride. We feel and we believe that it is our duty to create a history for Islam all over the world. In order to achieve that idea, we should supervise the molding of this history by sacrificing our money and our wealth, our efforts and our knowledge, and our time and our lives so as we can see our history being written in the best way we love to see."[13]

The MSA opposed assimilation within America's secular culture by adopting the motto of the Muslim Brotherhood: "We are Muslims first, and Muslims last, and Muslims forever. We should live as Muslims and we should die as Muslims."[14]

THE MONEY PIPELINE

The new organization was funded almost entirely by the Muslim World League, a Saudi organization established to encourage conversion to Salafism through *da'wah* (proselytization). Salafism is an austere form of Sunni Islam that attempts to effect a return to what its adherents believe to be unadulterated Islam, as practiced by Mohammed and his first followers. In order to achieve this objective, the Salafists seek to strip what they see as *bida*, or innovations, from the practice of Islam as it has developed over the centuries. According to Salafists, only pure Islam can solve the political, economic, and social issues that beset the Muslim community (*ummah*). This accounts for their insistence that all Muslim societies must be governed by *sharia* (Islamic law).[15]

With the creation of more and more chapters on American campuses, more and more millions poured into the MSA's coffers. By 1971, the group set up headquarters at the Al-Amin Mosque in Gary, Indiana. Four years later, the MSA purchased a large farm in Plainfield, Indiana, and established a general secretariat of full-time workers. Departments were created for education and publication, training, public relations, administration, and finance. By 1976, the finance department gave rise to the North American Islamic Trust, which held title to MSA properties including three hundred newly created mosques.[16]

In subsequent years, a number of additional Islamist organizations would grow out of MSA, whose website now proclaims: "MSA National was the precursor of ISNA [the Islamic Society of North America], ICNA [the Islamic Circle of North America], MAYA [the Muslim Arab Youth Association], IMA [the Islamic Medical Association of North America], AMSS [the Association of Muslim Social Scientists], AMSE [the Association of Muslim Scientists and Engineers], MYNA [Muslim Youth of North America], Islamic Book Service, and the North American Islamic Trust."[17]

OTHER EARLY ARRIVALS

In 1952, the relocation of the United Nations to Manhattan created a need of a place for Muslim dignitaries to worship. Three years later, the Islamic Center of New York was established at the Pakistan House on Sixty-Fifth Street, the home of the Pakistani delegation. Unable to secure the services of an imam due to the paucity of Islamists in the country, the center was forced to rely upon Dr. N. Saifor Fatemi, chairman of Princeton University's Department of Oriental Languages, to conduct the Friday prayer services. Eventually, the center imported Muhammad Shuaiba, who became the first of hundreds of imams to come to this country from Cairo's prestigious al-Azhar University, the academic center of Sunni Islam.[18]

CULTURE SHOCK AND SHIRK

But from 1965 to 1970, when they first began to arrive in droves, the Muslim immigrants were shocked to find no mosques, no imams, no muezzins calling believers to prayer, no madrassas, no Islamic community centers, no halal food outlets, no clothing stores selling hijabs and burqas, and no bookstores selling works in Arabic. The few men who appeared on the streets wearing kufis and ankle-length dresses were not orthodox Sunnis but Five Percenters, who declared that the black man collectively—not Allah—was God.[19] Worse, at the temples of the Nation of Islam, which many of the Islamic immigrants inevitably visited, the most vile form of *shirk* (blasphemy) was proclaimed from pulpits by so-called Muslim ministers, who insisted that all white people (including the newcomers from Palestine, Yemen, and Saudi Arabia) were devils who had been created by a mad scientist named Dr. "Big-Head" Yakub; that true Muslims came from the Moon; that Master Fard (Wallace Ford), an ex-con from San Quentin, represented Allah in the flesh; and that Mohammed was neither the greatest nor the final prophet.

The clash between these two ideologies resulted in the arrival of Tablighi Jamaat missionaries from Pakistan, India, and the Maghreb region of North Africa. Funded by Saudi sheikhs, the missionaries served not only to introduce African American Muslims to the sunnah and proper Islamic behavior (*adab*), but also to establish orthodox mosques within major American cities.[20] Another result was the awarding of full scholarships and generous stipends for NOI leaders and prominent black Muslims to study the Quran and tenets of orthodox Islam at such prestigious universities as al-Azhar in Cairo, the Islamic University of Medina, Ashrafia Islamic University in Lahore, the University of the Holy Quran and Islamic Studies in Lahore, and the King Saud University in Riyadh. The success of these efforts managed to convince King Faisal and the Saudi princes that the Islamic transformation of America was not a dream but a distinct possibility.

This realization was fortified by the oil embargo of 1973, which produced an incredible financial windfall for the Saudis, with oil profits skyrocketing from $1 billion in 1970 to $116 billion in 1980. "It was only when oil revenue began to generate real wealth that the Kingdom could fulfill its ambition of spreading the word of Islam to every corner of the world," Dr. Ibrahim Al-Assaf, Saudi minister of finance and national economy, said in 2003.[21] Between 1975 and 1987, the Saudis admitted to having spent $48 billion for "overseas development aid." By 2002, that figure rose to $70 billion. These sums, reported as state aid, did not include private donations to Islamic charities for the promulgation of Salafism.[22] The Muslims now had the money to change the religious landscape of the Western world, including America.

PHYSICS FORSAKEN

The rise of orthodox Islam in the United States did not comply with the third law of Newtonian physics by producing an equal and opposite reaction with the decline of the NOI. To the contrary, the presence of thousands of Sunni Muslims was accompanied by a sharp increase in NOI membership. This increase—fueled by the Black Power Movement—resulted in an unprecedented outburst of violence that came to be called the Zebra Murders.

CHAPTER 9
THE NIGHT OF THE NOI

Elijah Poole (Elijah Muhammad) responded to the complaints and outcries against his bizarre interpretation of Islam from the first wave of Sunni immigrants by proclaiming that they were pitifully ignorant of the teachings of Master Fard, the incarnation of Allah. He continued to insist that true Muslims came from the Moon and that whites (including the Palestinian and Egyptian refugees who now appeared at the NOI temples) represented a race of devils that had been created by the mad scientist Dr. "Big Head" Yakub. He continued to demand sharp segregation between the races and the creation of a separate state within the United States for black Americans. While the newcomers continued to condemn Poole's proclamations as shirk, the prophet announced his intent to send his minister to the Middle East in order to reeducate Muslims about "true" Islam.[1]

Although Poole's message was decried as shirk by the Muslim immigrants, it resonated throughout urban America in the 1960s and gave rise to a tremendous surge in NOI membership. By 1970, when the first Sunni mosques appeared in New York, Detroit, Cleveland, and Los Angeles, the NOI could boast to such scholars as C. Eric Lincoln and E. U. Essien-Udom of 100,000 to 250,000 members at seventy-five temples throughout the country.[2] Elijah Muhammad now stood as a hero of black power along with Stokely Carmichael (who later became Kwame Ture), Willie Ricks (later known as Mukasa Nada), and H. Rap Brown (now called Jamil al-Amin).[3] The white-hot rhetoric from these spokesmen helped ignite racial rioting in Los Angeles; Cleveland; Minneapolis–St. Paul; Baltimore; Hartford;

Chicago; Newark; Washington, DC; Plainfield, New Jersey; York, Pennsylvania; and other places throughout the country. But the most horrific outbreak of violence came from the NOI Muslims.

The killings began on October 19, 1973, when members of an elite group within the NOI, known as the Death Angels, kidnapped Richard and Quinta Hagueas as they were taking a stroll near their home on Telegraph Hill in San Francisco. The Muslims forced the couple into a white van and began to sexually molest the twenty-eight-year-old Quinta. When Richard protested, a member of the squad smashed his jaw with a wrench. Following the molestation, the Muslims proceeded to decapitate her with machetes. The cuts severed her cervical spine and ripped through her carotid arteries, jugular veins, epiglottis, and hypopharynx. "That girl's wounds screamed out hate," San Francisco Police Department detective Earl Sanders later recalled. "Whoever cut her didn't just cut through flesh, they cut through bone. They cut deep."[4] The killers next turned their attention to Richard, smashing his skull with the wrench and hacking away at his face and neck with their machetes.[5]

THE KILLINGS CONTINUE

Ten days later, Frances Rose, a twenty-eight-year-old physical therapist, was shot in the face at point-blank range by Jesse Lee Cooks, a member of the Death Angels, who blocked her car and demanded a ride as she drove up to the entrance of the University of California's Extension Campus on Laguna Street.[6]

Within the next two months, seven additional attacks took place on the streets of San Francisco, including a hit on Art Agnos, a member of the California Commission on Aging, and the murders of Ilario Bertuccio, an eighty-one-year-old maintenance man, Paul Dancik, a twenty-six-year-old street junkie, Saleem Erakat, a fifty-three-year-old grocer, and Marietta DiGirolamo, who worked as a janitor.[7]

On December 22, a member of the Death Angels gunned down nineteen-year-old Neal Moynihan in front of the Civic Center Hotel. Moynihan had just purchased a last-minute Christmas gift—a teddy bear for his kid sister. The assassin fled down a nearby alley to Gough Street, where fifty-year-old Mildred Hosler was waiting at a bus stop. He shot her four times in the left breast and then continued to jog down the street. The killer had eliminated two whites within three minutes.[8]

A CHRISTMAS TURKEY

On Christmas Eve, the Death Angels captured a homeless white man and transported him to the Black Self Help Moving and Storage Company, a business owned by the NOI, where they butchered him while he was still alive and trussed up his remains like a Christmas turkey, which they tossed into San Francisco Bay. The body was so mutilated that San Francisco police have never been able to come up with the name of the corpse. He remains known as John Doe no. 169.

The attacks by now had become so commonplace that the SFPD reserved radio frequency "Z" for communications related to the killing spree. For this reason, the crimes became known as the "Zebra Murders." It proved to be an ironically prescient handle, since the incidents involved random attacks by black militants on white victims.

MURDER WITHOUT END

The killings stopped for five weeks only to resume on January 28, 1974, with the murders of Tana Smith, a thirty-two-year-old secretary; John Bambic, eighty-four, an avid junk collector; Jane Holly, forty-five, a social activist; and Vincent Wollin, who was celebrating his sixty-ninth birthday by treating himself to a doughnut and a cup of coffee. The rampage continued with the shooting of Roxanne McMillan, a twenty-three-year-old housewife and mother of a four-month-old baby, who would spend the rest of her life in a wheelchair, and Thomas Bates, a twenty-one-year-old student who was shot three times while hitchhiking near Emeryville.

On April 1, a Death Angel stalked and shot Thomas Rainwater, nineteen, and Linda Story, twenty-one, as they walked away from the Salvation Army School for Officers' Training, where they were first-year cadets. Rainwater, who was plugged three times in the back with a .32 caliber, was dead at the scene. Story was shot twice while she sought to escape from the killer's clutches. The bullets narrowly missed her spine, and she later recovered.[9]

On Easter Sunday, April 14, Black Muslims killed nineteen-year-old Ward Anderson and wounded fifteen-year-old Larry White on the corner of Fillmore and Hayes, where the teenagers were waiting for a bus. Two days later, they executed Nelson T. Shields, twenty-three, heir to a prominent DuPont executive, in the Ingleside district of the city.[10]

THE ANGELS' WINGS

The break in the case came late in 1974, after the SFPD posted a $30,000 reward for any information leading to the arrests of the killers. Anthony Harris, a worker at Black Self Help, took notice. He was struggling to support a wife and baby, and $30,000 was a lot of dough to him. A few hours after he dropped a dime into a payphone, detectives took him into custody for questioning. Harris spilled his guts, telling the cops about the Death Angels and the point system within the NOI for killing white people.[11]

Angels, according to the system, gained their "wings" upon killing four white children and five white women, or, if they preferred, nine white men. Upon attaining this quota, a photo of the angel was taken with a pair of black wings affixed to his back. The photo was mounted on a board along with pictures of other successful candidates, and the board was displayed on an easel at Black Self Help Moving and Storage.[12]

In the predawn hours of May 1, more than one hundred cops carried out simultaneous raids. Forty officers were deployed to an apartment building on Grove Street, where J. C. X. Simon lived in apartment 2 and Larry Green lived in number 7. Twenty cops charged into Black Self Help Moving and Storage Company on Market Street, where two suspects lived. None of the men arrested in the raid offered resistance.[13]

THE TENTH LESSON

San Francisco mayor Joseph Alioto held a press conference to announce that the men taken into custody were members of NOI's Mosque no. 26, where they aspired to become "Death Angels." John Muhammad, the leader of Mosque no. 26, expressed indignation and demanded that the mayor apologize for his racist remarks.[14] Muhammad, however, refused to explain lesson ten of the NOI as penned by Elijah Poole (Elijah Muhammad):

> Lesson Number Ten: Why does Muhammad and any Muslim murder the devil [the white man]? What is the duty of each Muslim in regard to four devils? What reward does a Muslim receive by presenting four devils at one time? Answers: Because he [the devil] is 100 percent wicked and will not keep and obey the laws of Islam. His ways and actions are like a snake of the grafted type. So Muhammad learned he could not reform the devils, so they had to be murdered. All Muslims will murder the devil because they know he is a snake and also if he be allowed to live, he would sting someone else. Each Muslim is required to bring four devils, and by bringing and presenting four at a time his reward is a button to wear on the lapel of his coat. Also a free transportation to the Holy City, Mecca, to see Brother Muhammad.[15]

OUTCRY AND OUTCOME

Muhammad was not the only African American to express outrage at the mayor's remark. The Black Liberation Army sent a communiqué to FM rock station KSAN that called for an armed uprising of all radical groups—including the Symbionese Liberation Army, the Weather Underground, and the Death Angels—against the racist municipal government.[16]

The uprising never happened, and the legal proceedings took place without the spilling of blood. Of the seven suspects taken into custody, three were later released. The remaining four—Larry Green, J. C. X. Simon, Manuel Moore, and Jesse Lee Cooks were found guilty of first-degree murder and sentenced to life in prison.

Black Self Help was managed by Tom Manney, an NOI member and former St. Ignatius High School and City College football star. Manney lent his black Cadillac to the murderers, who used it to hunt down their victims, along with an illegal .32 pistol that was used in several of the killings. He was taken into custody only to be released for lack of evidence.[17]

UNREPORTED SLAUGHTER

In October 1973, when the killing spree started, there were fifteen divisions of the Death Angels within California. The California attorney general's office had compiled a list of seventy-one execution-style murders committed around the state, either with a machete or a pistol, in which the killers were always well-dressed and groomed youngish black men, and the victim always white. In addition to San Francisco, the murders were carried out in Oakland, San Jose, Emeryville, Berkeley, Long Beach, Signal Hill, Santa Barbara, Palo Alto, Pacifica, San Diego, Los Angeles, and in the counties of San Mateo, Santa Clara, Los Angeles, Contra Costa, Ventura, and Alameda. What they discovered was the NOI genocide campaign had actually begun approximately three years before the San Francisco killings.[18]

It took law enforcement officials several years to come to terms with the real enormity of the crime. From 1970 to 1974, the NOI was responsible for "just under 270" black-on-white murders in California alone.[19] How many killings occurred throughout the country has yet to be calculated.

Nor has the economic impact of the killings ever been assessed. However, clippings from the *San Francisco Chronicle* document that the city remained crippled by fear. Tourism fell to an all-time low, hotel prices plummeted, stores and restaurants closed for lack of business, and cultural events failed to attract audiences. When night fell, the City by the Bay became a ghost town.

The rampage made the NOI the bloodiest domestic terrorist group in US history. Yet no law enforcement or government figure, in this heyday of the civil rights movement, opted to take the Muslim organization to task, let alone to expose Elijah Poole as the instigator of mass murder. At the heart of the matter remained the fact that the Nation of Islam was a religion with thousands of adherents and even more supporters. As a religion, it was protected by a battery of constitutional rights. The first line of the first article of the Bill of Rights reads: "Congress shall make no law respecting an establishment of religion, or prohibiting the free exercise thereof." Doing anything that contravened these words would create a legal maelstrom that would result in the loss of a juridical or governmental position and personal costs beyond calculation. And so the real cause of the murders was neither addressed nor uprooted.

MORE MUSLIM MURDERS

The NOI killings in other states were equally horrific and underreported. On Friday, April 14, 1972, New York City police officers were summoned to Mosque no. 7 in Harlem, for a "ten-thirteen": an officer in need of help. Police entered the mosque and a conflict ensued, which left Patrolman Philip W. Cardillo dead and the city on the brink of a full-scale riot.[20] Sensing a potential crisis and conflict with the Nation of Islam and black militants, New York City mayor John Lindsey, Commissioner Benjamin Ward, and Congressman Charles Rangel acquiesced to the city's black leaders and ordered the police out of the mosque. Subsequently, the details of Officer Cardillo's murder and the events of what happened at the mosque were covered up, and an investigation was never truly launched. It remains one of the great scandals in the history of the New York Police Department.[21] The spiritual director of Mosque no. 7 at that time was Louis Farrakhan.

Another incident occurred in Washington, DC. Ernest T. McGee, also known as Khalifa Hamaas Abdul Khaalis, left the NOI after the death of Malcolm to form the Hanafi sect, which adhered to Sunni Islamic principles. On January 5, 1973, he publicly condemned the NOI and labeled Elijah Poole a "lying deceiver."[22]

On January 18, 1973, several NOI members set out for the townhouse of LA Lakers' superstar Kareem Abdul-Jabbar, which was being used by Khaalis in Washington, DC. Seven members of Khaalis's family were killed. Four of the victims were babies, aged between nine days and twenty-two months. The infants had been drowned in a bathtub and a sink. Khaalis's wife was shot. Though paralyzed, she survived.[23]

Murder was not the NOI's sole criminal activity. By 1975, members of the NOI forged an alliance with the Gambino crime family in New York and the Stanfa crime family in Philadelphia for the distribution of illicit drugs—heroin, marijuana, and PCPs—throughout the eastern seaboard. Some became elevated to the status of triggermen. But they were soon replaced by new Muslim arrivals from the Balkans who had mastered the art of cold-blooded killing.[24]

THE PASSING OF POOLE

Poole died a very wealthy man on February 25, 1975. Although borderline mentally retarded and responsible for an unprecedented wave of violence, Poole was lionized by the *New York Times* as follows in a front-page obituary: "Elijah Muhammad was a mystic. But his mysticism was applied; it always had a quite earthly purpose. Forerunning transcendental meditation and other modern popular sects, he saw the need for 20th-century religions to declare themselves based on science, not faith. Islam was a science and a 'way of life,' not a religion, he said."[25]

To this day, several of Poole's disciples insist that he didn't really die but rather had boarded the giant Mother-plane that is "even now flying over our heads."[26] Commenting in 2000 on the messenger's impact on American society, Daniel Pipes wrote:

> The wilder notions of Muhammad's religion are disappearing; but all African-American Muslims today can claim him as their patron, for nearly every one of them has a direct connection, personal or familial, to the NOI. Without Muhammad, the million or so African-Americans who are now Muslims would almost certainly still be Christians. Their numbers, moreover, are only likely to grow. Though Islam still exercises only modest appeal to white Americans, it has become a powerful and permanent presence among blacks, who by my rough calculation are 200 times more likely to convert to it than are whites. Nor is it hard to imagine such conversions beginning to cascade, in an Islamic pattern that, as the historian Richard Bulliet has established, goes back over a millennium. If that happens, Islam may well pull ahead of Christianity among blacks within a matter of decades.[27]

Poole did not leave the movement empty handed. Before his death, the messenger managed to solicit a gift of $1 billion from one of his ardent admirers: Libyan president Muammar al-Qadhafi.[28]

THE IMMACULATE CONCEPTION

Warith (Wallace) Deen Muhammad, the seventh son of Elijah Poole, now ascended to the throne of the NOI. His relationship with his father had been turbulent. In 1965, following the lead of Malcolm X, he had made the hajj and converted to orthodox Islam. His father immediately condemned him as a "hypocrite" and excommunicated him from the NOI. Three years later, jobless and penniless, Wallace repented of his lapse in faith in the teachings of his father. Upon his return to the NOI pulpit, Wallace began to claim that he had met with Master Fard on several occasions and that the long absent incarnation of Allah would soon return to planet Earth. One of Wallace's first acts as the NOI's new leader was to make the announcement that he, no less than Master Fard, was a manifestation of God: "Yes, I myself am an Immaculate Conception. You say, 'This man is crazy.' No, I'm not crazy. . . . After we explain it to you, you'll know that I'm not crazy. The world has just been in darkness. I can truthfully say that my physical father was not my father. I have never had a physical father. . . . You say, 'Who is your father?' Speaking in the language of the New Testament, My Father is God. . . . I am the Manifestation of God. . . . All praise is due to Allah."[29]

QIBLA: THE TURN TO MECCA

In 1976, Wallace maintained that the NOI was the dominant Islamic organization in America with seventy thousand members.[30] Such claims attracted the attention of the Saudis, who placed their riches at Wallace Muhammad's disposal in exchange for his service in leading his followers to a belief in orthodox Islamic teaching. The deal was struck. Wallace changed the Nation of Islam's name to the American Muslim Mission and proceeded to move the organization into mainstream Sunni orthodoxy.[31] His followers now upheld the Five Pillars of Islam and proclaimed that Mohammed was the last prophet. The fast of Ramadan, which was observed in December when Elijah Poole was alive, became celebrated according to the lunar calendar used by orthodox Muslims. In the NOI temples (now called mosques), worshippers faced east and sat on the floor to pray, as members of the NOI had not done in the past.[32] The Black Muslims, which members of the NOI were called since the publication of C. E. Lincoln's *The Black Muslims in America* (1961), now were called Bilalians, in honor of Bilal, the Black Arab, who had served as the Prophet Mohammed's muezzin.[33] And Wallace, now known as Warith Deen Muhammad, denounced Master Fard as a "witch doctor" who had been sent by *Iblis* (Satan) to misdirect African Americans.[34]

In 1977, Wallace led three hundred Bilalians on an all-expense-paid hajj to Saudi Arabia, where he met with King Khalid and received the title of *mujadid*, meaning "the re-newer of Islam."[35] All Saudi funding of new mosques and Islamic activities in America was to be funneled through his organization, and all American Muslims who wished to make the hajj were required to receive his certification.[36]

OLD FARDS AND FARRAKHAN

Naturally, some of the old Fards objected and refused to follow Warith's lead in embracing the blue-eyed Muslims of the Middle East. Rather, they opted to regroup under Louis Farrakhan, who responded to the spread of orthodox Islamic teaching by saying:

> We [the NOI] believe that Allah came to us in the name of W. Farrad Muhammad, the Messiah of the Christians and the Mahdi of the Muslim. . . . Many of my Muslim brothers say this is un-Islamic. . . . I visited Mecca and I sat down with the scholars and this is the main point we wrangled over. . . . And when I finished, they shut their mouths.[37]

Farrakhan's attempt to restore the NOI involved a long legal battle that resulted in the disgruntled minister gaining control of the movement's major temple and the former palatial residence of Elijah Poole in Chicago.[38]

But Farrakhan, no matter how hard he tried to regain a footing in the African American community, could only watch as the movement gradually slipped through his fingers. By 1975, there were four orthodox Sunni groups, in addition to Wallace Muhammad's American Muslim Mission, vying for NOI turf: the Islamic Revivalist Movement, the Muslim Islamic Brotherhood, the Islamic Party of North America, and finally the Dar ul-Islam, known as the DAR, whose members emerged as the biggest and baddest boys in the hood.

CHAPTER 10
DAWAH AND THE DAR

THE IDEAL CANDIDATES

The Tablighi Jamaat movement, which got underway in India during the 1920s, calls upon all Muslims to live under the exacting rules and regulations that governed the community in seventh-century Mecca in order to stay the rising tide of Westernization and secularization.[1] Its members uphold the dietary restrictions and rigid laws that regulated every aspect of daily life and never touch another person with their left hands (which are used for the necessary ablutions regarding excretion and urination), maintain the strict segregation of the sexes in their settlements, eschew beds for sleeping, and clean their teeth with twigs rather than tooth brushes.[2] The men replicate the dress and appearance of the Prophet by wearing flowing robes and leather booties and by shaving their moustaches while allowing their beards to grow long and wispy. The women are forbidden to appear in public without enveloping outer garments and face veils. Few Islamic sects are more exacting in belief and practice.

Although Tablighi Jamaat represents the largest Muslim movement in the world, with 150 million members in 213 countries, it remains without formal organization.[3] The Tablighis maintain no records of their finances, no roster of membership, no spreadsheet of their activities, and no files of shura decision making. Most knowledge of the workings of the movement comes from the three-day annual Tablighi gathering (*Ijtema*) in the small Pakistani town of Raiwind.[4]

The canon of the movement remains bare-boned, consisting of the following six principles:

Kalmah: "An article of faith in which the tablighi accepts that there is no god but Allah and the Prophet Muhammad as his Last messenger. This Kalima is for all Muslims and is not restricted to Tablighis only."

Salah: "Five daily prayers that are essential to spiritual elevation, piety, and a life free from the ills of the material world."

Ilm and Zikr: "The knowledge and remembrance of Allah conducted in sessions in which the congregation listens to preaching by the emir, performs prayers, recites the Quran, and reads Hadith. The congregation will also use these sessions to eat meals together, thus fostering a sense of community and identity."

Ikraam-e-Muslim: "The treatment of fellow Muslims with honor and deference."

Tas'hih-i-Niyyat: "Reforming one's life in supplication to Allah by performing every human action for the sake of Allah and toward the goal of self-transformation."

Dawt'o' Tableegh (dawah): "The sparing of time to live a life based on faith and learning its virtues, following in the footsteps of the Prophet Muhammad, and taking His message door-to-door for the sake of faith."[5]

Apart from the Quran and Hadith, the only literature Tablighis consider required reading is the *Tablighi Nisab*, a compilation of seven essays penned by a companion of Muhammad Ilyas, who founded of the movement in 1927. For this reason, the movement has not evolved in a monolithic manner: some Tablighis believe Muslims should pursue jihad through conscience (*jihad bin nafs*) while others advocate jihad through the sword (*jihad bin saif*). Yet all members remain united in their resistance to Western culture and their insistence that Muslims should avoid contact with all those who do not share their values and beliefs.[6] Aside from their practice of gathering at graves to venerate the dead, the Tablighis uphold an interpretation of Islam that is hardly distinguishable from the Wahhabism that is upheld by the Saud dynasty.[7] For this reason, they were viewed by the Saud dynasty as ideal candidates to effect the Islamic transformation of America.

The Tablighi missionaries, in turn, realized that the African American community represented fertile ground for the future of Islam. One explained the importance of the mission to a correspondent from *Dawn*, Pakistan's oldest and largest daily newspaper, by saying:

> The umma [Muslim community] must remember that winning over the black Muslims is not only a religious obligation but also a selfish necessity. The votes of the black Muslims can give the immigrant Muslims the political clout they need at every stage to protect their vital interests. Likewise, outside Muslim states like Saudi Arabia, Malaysia, and Pakistan need to mobilize their effort, money, and missionary skills to expand and consolidate the black Muslim community in the USA, not only for religious reasons, but also as a farsighted investment in the black Muslims' immense potential as a credible lobby for Muslim causes, such as Palestine, Bosnia, or Kashmir—offsetting, at least partially, the venal influence of the powerful India-Israel lobby.[8]

The Tablighi, with funds from the House of Saud, soon established the following mosques throughout the country: Dearborn Mosque, Dearborn, Michigan; Markaz New York, Brooklyn; Markaz, Masjid Falah, Corona, New York; Abdur Raqeeb, Guttenberg, New Jersey; Markaz, Los Angeles; Farouq Toorawa, Los Angeles; Masjid Al-Noor (Markaz), San Francisco; Vallejo Mosque, Vallejo, California; Naser Sayedi, Honolulu; Islamic Centre, Manoa, Honolulu; and Masjid Nur, San Diego.[9] The US headquarters of the group, according to reputable sources, became Masjid Al-Noor in Chicago.[10]

The Saudis were not alone in supplying millions for the work of Tablighi missionaries in America. The Libyan government, newly rich from the discovery of massive oil reserves in 1959, funded the work of Yusuf Muzzafaruudin Hamid, who established the Community Mosque of Washington (Masjid al-Ummah) and the Islamic Party of North America,[11] and Pakistani clerics provided support to Wali Akram, an American-born Tablighi, in his effort to transform the First Cleveland Mosque, a pseudo-Islamic Ahmadiyya establishment, into an orthodox center of Sunni worship.[12]

Nor were the Tablighis the only well-heeled Muslim missionaries to arrive with the goal of spreading Salafi/Wahhabi beliefs throughout the New World. Others were affiliated with the Jamaat-i-Islami (JI), another Pakistani revivalist group, founded in Lahore by Muslim theologian Maulana Sayyid Abul Ala Maududi. The primary purpose of JI was the *Iqamat-e-Deen* or *Nizam-e-Mustafa*—the establishment of a pure Islamic state, governed by sharia law. By 1972, JI members and missionaries established the Islamic Circle of North America and a string of mosques, including Masjid As-Salam in Albany, New York.[13] Mohammad Hossain, the founder of the Albany mosque, and Yassin Aref, its imam, were eventually indicted for taking part in a plot involving the sale of a shoulder-fired missile that was used to assassinate a Pakistani diplomat in New York City, and for conspiracy to provide material support to Jaish-e-Mohammed, an organization that has been classified as a terrorist organization by the US Department of State.[14]

THE DAWN OF THE DAR

Hafis Mahbub, the first Tablighi missionary to America, arrived in Brooklyn in the summer of 1960 to serve as a Quranic teacher at the State Street Mosque. The mosque was really a brownstone townhouse owned by Sheikh Daoud Faisal, a former member of the Moorish Science Movement. Faisal had upheld many of the teachings of Timothy Drew, including the claim that African Americans were not "Negroes, but Muslims."[15] When his teachings were questioned by the new Arab Muslim immigrants, Faisal made contact with al-Azhar University in Cairo and secured the services of Imam Mahbub.

By 1962, the newly arrived Tablighi missionary had attracted a dedicated circle of disciples, including such former members of the NOI and the Moorish Science Movement as Rijab Mahmud, Yahya Abdul Karim, Sulaiman al-Hadi, Muhammad Salahuddin, Hajj Muhammad, and Abdul Karim.[16] Mahbub led them in fayr prayer every morning and taught Arabic from the Quran every night.

Tension within the State Street Mosque rose with the passage of the Hart-Celler Act and the presence of more and more immigrant Muslims at Friday prayer services. Many of the newcomers failed to differentiate between the Black Muslims who constituted the Nation of Islam and the black Muslim in their midst who professed a black-supremacy doctrine. To make matters worse, since the Black Muslims identified themselves not only by religion but also by race, Sheikh Faisal insisted that they must carry Sunni Muslim identification cards.[17]

The situation soon became untenable and Mahbub led 150 of his black followers on a hajj to Brooklyn, where they came to establish the Yasin Masjid on Saratoga Street. Mahbub's Muslims called their new location *Dar ul-Islam,* since it represented an area where they could unite against the world of unbelievers (*Dar ul-Kufr*). They called themselves "holy warriors," shaved their heads, donned traditional Islamic dress, grew wispy beards, and practiced polygamy. Their wives donned head coverings (*kemars*) and completely veiled their faces (*nijabs*) when appearing in public.

In addition to their Quranic and Arabic studies, the group trained in marital arts and spent weekends with semiautomatic weapons at a firing range in New Jersey. Immigrants were excluded from membership, since DAR existed "in order to exclusively convert African Americans to mainstream Islam."[18] Such converts were obliged to swear the following oath of bayat to the group:

> In the name of Allah, the Gracious, the Merciful; Allah is the greatest; Bearing witness that there is no God but Allah and that Muhammad (peace be on him) is His Messenger, and being a follower of the last Prophet and Messenger of Allah, I hereby pledge myself to the Shariah and to those who are joined by this pledge.

> I pledge myself, by pledging my love, energy, wealth, life and abilities. I also pledge myself to the Majlis (Imamate), whose duty is to establish, develop, defend and govern according to the precepts of the Shariah.

The first Tablighi missionary to the New World had succeeded in creating "an urban *mujahadeen.*"[19]

By 1970, cells of DAR soon sprouted up in Akron, Pittsburgh, Chicago, Philadelphia, Durham, Raleigh, Columbia, Atlanta, Dallas, San Antonio, Los Angeles, Cleveland, Washington, DC, and a score of other cities throughout the country. All cells were united under the command of Sheikh Yahya Abdul Karim, the newly elected imam at the Yasin Masjid.[20] Turf wars broke out throughout the country between the DAR and urban street gangs, and hundreds of "holy warriors" were collared for such crimes as murder, attempted murder, rape, aggravated assault, breaking and entering, firebombing, and theft. A considerable number, including Salih Ali Abdullah, Dawd Abdullah Ar-Rahm Yusef Abdul, and Shuaib Abdul Raheem (Earl Robinson, notorious cop killer) ended up in maximum-security prisons, including Attica and Green Haven Federal Penitentiary in rural New York.[21]

In 1973, the Yasin mosque relocated to a three-story brick building on Herkimer Place, which became the site of a violent shootout between DAR members and a gang of Black Muslims from the Mosque of Islamic Brotherhood (MOI) in Harlem. Four DAR leaders were killed in the melee, including deputy imam Bilal Abdullah Rahman.[22]

THE PRISON DAWAH

At Green Haven Federal Penitentiary, members of DAR, under the leadership of Yusef Abdul Mu'mim, demanded special privileges, which they obtained from prison officials who remembered Attica and remained fearful of another prison riot. The privileges included the right of Muslims to appoint their own imams and to establish a mosque—which they called *Masjid Sankore*—within a large storage area. DAR inmates also demanded and received the right to observe congregational salat not only in the mosque, but also in the exercise yard, a separate kitchen for the preparation of separate halal meals, separate hours for showers and toilets to ensure their privacy, and *sadaqa* (financial autonomy for their prison business endeavors, including the sale of incense, aromatic oils, and personal toiletries). They refused to submit to strip searching and frisking, claiming that such practices violated the Islamic code of *wuduzu*.[23] These concessions granted DAR the ability to corner the drug trade within the prison system. Sheikh Ismail Abdul Rahman, a DAR emissary to Green Haven, noted: "When you walked in there [Masjid Sankore], it was another world. You didn't feel like you were in Green Haven in a maximum security prison. Officers [prison guards] never came in. It was like going to any other masjid on the outside; you felt at home."[24]

Thanks to DAR, the Muslims emerged as a privileged class within the prison system—a class that could offer protection to other black inmates from Hispanic street gangs and white supremacists. By 1975, there were more converts at Masjid Sankore than at any mosque in the country, and the DAR prison committee started to receive annual stipends from the New York Department of Corrections to bring militant Muslim visitors to the prison mosque as lecturers and entertainers.[25] Shuaib Abdul Raheem, who became the new imam at Sankore, had been sentenced to life in prison for killing a New York City police officer while attempting to steal weapons from a sporting goods store with three other DAR members.[26]

The DAR Muslim ministry quickly expanded from Green Haven to other maximum-security prisons throughout New York, including Attica, Auburn, Clinton, Downstate, Five Points, Great Meadows, Shawangunk, Sing Sing, Southport, Upstate, and Wende. By 1978, the movement had established mosques and Muslim men's clubs in penitentiaries throughout the country, and members of DAR ascended to positions of prominence. Warith Deen Umar (Wallace Gene Marks), who joined the DAR at Green Haven, became the head of the National Associations of Muslim Chaplains, an organization that received millions in funding from Saudi Arabia. Jamil al-Amin (H. Rap Brown), a former Black Panther leader who became a Muslim while serving time in Attica, established the Community Mosque of Atlanta and became the spiritual leader of over thirty Islamic centers throughout the country.[27] Al-Amin said: "I was in prison in New York. The Dar-ul-Islam movement had a prison program and brothers would come in to conduct *juma* and for *da'wah* purposes."[28] Ihsan Bagby, who currently is an associate professor of Islamic Studies at the University of Kentucky, told the Associated Press in 2000 that "the Dar-ul Islam movement appealed to Al-Amin and many other black militants because it blended the rhetoric of black power with a call for strict devotion to Islam."[29]

THE MOVEMENT SOLIDIFIES

Throughout the 1970s, the organizational structure of the Dar ul-Islam movement remained hierarchical, with leadership "selected on the traditional criterion of being 'most knowledgeable' of the *Qur'an* and the *hadith*."[30] At the top of the organization stood the *majlis ash-shurah* (governing body), which made decisions affecting the growth of the movement, including the establishment of DAR mosques throughout the United States and Canada, with the guidance of Tablighi missionaries, including Ali Abdur Rashid.[31] Under the majlis ash-shurah were several ministries, each with distinct responsibilities, including propagation (*dawah*), defense, information, culture, education, health and welfare, and protocol.[32] By 1971, the ministry of defense had its own paramilitary wing called the *Ra'd*, meaning "thunder" in Arabic. Members of the Ra'd performed a variety of activities, including acting as personal bodyguards, providing building security and community protection, and "administering punishments to those who broke the laws of the community."[33]

Imam Yahya Abdul Karim remained in control of the overall movement, while individual communities had their own imams responsible for day-to-day operations. By the 1970s, the movement had "formed a federation of mosques around the country."[34] There were around twenty Dar ul-Islam mosques in the New York area alone, with affiliates in Canada and the Caribbean.[35] The movement remained funded by the Saudi royal family, with members offered all-expense-paid trips to make the hajj in Mecca and to study under Wahhabi scholars.[36] These funds were supplemented by private-sector business endeavors. In 1974, the DAR opened the country's first halal meat store on Atlantic Avenue in Brooklyn, a Muslim daycare center in Bedford-Stuyvesant, and an incense factory next to the Yasin Mosque.[37] In addition, the brothers produced a magazine called *Al-Jihadul Akbar*, which they hawked throughout New York and other urban areas, and they made plans to create their own Islamic army to wage jihad against infidels and nonbelievers.[38]

The DAR retained its separate identity from the Muslim immigrants that "foreign Muslims were accepting the racial conditions imposed upon them by non-Muslim Americans."[39] The group responded to the rapid growth of the Muslim Student Association as follows: "The M.S.A. has a lot of good brothers but a few have personal ambitions. It's the ambitious ones who want to direct Islamic affairs in this country. They are not from this country. Americans should control their own activity and they should 'assist' us."[40]

ENTER SHEIKH GILANI

The movement came to a screeching halt when Sheikh Mubarak Ali Gilani, another Tablighi missionary, arrived in Brooklyn to serve as the new imam of the Yasin Mosque. A practitioner of something called "Quranic psychiatry," Sheikh Mubarak Ali Gilani presented himself to the Brooklyn congregation as "the sixth Sultan ul Faqr," with a lineage that dates back to the Prophet Mohammed. He claimed to have supernatural powers that came from his regular reception of visits by jinn and "non-human beings."[41]

Sporting ammunition belts, Gilani called upon DAR militants to take part in the holy war against the Soviet occupation of Afghanistan. Hundreds answered the call and headed off to training camps in Pakistan, which had been established by Osama bin Laden and other members of the mujahadeen.[42] One such recruit was Abdullah Rasheed Abdullah (also known as Clement Rodney Hampton-El), who served as a field medic under the command of Gulbuddin Hekmatyar's *Hezi Islami* (Islamic Party) and went on to become a key planner of the 1993 bombing of the World Trade Center.[43]

THE DAR DIVIDES

Gilani gained a cadre of ardent supporters, including Abdul Kareem, who oversaw the prison ministry, and Imam Yahya Abdul Karim, the leader of the movement.[44] But other DAR members objected to Gilani's emphasis on a foreign war rather than the local issues of street justice and social reform.[45] They further took offense at the new sheikh's introduction of Sufi practices in their mosque, including the *zikhr*, or rhythmic chanting, and the increasing number of Muslim immigrants who now appeared at the Yasin Mosque on Friday afternoon for salat.[46] Several, including Sheikh Sulaiman al-Hadi, became convinced that Gilani was a CIA operative who had been assigned to destroy the movement.[47] Tensions mounted until the Yasin Mosque broke into two separate places of worship—both in Brooklyn: Masjid Mu'minim on Atlanta Avenue and Masjid Ikwa on Eastern Parkway. The cleft widened until the movement disintegrated into two splinter groups, each vying for dominance in the black community. One group united under Jamil al-Amin (H. Rap Brown) and became known as the National Ummah.

THE NATIONAL UMMAH

By 1994, the National Ummah, which sought to create Islamic enclaves within major American cities, could boast of ten thousand members and the creation of twenty-eight mosques.[48] The group's position on violence was expressed as follows by al-Amin in *Revolution by the Book*: "Islam is not non-violent. There is right to self-defense, and there is right to defend your faith. Allah says that fighting is prescribed for you."[49]

The Ummah gained national notoriety on October 28, 2009, when the FBI raided a warehouse and two houses in Detroit and arrested eleven Ummah members on charges of mail fraud, the illegal possession of firearms, trafficking in stolen goods, and altering vehicle identification numbers. In the course of the raid on the warehouse, Luqman Ameen Abdullah, the ringleader of the group, opened fire on the federal agents and was killed in the ensuing gunfight.[50]

ME AND MR. MOHAMMED

By 2012, Ummah enclaves cropped up in such cities as Cleveland, New York, and Dearborn and came to contain not only mosques, madrassas, and Islamic community centers, but also Islamic housing complexes. Many of these complexes were created with massive infusions of state and federal funds, as evidenced in the case of Kenny Gamble, the composer of such hit songs as "Love Train" and "Me and Mrs. Jones."

A convert to Islam, Gamble, now known as Luqman Abdul Haqq, collected more than $1.6 billion in government grants, foundation awards, and private sector funding for his "charitable" undertakings. In 1993, he set up the United Muslim Movement, whose corporate purpose was "to establish the religion of Islam with clear representation of the Qur'an and the Sunnah."[51] Gamble soon realized that his nonprofit organization's statement of intent would limit his sources of public funding, so in the same year he formed Universal Companies, another charity at the same address.

Universal Companies eventually managed to amass more than $1.6 billion in government grants, bequests from foundations, and other sources of funding. It developed one hundred new housing units between South and Federal Streets in downtown Philadelphia, operated a public elementary school and a charter school in the same neighborhood, set up a mosque and an Islamic Center, and provided healthcare services for the new Muslim residents. Gamble and his spokesmen claimed that their project served to clean up this blighted section of the city, but fears surfaced that Universal really used the public funding to create a Muslim ghetto. Rotan Lee of the Philadelphia YMCA described the transformation of the neighborhood as follows: "You look up and down the street and see men, women and children in traditional Muslim dress everywhere; you see the masjid right across from Kenny's house and security guards on the corners in kufis." Gamble himself offered testimony to support this contention that he was carving out a Muslim enclave within the inner city by saying: "We are not here for Universal, we are here for Islam."[52]

At present, the Ummah remains under the control of al-Amin, who is serving a life sentence in a maximum-security prison after being convicted in 2002 of killing a Georgia police officer.[53]

The other DAR members remained under the leadership of Sheikh Gilani and adopted the name Jamaat ul-Fuqra ("Community of the Impoverished"). From this group would emerge a torrent of violence without precedence in the religious history of the United States.

THE DAR LEGACY

Dar ul-Islam, once the most powerful Islamic movement in America, now ceased to exist. But the group had forged a path for the future of Sunni Islam in America. The vast majority—over 90 percent—of converts to the faith would be African American, and 60 percent of such converts would come from the prison system. By 2005, approximately 350,000 these inmates would find faith in Allah while incarcerated. By 2008, prison conversions would take place at the astonishing clip of forty thousand a year.[54] All of this would come to pass from the work of Hafis Mahbub, an individual who would produce greater changes in American religious life than Timothy Drew, Elijah Muhammad, Malcolm X, or any of his quasi-Islamic precursors. Yet no monument to his work has been erected and no account of his accomplishments has been recorded.

The Muslim prison ministry, which originated with Mahbub and the DAR, remains funded by the Saudi government through the Islamic Society of North America (ISNA). Abdel al-Jubeir, foreign policy spokesman for Saudi Arabia's King Abdullah, told the *Wall Street Journal*: "The Saudi government pays for prison chaplains, along with many other American Muslims, to travel to Saudi Arabia for worship and study during the *hajj*. . . . The trips typically cost $3,000 a person and last several weeks."[55]

At present, there are fifteen thousand Tablighi missionaries at work in the United States. Graham E. Fuller, a former CIA official, characterizes the Tablighi as "a peaceful and apolitical preaching-to-the-people movement."[56] But many law enforcement officials and counterterrorism experts do not agree with this assessment. "If al-Qaida needed a fresh set of bodies in order to pull an operation, one of the places that they would go to for that fresh set of bodies would be Tablighi Jamaat, whether it's in the United States or not," says former FBI agent Steve Denny, who has investigated members of Tablighi for the past decade.[57] For proof of this contention, Denny points to Islamberg and other settlements that have sprouted up throughout the country.

CHAPTER 11
WELCOME TO ISLAMBERG

In 1979, eighty-five thousand Soviet troops invaded Afghanistan to prop up the communist government of Noor Takaki. Religious teachers and clerics throughout the Muslim world called upon young men to take up arms in a jihad to liberate their Muslim brothers. The calls were heard in the United States, particularly at the Yasin Mosque in Brooklyn. Shiekh Mubarak Gilani, the leader of the Dar ul-Islam movement, convinced scores of his followers to head off to guerilla warfare training camps in Pakistan with an offer of thousands in cash and the promise of seventy houris in seventh heaven, if they were killed in action. Gilani, in his efforts, was reportedly funded not only by members of the Saud dynasty but also by the CIA.[1]

The US State Department's support of the sheikh's activities purportedly began in 1979 and persisted throughout the 1990s. It was prompted by a bipartisan desire to tip the scales against the Soviets. President Carter provided the mujahadeen in Afghanistan with $30 million in covert aid. This amount increased under the Reagan administration, and so did the carnage and the number of refugees. By 1985 the Afghan rebels were receiving $250 million a year in covert assistance to battle the 115,000 Soviet troops occupying the country. This figure was double the number of Soviet troops in 1984. The annual payments to the guerillas reached $700 million by 1988. By this time, the CIA was even shipping Tennessee mules to Afghanistan to carry all the US weapons into the hills.[2]

Realizing that it would be financially advantageous to train new recruits for the holy war on American soil, Sheikh Gilani set up his first paramilitary training camp within the dense forest among the foothills of the Catskill Mountains on the outskirts of Hancock, New York. The seventy-acre complex, known as Islamberg, was surrounded with "no trespassing" signs. The rocky terrain was infested with rattlesnakes, and the woods were home to black bears, coyotes, wolves, and a few bobcats. The entrance to the community was located at the bottom of a very steep hill that is difficult to navigate even on a bright, sunny day in May. The road, dubbed Muslim Lane, remained unpaved and marred by deep crevices that could only be navigated by all-terrain vehicles. A sentry post was established at the base of the hill.

On the other side of the hill, where few nonresidents would dare to go, was a tiny village replete with a makeshift learning center (dubbed the "International Quranic Open University"); a shack that served as a laundry facility; a small, green community center; a small and rather squalid grocery store; a masjid, over forty clapboard homes; and scores of rusty old trailers.

The training took place at the eastern perimeter of the property, an area equipped with ropes hanging from tall trees, wooden fences for scaling, a makeshift obstacle course, a firing range, and large underground bunkers that had been stationed throughout the complex.[3]

Islamberg became off-limits to all outsiders—even to the local undertaker, who delivered bodies to the complex from the local hospital but never gained entrance. "They come and take the bodies from my hearse. They won't allow me to get past the sentry post. They say that they want to prepare the bodies for burial. But I never get the bodies back. I don't know what's going on there but I don't think it's legal."[4]

The neighbors were now treated to the sounds of gunfire and explosions erupting day and night from the bucolic site. "If you go there, you better wear body armor," a customer at the Circle E Diner in Hancock told a team of reporters. "They have armed guards and if they shoot you, nobody will find your body."[5] But despite the complaints, the training continued because the complex supposedly served a covert purpose.

In public statements, Gilani presented Islamberg as a peaceful settlement where world-weary Muslims could retreat for prayer and meditation. For this reason, he named the governing organization of the settlement Jamaat ul-Fuqra (Community of the Impoverished) and established its headquarters in Lahore, Pakistan. The American arm of Jamaat ul-Fuqra became the Muslims of the Americas (MOA), a tax-exempt corporation with Gilani's mosque in Brooklyn as an address.[6]

Soon other *jamaats* (settlements)—all similar to Islamberg and all under the corporate protection of the MOA—appeared in Red House, Virginia; Commerce, Georgia; York, South Carolina; Dover, Tennessee; Buena Vista, Colorado; Macon, Georgia; Squaw Valley, California; Marion, Alabama; Talihina, Oklahoma, and a score of other sites in rural America.[7]

By 1985, the international press began to report that an unspecified number of African American Muslims—all related to ul-Fuqra—had joined the ranks of the mujahadeen in Afghanistan and that several had been killed in action.[8] Later, when questioned, several of the jihadis imported from America would testify that they were agents of the CIA.[9]

THE INTERNATIONAL QURANIC OPEN UNIVERSITY

Along with the paramilitary training camp in Islamberg, Sheikh Gilani also opened the International Quranic Open University, a one-room schoolhouse. In a recruitment video, Gilani stated the purpose of the new facility: "We give [students] specialized training in guerilla warfare. We are at present establishing training camps. You can easily reach us at Open Quranic offices in upstate New York or in Canada or in South Carolina or in Pakistan." Similarly, in a handbook, published by the university, Gilani wrote that the foremost duty of all students at the school was to wage war against "the oppressors of Muslims."[10] Those who enrolled were expected to sign an oath that read, "I shall always hear and obey, and whenever given the command, I shall readily fight for Allah's sake."[11]

HOLY WAR ON THE HOMEFRONT

From 1982 to 1992, members of Jamaat ul-Fuqra initiated a wave of terror attacks throughout the country and became convicted of such crimes as homicide, conspiracy to commit murder, firebombing, gun smuggling, grand theft, counterfeiting, and workers' compensation fraud. Others remain leading suspects in criminal cases throughout the country, including ten unsolved assassinations and seventeen firebombings between 1979 and 1990.[12]

The first violent outings reflected the sheikh's close ties to Kashmir, his alleged association with Pakistan's Inter-Service Intelligence (ISI), and his hatred of ethnic Indians and Indian sects, including Hare Krishna and yoga societies. They also crystallized his intent to cleanse Islam of heterodoxy, such as the Ahmadiyya movement, through violence. A partial listing of these attacks is as follows.

July 1983: Portland, Oregon—A hotel owned by the Baghwan Shree Rajneesh, an Indian guru, was firebombed by a member of ul-Fuqra. Three pipe bombs were placed in a room on the fourth floor of the hotel by Stephen Paul Paster, one of the organizers of ul-Fuqra in the United States. Paster was convicted of the crime and sentenced to twenty years in a federal prison. He served four years, was released on good behavior, and relocated to Lahore, Pakistan, where he continues to train ul-Fuqra members in the use of explosives.

August 8, 1983: Canton, Michigan—A leader of the Muslim Ahmadiyya sect, Dr. Mozaffar Ahmad, was executed and the Ahmadiyya Center of Detroit was set ablaze. The two crimes were interrelated. William Cain, an ul-Fuqra follower from Akron, Ohio, was identified by authorities as Ahmad's murderer. Both Cain and an accomplice, Calvin Jones, were killed in the fire that had been set by Ahmadiyyans in retaliation for the assassination.

June 16, 1984: Philadelphia, Pennsylvania—The Hare Krishna Temple of Philadelphia was firebombed by ul-Fuqra thugs.

June 17, 1984: Seattle, Washington—Members of ul-Fuqra firebombed the Integral Yoga Society, a Hindu religious institution, and the Vedanta Society, a Sikh religious institution.

June and July 1984: Kansas City, Missouri—A defective bomb was found at the Vedanta Society. Authorities maintained that ul-Fuqra was attempting to duplicate its success in Seattle.

August 1, 1984: Denver, Colorado—A Hare Krishna temple was firebombed, causing $150,000 in damage. James Williams and Edward Flinton, two members of the ul-Fuqra sect, were charged in March of 1993 with conspiracy to commit murder in relation to the incident.

August 1, 1984: Overland Park, Kansas—Srinivasu Dasari, a Hindu physician, was kidnapped and presumed murdered by ul-Fuqra assassins.

August 1, 1984: Tacoma, Washington—Three East Indians were shot to death in a suburb of that city by alleged agents of Sheikh Gilani.

May 28, 1986: Bethany, West Virginia—Associates of ul-Fuqra attacked Randall Gorby, a member of a Hare Krishna temple in Philadelphia.

September 17, 1988: Augusta, Georgia—A Hindu doctor was shot to death in front of Humana Hospital by ul-Fuqra triggermen.[13]

By the time of this incident, Jamaat ul-Fuqra had established ties to violent African American gangs throughout the country, including New York's Black Panthers and Chicago's El Rukn. The latter organization was particularly well-heeled, since it had received $2.5 million from the Libyan government to act as a fighting force on call in case an armed struggle erupted between Libya and the United States. When large numbers of El Rukn were incarcerated, many members of the gang sought sanctuary within the ranks of ul-Fuqra.[14]

A RAID ON THE COLORADO COMPOUND

In 1989, federal law enforcement officials conducted a raid on the 101-acre *jamaat* in Colorado Springs, Colorado. The officials recovered a multitude of handguns with silencers and obliterated serial numbers, semiautomatic weapons, thirty to forty pounds of explosives, three large pipe bombs, improvised explosive devices, shape charges, blank birth certificates, counterfeit social security cards, sets of Colorado drivers' licenses with identical photos and different names, and manuals titled "Guerilla Warfare" and "Counter-Guerilla Operations." They also came upon several silhouettes for target practice, including one with the words "FBI Anti-Terrorism Team" written on the target's torso bullseye. In the course of a subsequent raid on the complex, the feds uncovered a weapons cache of military rifles that included American M-16s and M-14s and Soviet AK-47s.[15]

The government now knew that a militant organization of thousands of African American Islamists was conducting paramilitary training at the sites, but no measures in the halcyon days before 9/11 were adopted to ban the group or to shut down the other compounds. Moreover, the Colorado state officials in their report failed to make note of the fact that the Buena Vista compound had been deeply mined and contained vast underground bunkers that were connected by a series of tunnels.

THE 1993 WORLD TRADE CENTER BOMBING

The first bombing of the World Trade Center was executed, in part, by members of the al-Farouq mosque under the guidance of blind sheikh Omar Abdel Rahman, one of Gilani's close friends and compatriots. The blind sheikh's photograph still adorns the meeting halls and learning centers of ul-Fuqra compounds. The bombing—which occurred on February 26—killed six people and injured

1,042 more, and produced more hospital casualties than any event in US history apart from the Civil War. It was commandeered by Ramzi Yousef, a Kuwaiti radical who established headquarters in the Brooklyn mosque. His key planner was Clement Rodney Hampton-El (also known as "Rashid" and "Dr. Rashid"), one of Gilani's first recruits for the Afghan war and a prominent figure within the ul-Fuqra movement.[16]

Following the success of this attack, Sheikh Omar Rahman drafted plans to bomb the Lincoln and Holland tunnels, the United Nations, the FBI headquarters, and other federal buildings in Lower Manhattan. To create the bombs, they began mixing hundreds of pounds of Scotts® Super Turf Builder® with 255 gallons of diesel fuel within a safe house in Queens, New York. Neighbors became suspicious of the strange comings and goings of Muslim men in robes and skullcaps. A call was made to FBI headquarters, resulting in a raid on June 23, 1993. Eleven men were collared, including Sheikh Omar Rahman, Rodney Hampton-El (Dr. Rashid), and Iyman Faris, an al-Qaeda operative with strong ties to ul-Fuqra.[17]

CRIME FROM THE "CITY OF GOD"

After the news of ul-Fuqra's involvement in the World Trade Center bombing came to light, the criminal activities of the group came to a sudden standstill. The only incident of major significance occurred on August 21, 2001, when Fresno County sheriff's deputy Erik Telen was fatally shot while responding to a burglary. The shooter, who surrendered after a six-hour standoff, turned out to be nineteen-year-old Ramadan Abdur-Rauf Abdullah, who had been born in Islamberg and raised in the Red House compound. He had traveled to California to settle within an ul-Fuqra compound in Mira Monte, California, known as Baladullah.[18]

Baladullah (Arabic for "City of God") was located on the eighteen-hundred-acre site of the former drug-recovery cult

Synanon. It contained not only a firing range and obstacle courses, but also a large landing strip and a U-Haul® truck-rental center. Several months before Abdullah's arrest, James Hobson (also known as Umar Abdussalam), another resident of Baladullah, was taken into custody for running guns and ammunition between South Carolina (the site of Holy Islamville, another ul-Fuqra compound) and Gilani's mosque in Brooklyn, New York.[19]

At Baladullah, ul-Fuqra established the Gateway Academy Charter School. In 2000, the school opened for business, having received $1 million in funding from the California Department of Education and the Fresno School District. Realizing they had stumbled upon a great way to bilk money from Uncle Sam, members of the compound established thirteen additional schools under the original charter. In this way, they managed to amass an additional $5.5 million in state aid by claiming a highly inflated enrollment of twelve hundred students. With money pouring in at the rate of $4,600 per reported pupil, the compound members hired illiterate ex-cons to instruct the one hundred or so children of residents of the compound in the teachings of the Quran, the doctrines of Wahhabism, and, of course, the writings of Sheikh Gilani.[20] By the time law enforcement officials became aware of the scheme, millions had left Gateway's coffers and had been sent overseas. In 2004, Khadjiah Ghafur, the head of the phony educational enterprise, and two other members of Baladullah, were arrested on fraud and grand theft charges. The money was never recovered.[21]

The Baladullah boondoggle was reminiscent of an earlier scam in which the ul-Fuqra compound in Buena Vista managed to bilk the Colorado Workers' Compensation Fund for an amount in excess of $350,000. The money was laundered through Professional Security International (PSI), an ul-Fuqra security firm, and sent to terrorist groups in Pakistan.[22]

UL-FUQRA AND 9/11

In 2001, Khalid Sheikh Mohammed, the al-Qaeda leader in charge of 9/11, sent Zacarias Moussaoui to live with ul-Fuqra member Melvin Lattimore (also known as Mujahid Abdul-Qadder Menepta) in Norman, Oklahoma, so that Moussaoui could attend flight school with Mohammed Atta and other 9/11 operatives at the Airman Flight School. The gracious Lattimore opened his doors not only to Moussaoui, but also to Nawaf al Hazmi (also known as Rabia al Makki) and Marwan al-Shehhi, two of Atta's fellow hijackers.[23]

Lattimore had been convicted in 1979 of stockpiling weapons and explosives in a St. Louis mosque, and his credit card was used to purchase materials for the 1993 bombing of the World Trade Center. In 1995, while residing at the ul-Fuqra compound in Talihina, Oklahoma, he was spotted on several occasions in the company of Oklahoma City bomber Timothy McVeigh. Despite this, Lattimore was never taken into custody and subjected to an extensive grilling. His name does not appear in the 9/11 Commission Report. He received favored status from the Justice Department because he was listed as an FBI informant.[24]

THE SHEIKH AND THE SHOE BOMBER

On December 22, 2001, Richard Reid, a twenty-nine-year-old British citizen, attempted to blow up a transatlantic jetliner with explosives that he had concealed within his shoe. At the time of his arraignment in federal court, Reid admitted his intention to blow up the plane and kill the eight crewmembers and 197 passengers. "I'm a follower of Osama bin Laden," Reid said, "and I'm an enemy of your country."[25]

Reid was also a follower of Sheikh Gilani and an affiliate of ul-Fuqra. On January 6, 2002, the *Boston Globe* published an investigative report stating that Reid had been a guest on several occasions at the sheikh's walled fortress in Lahore, Pakistan.[26] Few in the media at that time had focused on Gilani, and fewer still had made the connection between ul-Fuqra and al-Qaeda. But the report intrigued *Wall Street Journal* reporter Daniel Pearl, who made arrangements through his ISI (Pakistan's Inter-Service Intelligence agency) contacts to meet the elusive sheikh in Lahore. He was kidnapped on his way to the meeting and, several weeks later, beheaded. The actual beheading was performed by Khalid Sheikh Mohammed, an al-Qaeda chieftain now in federal custody.

THE SHEIKH'S PEARL

In his memoirs, titled *Pillar of Lies,* Gilani writes that he was not involved in the murder of the reporter, but he adds that Pearl deserved his fate because he was not an actual journalist, but an agent of the CIA. "Obviously," he insists, "Daniel Pearl was to target me and then an assassination team would be sent to kill me."[27]

Gilani, thanks to Pearl, finally had captured the attention of the national press in America. On February 11, nineteen days after Pearl's kidnapping, CBS reporter George Crile of *60 Minutes* arrived in Islamabad and interviewed Khalid Khawaja, a leading Islamic militant who was close friends with bin Laden and Sheikh Gilani. "I am telling you," Khawaja said, "Osama doesn't have many people in America. But here (in Pakistan), he has lots and lots of followers there and followers who are, I am telling you, I am sure of one thing, Osama does not have even one of his followers as committed as Sheikh Mubarak Gilani. Osama does not have even one as committed as the least of his people."[28]

On February 12, CBS reporter George Crile interviewed Gilani at the sheikh's fortress in Pakistan. Gilani professed to know nothing of Daniel Pearl or Richard Reid and maintained that he had nothing to do with al-Qaeda. "Why should I be part of it?" he asked. "I'm a reformer, educationist. And I am not part of anybody. . . . I mean, I keep to myself. And I do what I think is best for the people who follow me. First is peace. You know, another is they should work hard for a living. And they should be honest, good, trustworthy. That's all I told them. I know—if anybody does anything wrong, why blame me? Will you blame the pope if somebody, some Christian, does something wrong?"[29]

Gilani went on to say that the terrorist attacks within the United States were not a result of Islamic fundamentalism but rather of malevolent invisible powers. "There are beings who are not visible to you," he told the CBS reporter, "but they inhabit this earth. And they are damaging, causing psychotic diseases, fits, epilepsies. And controlling the agents, controlling the human beings." Gilani said that he possessed the power to control those forces, and could, if he so desired, bring about the salvation of America and the Western world. To clarify this claim, Gilani turned to *The X-Files*, his favorite American television program: "What is an X-file? Most of things—could have happened or will happen. Human beings can be made to do things against their will. They can be made to commit crimes. They can be made to go and kill people. You know? And all your missiles, all your rockets, space ships go up. And electronics, they can be damaged, influenced, and misdirected through the agencies of jinn beings."[30]

In the wake of the interview, authorities discovered that the Pearl kidnapping was engineered by Ahmed Omar Saeed Sheikh, the son of a wealthy Pakistani manufacturer. Ahmed Omar Saeed Sheikh was an ul-Fuqra agent who served as the intermediary between bin Laden and the ISI. The close ties between ul-Fuqra and al-Qaeda no longer could be disputed, but few expressed alarm that the sheikh had established paramilitary compounds throughout the United States and had assembled an army of violent street thugs to do his bidding.

THE BELTWAY SNIPERS

The bloody saga of ul-Fuqra did not end with the beheading of Daniel Pearl. It continued with the random killings of ten people and fifteen attempted assassinations in the vicinity of Washington, DC, by the "Beltway snipers"—John Allen Muhammad, forty-one, and Lee Boyd Malvo, seventeen. During their murder spree, the gunmen reportedly holed up in the Red House compound. Muhammad and Malvo were quite familiar with life among ul-Fuqra. They reportedly had spent some time at one of the group's paramilitary compounds near Macon, Georgia.[31]

CHAPTER 12
THE PAKISTANI'S VISION

Sheikh Gilani, the founder of Islamberg, was only one of five hundred thousand Pakistanis who arrived in America with the second wave of Muslim immigrants. This wave emerged from the 1971 war between West Pakistan and East Pakistan—a war that resulted in the creation of Bangladesh, the deaths of 3 million Bangladeshis, and the emergence of 10 million refugees, with hundreds of thousands eventually making their way to the United States of America.[1]

By the time the Pakistanis appeared in considerable numbers, the Palestinians, who had preceded them, had created mosques throughout the country. Most were makeshift establishments that served as stores, restaurants, even residential units as well as houses of worship. Others were converted factories, retail outlets, churches, and movie theaters. Such mosques included the al-Farooq Mosque in Brooklyn; the Bridgeview Mosque in Chicago; the al-Fajr Mosque in Indianapolis; Masjid Annur in Santa Ana, California; the Dearborn Mosque in Dearborn, Michigan; and the Quincy Mosque in Quincy, Massachusetts. All of these mosques received Saudi funds and remained, in part, under Saudi control, thereby providing the Pakistani immigrants with indoctrination in the tenets of militant Salafism.

A MINARET RISES IN QUEENS

Many of the Pakistani newcomers settled in Queens, New York, where, in 1983, they built the Islamic Center of Corona (Masjid

Al-Falah), New York's first structure that was planned and conceived as a mosque, on National Street. The dome and minaret of this Islamic house of worship, which contained two prayer rooms and a funeral home, hovered over the largely Puerto Rican and Columbian neighborhood.[2] Pakistani Shiites, without a place of worship within the five boroughs of New York, began to join with the Sunnis at Al-Falah, a development that would have never occurred within their native country.[3] The new Pakistani mosque in Queens underwent several attacks of vandalism, including attempts to set it on fire. Anwer Ali, the imam, said that the Puerto Ricans had targeted the Muslims for taking away their jobs, housing, and businesses.[4]

Shortly after the construction of Masjid Al-Falah, Pakistani taxi drivers and mechanics established Masjid Fatima at the corner of Fifty-Eighth Street and Thirty-Seventh Avenue in the desolate factory district of Queens.[5] Within a decade, twenty additional mosques for central Asians sprouted up throughout New York.

THE AFGHANIS ARRIVE

Throughout the 1980s, Pakistanis arrived here at the rate of six thousand a year, swelling the ranks of this ethnic group, according to the US embassy in Islamabad, to more than seven hundred thousand by 2010.[6] Afghanis, uprooted by the Soviet invasion, also began to arrive, with over 2,800 reaching these shores in 1986.[7] By the close of the Afghan war, over ten thousand Afghanis had joined the thousands of worshippers at the mosques in Queens and Brooklyn and had organized the Afghan Community in America to rally public support for the mujahadeen rebels.[8] Such support came with the proclamation of March 22, 1988, as "Day of the Afghan Refugee" by New Jersey governor Thomas Kean and covert aid from the Reagan administration to establish the al-Kifah Refugee Center, which later became a cell of al-Qaeda, within the al-Farooq Mosque on Atlantic Avenue in Brooklyn.[9]

LITTLE PAKISTANS

By 1982, Chicago experienced a sharp influx of Pakistanis and Afghanis, who converted an old movie palace into the Muslim Community Center, where more than a thousand gathered every week for Friday prayer. The Muslim newcomers settled in clusters along Devon Avenue, which came to resemble a thoroughfare in Islamabad, with halal restaurants, Islamic bookstores, clothing shops with wedding saris for women and long, elaborate shirts and gilded slippers with curled toes for men, and a chain of rudimentary mosques that have the reputation for being far more conservative than those elsewhere in the city.[10] Little Pakistans also appeared in Middlesex County, New Jersey; Hudson County, New Jersey; and King of Prussia, Pennsylvania.

The migration of Muslims from Pakistan and Afganistan continued throughout the final decades of the twentieth century due, in part, to the Hindu-Muslim clashes in India, the Soviet-Afghani war, the rise of the Taliban, and the US-led invasion of Afghanistan. Some came as refugees; others came with student and work visas—almost all of whom remained in the United States as illegal residents when their visas expired. At present, 40 percent of the Muslims in America are African Americans, followed by the Indo-Pakistanis, who constitute about 29 percent. Arabs make up approximately 12 to 15 percent. The remaining roughly 17 percent come from Iran, Russia, China, Indonesia, sub-Saharan and southern Africa, and South America.[11]

SUCCESS STORIES

Most of the Pakistanis who arrived in the 1970s were drawn by jobs in academia, medicine, and engineering. It was only in the late 1980s and the 1990s that Pakistanis came to work blue-collar jobs as taxi drivers and shopkeepers.[12] The presence of so many professional and highly trained Pakistanis resulted in the ethnic group's advancement over Arab American Muslims with respect to occupational level and salaries.[13] The census calculated that mean household income in the United States in 2002 was $57,852 annually, while that for Pakistanis and Afghanis was $70,047.[14]

In 1979, the first session of the Association of Physicians of Pakistani Descent of North America (APPNA) was held in Dearborn. The event was attended by twenty physicians. By 1992, membership in this association rose to two thousand. In 2012, it stood at fifteen thousand.[15]

A TELLING INTERVIEW

Because the Pakistanis now represented the largest group of immigrant Muslims in the United States, they gained control over many Islamic organizations that had been established by Arab Americans, including the Islamic Circle of North America (ICNA), which launched a multimillion-dollar campaign in 2012 to promote *sharia* (Islamic law) throughout the country.[16] On its website, the ICNA, which presents itself as the "flagship" of Sunni orthodox organizations in America, states that its purpose is "to establish the Islamic system of life" as "spelled out in the Quran and the Sunnah [the oral tradition] of the Prophet Muhammad."

In an interview with Akbar Ahmed, author of *Journey into America*, Khurshid Khan, a Pakistani immigrant who now serves as the president of the ICNA, proclaimed, "I am an American, but first I am a Muslim." After saying this, Mr. Khan proceeded to lament that 95 percent of the Muslims throughout the country are now in "the melting pot." If they assimilate, he continued, Islamic values "may disappear within three or four generations." At the conclusion of the interview, Mr. Khan spoke of the "Zionist conspiracy" to destroy Islam, including the attacks of 9/11.[17]

THE AMERICAN *DEEN*

One of the most influential Pakistani newcomers to arrive with the second wave was Shamim A. Siddiqi, who arrived in 1976 to form the Forum of Islamic Work in Brooklyn. Siddiqi believed that most Americans had the wrong conception of Islam, since they viewed it as a religion. "Islam," he wrote, "is a *Deen* (a way of life) not a religion, as the West mostly understands it. It is an ideology, a code of conduct that governs the entire spectrum of human life both individual and collective, from birth to death. It regulates all the aspects of human life—personal and private, social and cultural, economic and political, war and peace, trade and commerce, human rights and obligations, national and international affairs, moral and spiritual bonds. Nothing lies beyond its domain."[18] For this reason, he concluded, no true Islamist could assimilate within American culture. "It's [the Dawah program] call on The Muslims of America to decide once and for all that they are to live in the country like true Muslims as enjoined by Allah and his Prophet or perish in this permissive society like vermin."[19]

Yet Siddiqii maintained that the Islamic takeover of the United States was imminent. The vast majority of Americans, he argued, remain hungry for the Islamist message, since it "pinpoints the shortcoming of capitalism, elaborates the fallacies of democracy, [and] exposes the devastating consequences of the liberal lifestyle." A substantial number of Americans, he argued, are perplexed by moral turpitude that surrounds them at work, at play, and even within the privacy of their living quarters. They decry gay rights, same-sex marriages, abortion, pornography, illicit drugs, lawlessness, radical feminism, and widespread promiscuity and will welcome sharia as the law of the land. The process of Islamization, the scholar added, can be accelerated by the migration of Muslims to certain states and municipalities where they can establish political-action groups, lobby for Islamic interests, and elect their own candidates to local, state, and federal office.[20]

Moreover, Siddiqi pointed out that the United States *permits*

Islamists to pursue their political agenda without the necessity of violence. It is the proverbial lamb that can easily be led to the halal slaughter house. The Constitution, Siddiqi maintained, guarantees complete governmental neutrality toward religion and allows Muslims to achieve their aim of making America an Islamic nation without fear of political or military resistance.[21] The courts, he says, have proven to be an important ally in the process of permitting the takeover, granting concession after concession to Muslim activists.

THE STEPS TO SUBMISSION

In *Methodology of Dawah Ilallah in American Perspective,* published in 1989, Siddiqi advised his fellow Islamists to adopt the following measures in order to ensure the takeover:

1. *The promotion of Islamic rituals and customs in public schools and institutions.* This entails the permission of Muslim students to recite the basmallah in classrooms, the broadcast of calls to prayers over loudspeakers on college campuses and within places of employment, and the installation of prayer rooms and foot baths in airports and publicly owned buildings.
2. *The demand of special privileges for Muslims.* This includes public support for Islamic schools, mosques, and civic centers, the inclusion of Muslims in affirmative-action plans, and the insistence upon special allowances for Muslim employees, including their right to retreat from their work stations at designated times of the day for prayer.
3. *The restriction of rights of others.* This consists of penalties for those who dare to show disrespect for the Quran and the tenets of the Muslim religion, the curtailment of critical analysis of Islam by "Occidentalists" ("non-Muslim scholars"), and the prohibition of activities like drinking and gambling that are offensive to believers.[22]

Siddiqi saw Islamists gaining control of the White House and the corridors of executive, legislative, and judicial power before 2020.

During his stay in the United States, Siddiqi served as the director of the *Dawah* and Publications Department at the Islamic Law Council (*Fiqh*) of North America. The ICNA, which remains the largest Islamic organization in the United States, was an outgrowth of the Muslim Student Association (MSA) and, in turn, the Muslim Brotherhood,[23] which came to adopt the Pakistani scholar's plan for the Islamic transformation of America.

THE ENGINEERS OF ISLAMIZATION

The Muslim Brotherhood (*al-Ikhwan al Muslimun*), an international organization with over 100 million members, associates, and supporters, was founded in March 1928 by Hasan al-Banna, a disgruntled Egyptian social reformer who sought to revive the political aspects of Islam that had fallen into retreat with the demise of the Ottoman Empire. Al-Banna wrote that "it is a duty on every Muslim to struggle toward the aim of making every people Muslim and the whole world Islamic, so that the banner of Islam can flutter over the earth and the call of the muezzin can resound in all the corners of the world: *Allahu akbar*."[24] The Egyptian radical also coined the term "Islamists" to mean individuals who believe that Islam must become a comprehensive guide to all aspects of social, economic, and political life.[25]

By 1938, cells of the Muslim Brotherhood popped up in Lebanon, Transjordan, Bahrain, Syria, Jordan, Saudi Arabia, Palestine, Kuwait, Algeria, Sudan, Somalia, Tunisia, and Libya. The members upheld this motto: "Allah is our objective. The Prophet is our leader. The Qu'ran is our law. Jihad is our way. Dying in the way of Allah is our highest hope."[26]

At the close of World War II, the Muslim Brotherhood initiated a campaign of killings that resulted in the assassination of Egyptian prime minister Mahmud Fahmi Nakrashi. In 1948 the group was outlawed by King Farouk and forced to go underground. By this time, the movement boasted over fifteen hundred chapters and a membership of 2 million.[27] Sayyid Qutb, upon his return to Egypt from the Colorado University's College of Education, became a key figure in promoting the dream of the caliphate and the objectives of al-Banna's organization, including armed jihad against all non-Muslim states and the replacement of existing Muslim governments with strictly Islamic regimes.[28] In 1987, the Muslim Brotherhood established the Islamic Resistance Movement (Hamas) to destroy Israel; one year later, it assisted in the creation of al-Qaeda as a "base" for the holy war against the Western world. Members of the organization came to include blind sheikh Omar Abdel Rahman, the architect of the 1993 bombing of the World Trade Center; Dr. Ayman al-Zawahiri, the founder of the Egyptian Islamic Jihad and Osama bin Laden's chief deputy; Abdullah Azzam, the cofounder of al-Qaeda; and Khalid Sheikh Mohammed, the mastermind of the 9/11 attacks.[29]

THE SECRET MEMO

The Muslim Brotherhood's project for the conquest of America was revealed in a document titled "An Explanatory Memorandum on the General Strategic Goal for the Group in North America," which came to light during the 2007 trial of the Holy Land Foundation for Relief and Development, the largest Islamic charity in the United States. The memorandum had been written by Dr. Mohamed Akram Adlouni, a former director of the United Association of Studies and Research in North Virginia. It received the unanimous endorsement of the Muslim Brotherhood's *shura,* or "planning council," on May 22, 1991.[30]

In the document, Adlouni wrote that Muslims "must understand that their work in America is a kind of grand jihad in eliminating and destroying the Western civilization from within and sabotaging its miserable house by their hands so that Allah's religion is victorious over all other religions."[31] This task, Adlouni maintained, can be accomplished by the slow and steady process of "absorption"—a kind of reverse assimilation by which Muslim immigrants and converts gradually impose their values and, ultimately, their laws upon compliant American Christians and Jews.[32]

The Islamization of America, Adlouni continued, is not a fantastical goal but an achievable objective: "The U.S. Islamic arena is full of those in waiting. If we ask for money, a lot of it would come, and if we ask for men, they would come in lines. If we examined the human and financial resources the Ikhwan [Muslim Brotherhood] alone owns in this country, we and others would feel proud and glorious. And if we add to them the resources of our friends and allies, those who circle in our orbit and those waiting on our banner, we would realize that we are able to open the door to settlement and walk through it seeking to make Almighty God's word the highest."[33]

Adlouni called upon the Muslim Brotherhood to create charities and nonprofit organizations to further the cause of Islam in America. Such organizations, he said, can be used as battering rams to break down all obstacles to the ascent of Islam that may be raised by government officials and petty bureaucrats. Adlouni wrote: "We must say that we are in a country which understands no language other than the language of the organizations, and one which does not respect or give weight to any group without effective, functional, and strong organizations."[34] He noted that many Muslim organizations that can be of service to the great jihad are already in place: "All we need is to tweak them, coordinate their work, collect their elements and merge their efforts with others, and then connect them with the comprehensive plan we seek."[35]

THE NEW VISION OF THE NEW WORLD

The conquest of America will not happen overnight, according to Adlouni, but the day will soon dawn when Muslims in the United

States will form their own political party to place devout believers in positions of power, operate their own television network, publish their own newspapers, oversee the curricula in public schools and colleges, establish Islamic universities to train Islamic scholars and teachers, set up an "Islamic Central Bank" that will provide interest-free loans to all believers, institute Muslim attorneys' societies to champion the cause of Islam, and create a "Central Islamic Court" that will establish Islamic law throughout the land.[36]

In this brave new world of Islam in America, all *shirk* (polytheism/idolatry) will be restricted: women will be obliged to dress modestly and to obey the commands of their husbands, girls will be forbidden from visiting a doctor or receiving treatment at a hospital without a male relative, homosexuality and pornography will be outlawed, the sale of alcoholic beverages will be prohibited, musical instruments of all types will be unlawful, cinemas will be shut down, television programs will be heavily censored, Jews and Christians will be obliged to wear the distinctive dress of dhimmis, all non-Muslims will pay a poll tax, fornicators will be fined and imprisoned, those who engage in adultery will be stoned, thieves will lose their hands, and apostasy will result in decapitation or crucifixion. The Muslim Brotherhood's success in America, for Adlouni and his Muslim brothers, will be the first step toward the establishment of "the global Islamic state."[37]

CHAPTER 13

SHIA SUNRISE

By the time the third wave of Muslim immigrants arrived in 1979, with three hundred thousand Iranians, the Islamic transformation of America became visible in places like Brooklyn, Queens, Chicago, Dearborn, Minneapolis, Los Angeles, and Houston, Texas, where more and more male newcomers appeared wearing head coverings, such as a *kufi*, a skullcap usually made of African kente cloth; a *tarboosh*, a cylindrical red hat that was popular in the Middle East, or a *kuffiyeh*, an Arab headdress secured by a band around the head. Such men often wore full-length robes, including the *thobe*, an ankle-length, often white garment, or a *jellaba*, a woolen cloak. Other men donned the *shalwar kameez*, a combination of loose pants and a tunic. Their female counterparts, for the most part, chose *hijabs*, head scarves often sewn from cotton or silk, and loose-fitting, full-length garments called *jilbabs*. A few walked the streets in *niqabs*, which covered every part of their body, save their eyes.

New Muslim grocery stores and butcher shops sprouted up in neighborhoods in which mosques had been established. The butcher shops slaughtered animals following the *sharia*, or Islamic law guidelines, which made meat *halal*, or permissible to eat. Instead of shooting, clubbing, or electrifying the animal to death, Islamic butchers used a sharp knife to slit the animal's neck, causing it to bleed to death. Such meat was sold to Muslim restaurants in which neither pork nor alcohol were served, since both were *haram*, or prohibited by the dictates of sharia.

The sudden demand for Islamically compliant products gave

rise to Muslim-owned wholesale supply and mail-order businesses. Midamar, established in Cedar Rapids, Iowa, in 1974, offered a whole line of halal food products, which included pizza toppings, sausages, deli meats, samosas, and chicken nuggets. Such items were sold in such Muslim American publications as the *Muslim Journal* and *Islamic Horizons*.[1]

IRANIAN STUDENT INVASION

In 1973, the Nixon administration discontinued the involuntary conscription of young men between the ages of eighteen and twenty-six in the armed forces. The selective service system remained in place only as a contingency plan. American colleges and universities no longer served as safe havens for those seeking to avoid or delay enlistment, and many institutions began to experience precipitous declines in enrollment. In 1968, 64 percent of high school students went on to college. Ten years later, that number dropped to 49 percent.[2] Several colleges, which had thrived during the war years, closed; others adopted open-admissions policies; still others attempted to ward off economic and academic disaster with the recruitment of foreign students from Muslim-majority countries, including Iran.

By 1977, Iran was in the midst of an upheaval. The white revolution of Shah Mohammad Reza Pahlavi had produced an antithetical revolution in the form of militant Islam. To escape the turmoil, young men and women enrolled in US educational institutions. As the situation worsened, unscrupulous American entrepreneurs began to sell student visas—which had been signed by the directors of admissions at US colleges and universities that had adopted policies of open admissions—to the highest bidder.[3]

During the 1977–1978 academic year, of about one hundred thousand Iranian students abroad, 36,220 were enrolled in US institutions of higher learning. During the 1978–1979 academic year, on the eve of the Iranian Revolution, the number of Iranian students enrolled in American institutions rose to 45,340, and in 1979–1980 the number reached 51,310. More students from Iran than from any other foreign country were enrolled in American universities. Out of a total of 263,938 foreign students enrolled in the United States in the 1978–1979 academic year, 17 percent were from Iran, and almost all of these were Muslims.[4] These Iranian students, for the most part, remained in America after graduation because of the economic deterioration that occurred in their homeland as a result of the revolution and the Iran-Iraq war, which raged from 1980 to 1990.[5]

IRANIAN AMERICAN PROFILE

The monumental influx of Iranian students into the country's colleges and universities is reflected in statistical findings. According to the 2000 census, 50.9 percent of Iranian immigrants have attained a bachelor's degree or higher, compared to a 28 percent national average.[6] According to the latest census data available, more than one in four Iranian Americans hold a master's or doctoral degree, the highest rate among sixty-seven ethnic groups studied.[7] The Small Business Administration (SBA) recently conducted a study that found Iranian immigrants among the top twenty immigrant groups with the highest rate of business ownership, contributing substantially to the US economy. According to the report, there are 33,570 active and contributing Iranian American business owners in the United States, with a 21.5 percent business-ownership rate. The study also found that the total net business income generated by Iranian Americans is $2,559,450,000.[8]

Before 1979, no Iranian Islamic community existed in America[9]—but suddenly Shia mosques—established by Iranians—began to pop up in such US cities as Los Angeles, San Diego, New York, Detroit, Houston, Rochester, and Washington, DC. Within Dearborn, Michigan, seven Shia masjids appeared within the span of a decade.[10] In most cases, these masjids became the centers of Iranian immigrant life.

THE NEW MUSLIM STUDENT ASSOCIATION

The arrival of tens of thousands of Muslim students from Iran gave rise to the Muslim Student Association's Persian-Speaking Group (MSA-PSG), which became centered at Florida Atlantic University in Boca Raton, Florida.[11] This group, also known by its Farsi name *Anjoman Islamie*—far from lamenting the fall of the shah and the rise of Ayatollah Khomeini—was elated by the Islamic Revolution and the spread of militant Islam throughout the Middle East. At the Masjid Taqwa in San Diego—a house of worship that they shared with African American Sunnis—Iranian students maintained a hotline with Iran to convey the latest pronouncements from the ayatollah and his deputies to fellow Persians within their newly created MSA group.[12]

Throughout the three decades since its founding, the MSA-PSG has become increasing vocal in its support of Hezbollah, a group that, prior to 9/11, was responsible for more US casualties than any other terror organization. Among its victims was William F. Buckley, the CIA station chief in Beirut, who was abducted by Hezbollah in March 1984 and died after fifteen months of torture in a fetid prison, and William Higgins, a colonel in the Marine Corps and commander of the UN peacekeeping mission in Lebanon, who was seized by Hezbollah in February 1988, tortured, and eventually hanged.[13] At their annual gatherings, the MSA-PSG fly the Hezbollah flag and chant, "Long live Hezbollah!" More troublesome is the fact that the group has been accused of being a source of US intelligence for the Iranian government. Testifying before a US Senate subcommittee in 1998, then chief of the International Terrorism Section of the FBI Dale Watson said that the MSA-PSG "provides a significant resource base which allows the government of Iran to maintain the capability to mount operations against the United States."[14]

THE ISLAMIC REVOLUTION—IN AMERICA

By the end of 1979, Ayatollah Khomeini, in an effort to export his revolution, began to send militant Shia clerics to the New World. One such missionary—Shahryar Rouhani—told an enthusiastic group of American Muslims: "The Iranian revolution surpassed all such revolutions; it drew all segments of society to action." He went on to credit the spirit of the uprising to a wide array of Islamic activists, including Hasan al-Banna, the founder of the Muslim Brotherhood, and Malcolm X. The revolution, he insisted, was "for all Muslims."[15]

This claim did not fall upon deaf ears. Militant Muslims throughout the country believed that the Iranian Revolution had "vindicated Islam as an instrument of change."[16] Georgetown professor Yvonne Yazbeck Haddad, who has studied the impact of the revolution on Islam in North America, wrote:

> The joy expressed at the passing of the Shah's regime was shared by Muslims I interviewed from 18 different countries then residing in North America. For most of them (85 per cent), the most significant aspect of the revolution was that it demonstrated the ability of a people to withstand the pressures of the "greatest power in the world" [the USA] and be able to affirm its will in designing its own destiny. The Islamic nature of the revolution was seen by many as the guarantee of the search for indigenous answers to local problems. . . . All Muslims questioned about their reaction to the Iranian revolution said that it had enhanced their pride and provided them with a positive affirmation of identity.[17]

American Muslims, according to Haddad, became more fervent in their religious beliefs after the revolution. Some had celebrated Christmas and imbibed spirits in 1978, but they abandoned such practices in 1979.[18] Most became more observant of dietary laws and the rulings regarding modest dress and behavior. And Shia groups at such places as the al-Khoei Islamic Center in Queens performed bloody acts of self-flagellation, involving swords or chains with blades, on the Day of Ashura, the annual festival of mourning for the martyrdom of Husayn ibn Ali, the grandson of the Prophet Mohammed, before horrified onlookers.[19]

Massive photographs of the austere Khomeini came to adorn the interiors of Shia mosques throughout the country, including the Islamic Insititute (*Majmah*) in Dearborn. Shaykh Abdul Latif Berri, an Iranian missionary who served as the spiritual leader of Majmah, warned his congregants not to be tolerant of Western ways. He insisted that women cover their hair, arms, and legs; that men refrain from shaking hands with women and all *kafirs* (nonbelievers); that women should save their makeup for their husbands' eyes only; and that neither men nor women should wear gold jewelry. Small wonder that sociologist Linda S. Walbridge found "no assimilated Muslims hoping for a dialogue with Christian Americans" at the Majmah.[20]

SHIA POPULATION EXPLOSION

Along with the Iranian missionaries came thousands of additional Shia from Lebanon. These Muslims had been uprooted by the civil war that raged within their country from 1975 to 1990, resulting in the deaths of forty thousand Palestinians and Lebanese, the wounding of a hundred thousand more, and the creation of half a million refugees. Approximately twenty-three thousand of these refugees made their way to America from 1980 to 1985, helping to further secure a firm footing for Hezbollah on US soil.[21]

The population of Shia in the United States continued to swell with the arrival of Iraqis in the wake of the Persian Gulf War of 1991. By 2000, ninety thousand Iraqis had settled in such cities as Chicago, Detroit, Boston, Houston, Dallas–Fort Worth, New York, and Washington, DC. [22] Thirty thousand more came because of the US-led invasion of Iraq in 2003. Although many had worked as doctors, teachers, scientists, and interpreters—often for Americans—in their native country, they found that overseas credentials did not always apply in the American marketplace and ended up competing for lower-skill jobs. Few other immigrant groups had encountered similar difficulty. "I've never seen a population where the trauma is so universal," said Robert Carey, vice president for resettlement and migration policy at the International Rescue Committee."[23]

CULTURAL DIFFERENCES

In 1996, an Iraqi refugee living in Omaha, Nebraska, arranged the marriages of his two daughters, aged thirteen and fourteen, to fellow Iraqi immigrants. The ceremonies were conducted by an imam from Ohio. One groom was a thirty-four-year-old cook; the other, a twenty-eight-year-old factory worker. The husbands took their "brides" home and "consummated" their marriages. The two men were charged with child abuse and statutory rape.[24]

The defendants were outraged by the charges and argued that they had committed no crime, since the weddings were in keeping with the tradition of their religion and the example of the Prophet Mohammed. "What we have here is an example of a cultural gulf, no doubt about it," said Terrell R. Cannon, the lawyer for the grooms. "These guys still can't understand why they were arrested. They really don't think they did anything wrong. There was no intent to break the law."[25]

But in Nebraska, the law was clear. People must be at least seventeen to marry, and it is illegal for anyone eighteen or older to have sex with someone who is under eighteen, even if the child consents. The grooms, much to their dismay, were sentenced to four to six years in state prison.[26]

NYPD ALARM

In 2006, the New York Police Department recommended increased surveillance of a dozen Shia mosques from central Connecticut to the surburbs of Philadelphia because of their ties to Hezbollah and the radical mullahs of Iran. The mosques, in a confidential report, were listed as follows:

Al-Hussini Madressa, New York
Masjid Al-Rahman, Brooklyn, New York
Al Mahdi Foundation, Brooklyn, New York
Shiia Ithna-Asheri Jamaat of New York, Woodside, New York
Shiia Association of North America, Delran, New Jersey
Muslim Foundation, Inc., Bloomfield, New Jersey
Astane-Zahra, Englishtown, New Jersey
Bait ul-Qaim, Delran, New Jersey
Mehfile Shahe-Khorasan, Englewood, New Jersey
Imam a-Zamana Foundation of North America, Freehold, New Jersey
Islamic Institute of Ahl' al-bait, West Hartford, Connecticut
Al-Khoei Center, Jamaica (Queens), New York[27]

The above mosques, according to the 2006 report, were considered to represent a threat to New York City in the event of US action against Iran.[28] This document further stated that the Shia population of New York City exceeded thirty-five thousand.

THE ALAVI FOUNDATION

Many of the Shia houses of worship in the United States that support Hezbollah receive funding from the Alavi Foundation, a nonprofit, tax-exempt organization with headquarters on Fifth Avenue in New York. "The Alavi Foundation has effectively been a front for the government of Iran," United States attorney Preet Bharara said in a statement. "For two decades, the Alavi Foundation's affairs have been directed by various Iranian officials, including Iranian ambassadors at the United Nations, in violation of a series of U.S. laws."[29] Specifically, the foundation was charged with transferring funds on a continuous basis to Bank Melli, a financial institution wholly owned and controlled by the Islamic Republic of Iran. Mohammad Mahallati, the former president of Alavi, had been investigated by the US Department of Commerce for attempting to purchase botulinum toxins for use in the manufacture of biological weapons.[30]

In 2009, federal prosecutors seized over $500 million of Alavi's US assets, including a thirty-six-story glass skyscraper in midtown Manhattan, the Islamic Education Center of Greater Houston, the Islamic Education Center of Rockville, Maryland, the Islamic Institute of New York in Queens, and an Islamic Institute in Carmichael, California. These properties, according to an FBI report, were under the complete control of the government of Iran and served as massive money-laundering operations.[31] In the past, the Alavi Foundation has provided millions in funding to radical Sunni mosques, including the notorious al-Farooq Mosque in Brooklyn and the Al-Salaam Mosque in Jersey City.[32]

Reacting to the government action, Ibrahim Hooper, the communications director of the Council on American-Islamic Relations (CAIR), said: "Whatever the details of the government's case against the owners of the mosques, as a civil rights organization we are concerned that the seizure of American houses of worship could have a chilling effect on the religious freedom of citizens of all faiths and may send a negative message to Muslims worldwide."[33]

Since its founding in 1986, Alavi has provided to the following Shia centers and organizations:

Islamic Education Center, MD
Jafaria Association of North America, NY
Shia Ithna Asheri Jamaat of Pennsylvania
Sahebozzaman Islamic Center, GA
Idara-e-Jafferia, MD
Irshad Learning Center, IL
Islamic House of Wisdom, MI

Islamic Institute of Ahlalbait, Inc., CT
Shia Association of Bay Area, Inc., CA
City of Knowledge School, CA
Bab ul Ilm Islamic Center, CA
Az-Zahra Center, KS
Aramgah Memorial Garden Foundation, PA
American Moslem Foundation, WA
Al-Zahra Islamic Center, TN
Al-Zahrah Islamic Center, KY
Alrasool Islamic Center, UT
Al-Mahdi Benevolent Foundation, AZ
Islamic Education Center of San Diego, CA
Razi School, NY
Jafaria Association of Connecticut, Inc., CT
Zainabia Nonprofit, Inc., GA
Islamic Center of Portland, OR
Manassa Masjid Muslim Foundation, Inc., NJ
Noor Center Corp., NJ
Hejrat Foundation, CA
Shia Islamic Education Center, MO
Anjuman-E-Haideri, TX
Masjid al-Islam, DC
Muslim Community School, MD
Ahlul Bayt Mosque, Inc., NY
Al-Mahdi Islamic Center, TN
Quran Account Inc., MD
Universal Muslim Association of America, MD[34]

MODERATE SHIA VOICES

But a number of the Shia houses of worship were neither radical nor a threat to national security, including the country's largest mosque—the Islamic Center of America—which was constructed in 2005 in Dearborn. The leaders of the new Dearborn house of worship became leading proponents of moderate Islam by decrying violence and voicing patriotic sentiments. Eide Alawan, the chief adviser to Imam Hassan Qazwini, made this comment in the wake of the London bombings by Islamic fanatics:

> If anybody preached in favour of bombing in this mosque, the community would be on top of them. They'd report it to the board [of the mosque] and he'd be fired. There's no room for a "but" about condemning violence. If you kill me, you kill the whole of humanity. If you've got a problem about Israel, sure, bring it up. But bring it up another time. Don't relate the two. If I heard about any kids talking about America as the Great Evil, or planning something dangerous, I'd turn them in. I've seen angry kids here. They may hate what's going on in America but so do a lot of non-Muslims. I've never heard a kid say, "I want to strap a bomb on me and blow up a lot of people." Our kids are American. They realise what this country has done for our people.[35]

THE MUSLIM CONGRESS

But similar words of moderation were not raised at the 2009 annual convention of the Muslim Congress, a Shia organization that was formed "to promote and propagate the true teachings of Islam as guided by the Holy Prophet and his purified progeny."[36] The event was held at an upscale hotel in Dearborn that caters to business executives visiting the nearby headquarters of the Ford Motor Company. Islamic dress was required at all times for those in attendance, and "just wearing a small hijab (veil) is not Islamic attire," one speaker warned. Most of the women wore tunics and tight-fitting headscarves that covered their necks up to their chins.[37] The organizers of the congress placed the men and women in separate dining halls.

The session got underway with Imam Mohammad al-Asi, the former prayer leader of the Islamic Center of Washington, DC, enumerating a list of US transgressions against Muslims from supplying Israel with bombs to building US military bases in Islamic countries. "Can't you see the *shaytani* character of the U.S. government?" al-Asi asked the crowd, using the Arabic word for "Satanic." The following speaker—Abdul Alim Musa, the imam of Masjid al-Islam in an economically ravaged neighborhood of Washington, DC—distributed fliers calling the US government "Zionist occupied" and the FBI the "Gestapo" and accused US leaders of fabricating a Muslim threat to national security so Americans could stop the global spread of Islam. Finally, Sheikh Abbas Ayleya, a Muslim Congress board member and a lead scholar at the Zainab Center in Seattle, told the audience, "There is no room for pluralism in Islam. It is un-Quranic." At the conclusion of the congress, Sheikh Mohammad Baig, when asked if Shia should vote in American elections, said: "That's up to the people." He then rose and walked away. Mr. Baig is the spiritual leader of the Madinatul Iim Islamic Center in Tampa, Florida.[38]

SHIA AMERICA

Islamic scholars such as Jane I. Smith and Yasin al-Jibouri estimate that the Shia presently constitute 15 percent to 20 percent of the country's total Muslim population, which they calculate exceeds 7 million.[39] In the absence of accurate statistical data, it is impossible to verify this contention, although vibrant Shia mosques, schools, and centers now appear not only within major metropolitan areas but also in small towns and villages throughout the land, including Medina, New York, to which Shia purportedly migrated in droves because they liked the name.

CHAPTER 14

RESETTLING SOMALIS

The first wave of Somali immigrants arose in 1991, following the fall of the regime of Mohammed Siad Barre (who had ruled the Somali Democratic Republic since 1969), the collapse of the centralized authority, and the bloody war between several Islamic clan lords, including Mohamed Farah Aideed and Ali Mahdi Mohamed.[1] The chaos disrupted agricultural production and food distribution and produced a famine that killed over three hundred thousand people. As the civil war continued to rage throughout the ensuing two decades, 1.46 million internally displaced Somalis came to inhabit refugee camps, including the malaria-plagued and scorpion-infested camps of northern Kenya. Thanks to the Refugee Act of 1980, hundreds of thousands were resettled in the United States.[2]

By 2005, the Somali American Chamber of Commerce was established to service the seventy-five thousand Somalis who now reside in central Ohio,[3] and the Somali American Community Association was set up "to protect, promote, and improve" the well-being of the four to six thousand Somali refugees in Washington, DC, and its environs.[4]

STRANGERS IN A STRANGE LAND

The Somalis were unlike other Islamic newcomers. Many had been victims of rape, torture, and starvation. The Somali children displayed an autism rate of 3.6 percent (360 per 10,000), five times that of the US national average.[5] Few possessed even a rudimentary education, and fewer still had marketable job skills. Some obtained jobs as housekeepers, janitors, dishwashers, cabdrivers, and workers in food-processing plants; others relied on continued benefits from public and private welfare agencies for basic subsistence. By 2009, over 60 percent of the Somalis in America were living below the poverty line.[6]

A FAILURE TO ASSIMILATE

Of all the Islamic newcomers, the Somalis were the most resistant to assimilation within American culture. They continued to speak in Somali (which has only been a written language since 1972),[7] to dress in traditional Islamic attire (including full burqas for the women), to cut their hair at Somali barber shops, and to organize themselves along the same clan lines that existed in their native country, calling upon tribal elders to settle family disputes and community problems.[8] Some also persisted in the practice of female genital mutilation.

Dubbed "female circumcision," this Bantu practice consists of the removal of the clitoris without the benefit of anesthesia or surgical instruments. Broken bottles or tin can lids occasionally serve as scalpels.[9] Recent statistics show that forty-one thousand Somali and other North African Muslims in Brooklyn and the other boroughs of New York City have been subjugated to this ordeal.[10]

THAT DARNED KHAT

Many Somalis refused to relinquish other quaint customs of their homeland, including the chewing of *khat*, the fresh leaves, twigs, and stalks of the evergreen shrub *Catha edulis*. In the dry soil of Somilia, khat (known as *qat* in Yemen, *tschat* in Ethiopia, and *miraa* in Kenya) grows twenty feet high and is available at grocery stores, restaurants, bars, and smoke shops throughout the country. The Somalis and other East Africans boil it into tea, smoke it, and even sprinkle it on their food.[11]

Khat is a narcotic and a hallucinogen. Its psychoactive ingredient, cathinone, remains listed in Schedule I of the Controlled Substance Act, the Drug Enforcement Administration's list of the world's most dangerous substances. Within Somalia, a country with a population of 6 million, a GNP of $6 billion, and an average per capita income of $400, the daily spending for khat exceeds $300,000 a day—or over $100 million per year—enormously increasing the crippling poverty.[12]

The US Customs Service estimates that the amount of any controlled substance that it confiscates in a given year is less than 10 percent of the total substance that makes its way into the country. In 2001, US Customs seized forty tons of khat, more than doubling the amount it interdicted in 1996. In 2002, US Customs confiscated over seventy tons. Using the established rule of thumb, this means that seven hundred tons of khat were chewed, smoked, boiled, and brewed throughout America in the first two years of the twenty-first century.[13]

PERISHABLE LETTUCE

By 2005, US Customs was seizing half a ton of khat a week at John F. Kennedy International Airport in New York. In 2004, over ninety thousand pounds of the narcotic was seized there. Manifests for the shipments, which arrived from Yemen, Kenya, and England, listed their contents as coffee, tea, herbs, tobacco, perishable lettuce, and molokheya (an Egyptian vegetable).[14] From 2000 to 2005, a thousand couriers were caught smuggling khat into New York—but none was arrested or prosecuted.[15]

Muslim Africans chew khat at social gatherings, a tradition older than the drinking of coffee. The chewing releases cathinone, whose amphetamine-like effect alleviates fatigue and reduces appetite. Some of the common side effects are anorexia, heart disease, hypertension, insomnia, constipation, gastric disorder, and blackened teeth.[16]

TOWNS BECOME *TUULAS*

The Somalis settled in clusters in such states as Ohio, New York, and Washington. Almost overnight, gangs of thugs from the Horn of Africa—the Somali Hot Boyz, the Somali Mafia, and Madhibann with Attitude—became a major crime element in such cities as San Diego, California, and Nashville, Tennessee.[17] Small towns throughout the country—including Greeley, Colorado; Clarkston, Georgia; Jamestown, North Dakota; and Garden City, Kansas—became transformed into *tuulas* (Somali villages).[18]

In 2007, when Tyson Foods began to replace its illegal Hispanic work force at its poultry processing plant in Shelbyville, Tennessee, with Somali émigrés, approximately 1,100 Somalis suddenly popped up in the sleepy Southern town.[19] More Somalis made their way to Shelbyville in 2008, when Tyson downsized its labor force at its plant in Emporia, Kansas.[20] To accommodate its new workers, the plant replaced Labor Day with *Eid al-Fitr* (the Festival of the Breaking of the Fast at the end of Ramadan) as a paid holiday and set up two prayer rooms so that the Somalis could pray at regular intervals without leaving the facility.[21] Later, due to a national uproar, Tyson rescinded its decision concerning Labor Day.

SO MUCH FOR SOUTHERN HOSPITALITY

The seventeen thousand residents of Shelbyville, who are known for their Southern hospitality, did not take too kindly to the new folks in town whom they found "very, very rude, inconsiderate, and very demanding."[22] The Somalis, according to published reports, demanded the right to haggle over prices in stores, including Walmart and grocery chains; refused to deal with female clerks and cashiers; protested women teaching their children in public schools; insisted upon free daycare; practiced poor hygiene; and banned firefighters from entering their dwelling places to put out a blazing fire.[23]

One Shelbyville resident, who had lived in the apartment complex that the Somalis "took over," voiced the following complaint:

> They [the Somalis] had no respect for neighbors and bad odors would come from their apartment into the halls and then into other people's apartments. They also would hit other people's vehicles and then claim they didn't do it and also would get confrontational with other people and try and start arguments and fights. They would also run in and out all times of the night while yelling in the hallways and outside. My friends got to the point where they were afraid to come over. They totally brought the standard of living down at the apartment complex and it was a nice little place before that. I got tired of it after a while and moved into a house. They would be warned of the rules there but would continually break them and they didn't care . . . they thought they were above that and treated the rest of the residents as though they were the outsiders.[24]

When asked about the "rude and arrogant" behavior, the head of Catholic Charities in Shelbyville said that "this is just the Western perception of the Somali culture." She claimed that "since the Somalis have been refugees for so long, it is only through being rude and demanding that they have managed to get the little they have gotten to survive over the years in the camp."[25]

THE LURE OF LEWISTON

Another favorite location became the economically depressed town of Lewiston, Maine, where African Muslims, many from the Bantu tribe, began arriving in 2001 at the rate of about a hundred a month.

Mohammed Maye, the president of the African Community and Refugee Center in Clarkston, Georgia, posted a map of Lewiston on the wall of his office. "Go to Maine," he advised the Somali immigrants. Abdullahi Abdullahi, the president of the Somali Community Development Organization in Clarkston, upheld this advice by telling his fellow countrymen that, unlike Georgia, Maine has terribly cold winters, but "the welfare system is better."[26]

Lewiston, indeed, was better. The small town in Maine, with a population of thirty thousand, provided welfare to anyone in need, with the state picking up half the tab. Recipients, including the Muslim refugees, were allowed a generous five years of assistance before termination of benefits, and extensions for several additional years on the public dole were not difficult to obtain. Single parents could stay on welfare and go to college. Public housing was also available, although, with the influx of Somalis, the housing projects became packed to capacity. Many of the new project dwellers were single Somali mothers with large broods of children. Those who were unable to obtain public housing were handed Section 8 vouchers, which the federal government provided to subsidize their rent in private apartments.[27] The northern city, with its frigid climate, became welfare heaven for the arrivals from the vast desert areas of northern Africa.

EMPLOYMENT PROBLEM

The newcomers allegedly showed scant interest in securing employment. When Renee Bernier, president of Lewiston's city council, offered to hire thirty Somalis at the rate of eight dollars an hour to hold warning signs at construction sites, few displayed interest. The handful who did apply said that they were only willing to work between the hours of 10:00 a.m. and 2:00 p.m.[28]

In 2002, Lewiston mayor Laurier Raymond, in a public letter, asked the Somali leaders, including the administrators of the

African Community and Refugee Center, to discourage the migration to Lewiston. The mayor admitted that the city was "maxed out financially, physically and emotionally." The Somali leaders, in reply, labeled Raymond "an ill-informed leader who is bent toward bigotry." Two hundred of the town's Somalis and their white sympathizers from the National Council of Churches mounted a protest march from a downtown Methodist church to Lewiston's first mosque, a converted grocery store on Lisbon Street. The US Department of Justice was called upon to conduct an investigation to ensure that the Somalis in the small town were not victims of discrimination.

Mayor Raymond, a former probate judge, was quickly brought to his knees. He met with the Somali leaders and their white Christian activists at city hall and vowed to cooperate with the Somali community to reduce racial tensions and to assist in the assimilation process. "Like all families, we have our misunderstandings," the seventy-one-year-old Mayor said, "but families draw strength from resolving their issues."[29]

MINNEAPOLIS AS MECCA

Nearly one in three of the newcomers from the Horn of Africa settled in Minnesota. Some scholars place the number of Somali refugees in Minneapolis–St. Paul as high as eighty thousand.[30] Others insist that the real figure might be half this amount.[31] Regardless of this dispute over demographics, the Somali population, by all indications, will skyrocket within the next decade. While the median age of Minnesotans stands at thirty-seven years, the Somalis in Minnesota are more than a decade younger, with a median age of twenty-five years.[32]

The Somalis have transformed a section of the Twin Cities, less than a block away from the Mississippi River, into a Little Mogadishu. Life within this ethnic enclave remains a far cry from anything Mark Twain could have imagined. Men with orange henna-streaked beards and women in full-body hijabs stream past such places as the Maashaa

Allah Restaurant, the Alle Aamin Coffee Shop, the Kaah Express Money Wiring stall, and the storefront Al-Qaaniteen Mosque. Within this neighborhood stands a cluster of six tall public housing buildings called "the Towers." Approximately 80 percent of the five thousand inhabitants of the apartments within these buildings are Muslim newcomers from East Africa.[33]

THE CALL FROM AL-SHABAAB

By 2007, a dozen young Somali American men—many from the Towers—began to disappear from Minneapolis, only to show up in Somalia as raw recruits for al-Shabaab, a terrorist group with ties to al-Qaeda. They were recruited, according to US Justice Department officials, at the Abubakr As-Siddique Islamic Center, the largest mosque within the Twin Cities.[34] The call for recruits came when the Transitional Federal Government (TFG) of Somalia called in Ethiopian troops (who were largely Christian) to oust the Islamic Courts Union (ICU), a cartel governing Mogadishu and the southern portion of the country. There were reports of civilians being raped, being beaten, or having their homes looted. "The majority of Somalis here were opposed to the (Ethiopian) occupation," said Abdi Samatar, a University of Minnesota geography professor. "The Somali people did not ask for it, and the brutality was incredible. Anybody who's human-rights oriented and has a patriotic sentiment would be incredibly enraged."[35] The resistance to the occupation and the TFG was mounted by al-Shabaab (which means "the youth" in Arabic). By 2012, more than forty Somali Americans had left the United States to join the rebels, and fifteen had been killed in action.[36]

One recruit from Minneapolis, twenty-seven-year-old Farah Mohamad Beledi, became one of two suicide bombers who attacked a military base in Mogadishu on May 30, 2011, according to the FBI. Two African Union peacekeepers and a Somali soldier were killed in the attack. Beledi is the second confirmed American suicide bomber.

The first, Shirwa Ahmed, carried out a suicide bombing at the Ethiopian Consulate and the presidential palace in Hargeisa, which killed twenty-four people in October 2009.[37] FBI director Robert Mueller said he was "absolutely" concerned that the young American men may return to the United States with their passports and attempt to carry out an attack on US soil similar to the foiled plot in Australia, in which Somali Australians affiliated with al-Shabaab attempted to carry out a suicide attack on a Sydney army base after returning from the killing fields of Somalia.[38]

CHAPTER 15

THE MUSLIM MAFIA

Between 1941 and 1960, 144 Albanians entered the country, and most were Christian.[1] The small group of Muslim Albanians, for the most part, settled in Detroit, where they established the Albanian American Muslim Society. This society of fifteen members, who met in St. Andrew's Hall, published a newsletter called *Albanian Moslem Life* and, in 1954, purchased a farmhouse with eighteen acres of land southwest of Detroit for $25,000.[2] At this site, they set up a Sufi lodge called a *tekke* under Baba Rexheb, a celibate spiritual leader associated with the Bektashi order. Rexheb led the group in the New Year's celebration of Nevruz and the commemoration of Ashura in honor of the martyrdom of Husayn, the grandson of the Prophet.[3] Despite their celebration of these holy days, the early Albanian American settlers were not Shia and later joined the Sunni mosques, which were established by the Palestinians and Pakistanis, in Detroit and Dearborn.[4]

FROM KOSOVO TO KENOSHA

The real influx of ethnic (Islamic) Albanians took place as a result of political instability in their native country as well as in Kosovo, Serbia, Montenegro, and the Former Yugoslav Republic of Macedonia.[5] In May 1999, over four thousand Muslim refugees from war-torn Kosovo arrived at Fort Dix, New Jersey.[6] "We want to welcome these people to America the way we might wish our grandparents and great-grandparents had been welcomed to Ellis Island," US Army Brig. Gen. Mitchell M. Zais told troops assigned to Operation Provide Refuge. This is something that has happened in America before, from the Irish potato famine to the Jews driven from Europe before World War II to the Italians who came in great numbers, the commander said. "For many Americans," he said, "this resonated as something that was personally related to their family experience."[7] Being granted refugee status under the emergency consultation provision, the ethnic Albanians received social security numbers, which allowed them to work in the United States. They were also eligible for food stamps and federal welfare benefits.[8] By 2006, 168,644 new Muslim arrivals from the Balkans had passed through the US Refugee Resettlement Program. The number who entered as legal immigrants remains unknown, since many carried Yugoslav or Turkish passports.

Albanian mosques now appeared in such places as Kenosha, Wisconsin; Berkeley, Illinois; Dunedin, Florida; Taylor, Michigan; Waterbury, Connecticut; Garfield, New Jersey; Greenway, Arizona; Detroit; Philadelphia; Staten Island; and Brooklyn. These religious institutions remain united through membership in the Presidency of Albanian Muslim Community Centers, an organization that was established by Imam Vehbi Ismail in Harper Woods, Michigan.[9]

St. Louis, where Imam Muhammad Hasic presides over the Bosnian Islamic Center, which has sixty thousand to seventy thousand members, now contains the largest concentration of Muslims from the Balkans in the country. The ethnic Albanians moved into decaying and crime-ridden neighborhoods where they opened businesses and are widely credited with being the source of the inner city's revitalization.[10]

CULTURAL CLASH

In 1989, Sadri Krasniqi, an ethnic Albanian American, was arrested for sexually molesting his four-year-old daughter in full view of hundreds of onlookers in a crowded gymnasium on the outskirts of Dallas, Texas. Krasniqi admitted to authorities that he had placed his daughter on his lap and reached under her skirt to "fondle" her through her underwear while they watched Krasniqi's son compete in a martial arts tournament. He also could not understand why he had been taken into custody for a criminal offense.[11]

In the civil trial regarding the incident, a jury ruled that the parental rights of Krasniqi and his wife should be terminated and that the children should be adopted by their Christian foster parents. In the criminal trial, physicians testified that they were unable to provide physical evidence that Krasniqi's daughter had been sexually violated. Anthropologists said that the fondling of a child's private parts constitutes an act of pedophilia in the United States but that such touching is commonplace in Albania and is not construed as sexual molestation, since it does not result in sexual release or consummation.[12] The jury eventually acquitted Krasniqi of all criminal charges.

Upon his release from custody, Krasniqi expected to regain the custody of his children, only to learn that the termination of his parental rights and the adoption of the children by the Christian couple remained final and irreversible. In response, Muslims gathered from all corners of the state to mount a protest on the steps of the juvenile court, demanding a reversal of the court's decision and an apology from the judge who presided over the case.[13] Judge Hal Gaither refused to apologize and the decision was never rescinded.[14]

THE PIZZA CONNECTION

Since the majority of ethnic Albanians spoke Italian, they settled within the Italian neighborhoods of major American cities and gained jobs with Italian American employers in restaurants, hotels, and the building trades.[15] More than two thousand ethnic Albanians had settled in Dallas–Fort Worth. So many of these newcomers opened their own restaurants that, by 2000, Muslims from the Balkans came to own 50 percent of the pizzerias in the heart of Texas (with such names as Luigi's Italian Café, Alfredo's Pizza, and Brother's Pizza).[16] Others, being considerably more secular than their fellow Islamists, established strip joints and sports bars.[17]

With their fair complexion and in many cases blue eyes and blond hair, the Muslims from the Balkans integrated more readily into American life than their fellow Muslims from other countries. Their assimilation was facilitated by the fact that most of the men were clean-shaven and donned Western attire, including business suits. The only indication of their religion was their names, such as Muhammad and Mustafa.[18]

NEW GOODFELLAS

The influx of the ethnic Albanians spelled changes not only in the religious landscape but also in the structure of organized crime. By 2004, the FBI announced that an organized group of ethnic Albanians had replaced La Cosa Nostra (LCN) as America's "leading crime outfit."[19] Few Americans, including members of the national press, took heed of this startling development. Most continued to watch *The Sopranos* and believe that Italian American crime families controlled such organized criminal activity as prostitution, gun running, labor racketeering, drug trafficking, and hits-for-hire. But this was no longer the case. The Albanian Mafia, owing to their incredible propensity for bloodletting, gained ascendancy over long-entrenched LCN families in every major city along the eastern seaboard. "They are a hardened group, operating with reckless abandon," said Chris Swecker, assistant director of the FBI's Criminal Investigative Division.[20]

The emergence of the Albanian Mafia as the leading force in national organized crime was a result, in part, of the FBI's success in busting LCN. As a result of Operation Button Down (the FBI codename for the campaign to crush the Italian Mafia), the number of LCN families shrank from twenty-four to nine. The crackdown resulted in the incarceration of more than one hundred leading LCN members and their associates. By 2001, even the prominent New York City dons had been toppled. John Gotti of the Gambino family had died of throat cancer in prison. Vincent "the Chin" Gigante, the "Oddfather" and head of the Genovese family, was serving twelve years in a federal slammer for murder and labor racketeering. Steven Crea, the capo of the Lucchese family, was cooling his heels in a state facility on charges of enterprise corruption. Alphonse "Allie Boy" Persico, the Colombo family don, was confined to a federal cell for gun possession and loan sharking. And Joseph Massino, the Bonnano family head, was facing charges for three gangland slayings.

MEET THE MUSLIM MOB

The busts left a gap that was filled by the Albanians. Many had worked as enforcers for LCN families. Zef Mustafa, for example, became the chief "clipper" (hit man) for the Gambinos. Mustafa's capacity for violence was equaled only by his love of vodka. He drank from early morning until late at night, often consuming three quarts of vodka a day.[21] While Gotti remained in prison, Mustafa used the resources of the Gambinos to organize a $650 million Internet and phone heist through pornographic websites and "1-800" sex lines. He was arrested in 2002, pled guilty to fraud, and was sentenced to five years in federal prison.[22]

Abedin "Dino" Kolbiba also served as an assassin for the Gambinos. Dino was so adept at his craft, including a knack for making bodies disappear, that he was contracted out to the other crime families.[23]

The ruthless indifference of the Albanian Mafia to killing was evidenced by Simon and Victor Deday, two hit men for the Gambinos. They shot a waiter at the Scores restaurant in Midtown Manhattan to express their displeasure at his service. For good measure, they also shot the bouncer before he could utter a word of protest.[24] Then they sat down and finished their meal, placing their napkins on the table and making their exit shortly before the police arrived.

By 1990 several Muslim émigrés from Albania became kings of the drug underworld. Skender Fici operated a travel agency in New York that served as a front for a multibillion-dollar business in narcotics. Caught with a stash of more than $126 million in heroin, Fici and his Albanian associates issued a contract for a hit on the New York detectives who had arrested them and the federal prosecutors who had landed them in prison.[25]

Daut Kadriovski, yet another ethnic Albanian, escaped from a German prison in 1993 and came here under the Refugee Resettlement Program to pursue the heroin trade among street gangs in the Bronx. By 1998 Kadriovski's business had become so brisk that he established branches in Trenton; Philadelphia; Washington, DC; Richmond; Detroit; Chicago; and a host of other cities.[26]

THE RUDAJ ORGANIZATION

By 2004, the Rudaj Organization had become the leading Albanian criminal organization in New York. Members of this group under Alex Rudaj, a thug from Ulcinj, Montenegro, reportedly engaged in racketeering, attempted murder, extortion, loan-sharking, and the operation of a large-scale illegal gambling business. In 2001, Rudaj and sixteen members of his gang stormed Soccer Fever, a Gambino hangout in Queens, sending a brazen message to the Mafia that the club now belonged to them. The seven Albanian men ripped the dimly lit basement club apart, overturning gambling tables, shooting off their handguns, and pistol-whipping a patron. The move was bold—and, prior to this date, unthinkable.[27]

Gambino leader Arnold Squitieri decided to have a heart-to-heart talk with the rogue mobsters in order to teach them their place within the syndicate. The "sit down" took place at a gas station in a rest area near the New Jersey Turnpike. Squitieri showed up with twenty armed "soldiers" from his crime family. Rudaj, on the other hand, appeared with only six members of his crew. According to undercover FBI agent Joaquin Garcia, who infiltrated the Gambino crime family during this period, Squitieri told Rudaj that the fun was over and that they should stop expanding their operations. The Albanians and Gambinos then pulled out their weapons. Knowing they were outnumbered, the Albanians threatened to blow up the gas station with all of them in it. This ended the discussion, and the Gambinos pulled back.[28] In 2003, Rudaj and his gang laid claim to John Gotti's old table at Rao's, the exclusive East Harlem haunt of LCN.[29] Three years later, Rudaj and three of his lieutenants were sentenced to twenty-seven years in federal prison.[30]

BALKAN CRIME BUSTS

By 2005, the FBI had established a special unit in Kew Gardens, Queens, to probe the workings of the new Muslim presence in organized crime. The work of this unit resulted in indictments of the Albanian Mafia Crew of Myfit Dika, Gazmir Gjoka, and Kujtim Lika on March 12, 2009. Twenty-five members of the crew were charged with international heroin smuggling, support of Islamic terrorism, and a host of other criminal charges. Dika, Gjoka, and Lika vanished from their New Jersey homes as soon as the charges were revealed.

On July 13, 2011, thirty-seven members of an ethnic Albanian mob under ringmaster Arif "the Bear" Kurti were charged with conspiracy to smuggle and distribute massive amounts of illegal drugs, including hundreds of kilograms of cocaine, throughout the States and Europe. Kurti allegedly orchestrated the activities of the group from his prison cell in Albania. Three of the defendants, according to court documents, gave a "clean-cut" patron of a Bronx bar a vicious beating because they suspected he was an undercover officer who was following them, the court papers said. A dispute over a drug debt prompted two other ring members to track down another victim on June 4 at a busy Bronx bar, where they pulled guns, chased him out the door, and shot him in both legs, the court papers said.[31]

ALL FOR ALLAH

America was not alone. The Muslim Mafia also gained control over all criminal organizations in Europe, thereby becoming the leading perpetrator of drug smuggling, counterfeiting, passport theft, forgery, sex slavery, abduction, murder, and the trafficking in human body parts. Cataldo Motto, Italy's top prosecutor, recently maintained that the Albanian Mafia poses a threat not only to his country, but to all of Western civilization.[32]

Dusan Janjic, coordinator of the Forum for Ethnic Relations in Serbia, stated three reasons for the success of the Albanian Mafia: "Firstly, they speak a language that few understand. Secondly, its internal organization is based on family ties, breeding solidarity and safety. Thirdly, there is the code of silence and it is perfectly normal for anyone to die if he violates the code."[33]

But Janjic overlooked a fourth reason. Several members of the Albanian Mafia believed that their crimes served a religious purpose. This fact became evident when the Italian police began to monitor the telephone conversations of Agim Gashi, Milan's leading drug lord. In one conversation, Gashi told his Turkish suppliers to continue sending shipments of heroin during the holy month of Ramadan. This breach of Islamic law, he said, is necessary to achieve the ultimate goal of his organization, namely, "to submerge Christian infidels in drugs." Similarly, in another conversation, Gashi lauded the success of his billion-dollar business by saying: "We have discovered that drugs are not only a source of wealth but a tool to weaken Christendom."[34]

RETURN TO FORT DIX

Eight years after Brig. Gen. Mitchell M. Zais welcomed the Muslim refugees from Kosovo to Fort Dix, a group of six Islamists—including four ethnic Albanians—were arrested while plotting to attack the New Jersey military base and "kill as many soldiers as possible."[35] The Albanians, according to the *Washington Post*, were different from stereotypical jihadis. They were European rather than Middle Eastern, wore business suits, spoke fluent English, and exhibited jovial mannerisms. Their children, the *Post* reported, played soccer and videogames with the other neighborhood kids in Cherry Hill, New Jersey, and three of the men, who were brothers, hawked their roofing business to their fellow Muslims during Friday prayer services at the local mosque.[36]

As Akbar Ahmed discovered in his *Journey into America*, 50 percent of the Muslims from the Balkans, despite the relative ease they have experienced in assimilating within America's culture and society, uphold radical Salafi doctrines and oppose interfaith dialogue.[37]

CHAPTER 16

THE TURKS AND THE NEW ISLAMIC WORLD ORDER

About 360,000 immigrants from Ottoman Turkey, according to US government statistics, came to America between 1820 and 1950, but only an estimated 45,000 were Muslim Turks. The majority of arrivals were from the numerous minority groups within the Ottoman Empire, primarily Jews and Greek, Armenian, and Syrian Christians. Of the Muslim Turks, approximately 65 percent were Kurds; the remaining 35 percent were ethnic Turks from Harput, Elâzığ, Akçadağ, Antep, and Macedonia.[1] Most of these Muslims embarked from Beirut, Mersin, Izmir, Trabzon, and Salonica and declared themselves as *Syrians* and *Armenians* in order to avoid discrimination and gain easy access into the country.[2] Throughout the early part of the twentieth century, the Turks were the most feared and despised of all Muslims.[3] Turkey represented the last Islamic state to threaten the bastion of Western civilization and the first to engage in modern genocide with the slaughter of 1.5 million Armenian Christians between 1915 and 1917.[4]

ABNORMAL VICE

The early Muslim Turks in America were poor, rural, illiterate, and 93.1 percent male.[5] A sizable number made their way to Detroit to work at the automobile manufacturing plants. By 1920, according to one investigator, the Highland Park neighborhood of Detroit contained the largest colony of Muslims in the country, estimated at between two thousand to eight thousand residents, nearly all of whom were employees of the Ford Motor Company.[6] Others gained employment in Massachusetts at the leather factories of Lynn and Salem and the wire factories of Worcester. A 1914 report by the Commission on Immigration in Massachusetts describes the living conditions of the Turkish Muslims:

> In the Turkish colony at Worcester, of 400 or more men, there is probably not one Turkish woman. Occasionally, the men club together and hire a cook, each paying usually $1 a month. In most of the groups visited, however, the men do their own cooking, either acting each one as his own commissary, or taking turns at buying and cooking the food. . . . As is expected under the circumstances, the living and sleeping conditions of these men are far from good. In most cases economy leads them to choose houses for which rents are low, and which consequently are often in a most dilapidated condition. These houses are planned for a family of four or five persons, and are totally unsuited for the purposes to which they are put. The sanitary conditions are far from adequate. . . . The sleeping quarters are, of course, crowded. Frequently, the floor is covered with mattresses and pillows, and clothes are scattered about the rooms. Among the Turks, beds are seldom used. . . . Police and health officers testify that day and night shifts are frequently found. In one case an investigator was told that a house of seven rooms was occupied by fourteen Turks, sleeping two to a room. On a visit at five in the afternoon he found eighteen men who apparently lived there, while four others who worked at night were sleeping in an adjoining room.[7]

The report goes on to detail the "forlorn" state of these Muslim men without families and speaks of their isolation from the outside world. It further states that these men, without normal social relations and working long hours for low wages, were vulnerable to every temptation and that "abnormal vice" raged among them.[8]

SARACEN SOJOURNERS

Unlike other immigrants, the Muslim Turks did not come to America to settle but only to save enough money to buy land and livestock upon their return to their native country. Kemal Karpat, a Turkish American scholar, says that the Muslim Turks "looked upon America as a culturally alien land where they had been driven by sheer necessity and where they wanted to stay as little time as possible."[9] Consequently, Karpat continues, they refused to strike permanent roots, build mosques, and establish their own communities as Muslims.[10] By 1930, following the establishment of the Turkish Republic by Kemal Ataturk and the restrictive US immigration laws of the 1920s, 86 percent of the Turks in America—including almost all Muslims—had returned to their homeland. In the 1970s, sociologist Barbara Bilge could locate only twenty-four of the two thousand to eight thousand Muslims who had once inhabited Detroit.[11]

One factor compelling ethnic (Islamic) Turks to return home was the lack of suitable Muslim women for them to marry in the United States. Another was their inability to separate their ethnic identity as Turks from their religious identity as Muslims in a Judeo-Christian country. A third factor was the lack of a network of social organizations to integrate the Turkish newcomers within American society.[12]

THE NEW DIASPORA

By 1980, Muslim Turks started to migrate to the United States at the rate of two thousand a year. Many came in search of educational and occupational opportunities. By 2009, the annual rate increased to seven thousand and the total number of native-born Turks within the country reached 440,000.[13] In October 2010, the newly arrived Turks opened Brooklyn's largest mosque in Brighton Beach.[14]

These Muslim immigrants and refugees consisted mostly of professionals, including engineers, economists, and teachers, whose numbers tended to increase while the number of incoming doctors was decreasing due to a series of new qualifications requested by American medical authorities.[15] The newcomers also included many small businessmen, artisans, and skilled workers as well as unskilled laborers who found employment in a variety of occupations such as construction and building maintenance. A number of these latter immigrants, following the American interest in ethnic cuisines, opened restaurants serving Turkish food.[16]

LITTLE ISTANBUL

Like their Ottoman predecessors, these Turks settled in or around large urban centers, including Boston, Chicago, Detroit, Philadelphia, Minneaspolis, Dallas, and Los Angeles. South Paterson, New Jersey, became known as Little Istanbul, since it contains the largest ethnic Turkish enclave in the United States. Turkish flags decorate the barbershops, bakeries, restaurants, cafes, and halal grocery stores throughout the once-fabled Silk City. The former Orpheum Theater, Paterson's premier movie palace, has been transformed into a mosque that houses fifteen hundred worshippers. Nine other mosques are located within walking distance. Of the 149,222 residents of Paterson, over thirty thousand are Muslims and most are Turks.[17]

From 1992 to 2012, America witnessed the appearance of the Business Improvement and Development Center, the Turkish Cultural Center, the Council of Turkic American Associations, and the Amity Schools. All of these organizations are linked to the militant Fethullah Gulen, who has been called "the most dangerous Islamist on planet earth."[18] Gulen does not reside in Istanbul or Islamabad but rather in a remote mountain fortress in Saylorsburg, Pennsylvania.

Gulen governs one of the world's "most powerful and best-connected" Muslim networks.[19] He has been charged as being the "strongest and most effective Islamic fundamentalist in Turkey," an individual who "camouflages his methods with a democratic and moderate image."[20] His movement, which reportedly seeks to create a New Islamic World Order, has amassed approximately 10 million supporters, many of whom contribute between 5 percent and 20 percent of their income to his movement, and his tentacles now stretch from Central Asia to the the United States.[21] With an estimated $25 billion in assets,[22] the reclusive Islamist reportedly controls over one thousand schools in 130 countries, political action groups, newspapers (including *Zaman*, Turkey's leading daily), TV and radio stations, universities, a massive conglommerate called Kaynak Holding, and even a centralized bank.[23]

THE MOUNTAIN FORTRESS

In 1998, Gulen fled to the Pocono Mountains of Pennsylvania in order to avoid prosecution on charges that he was attempting to undermine Turkey's secular government. The indictment says that Gulen has established a network of schools as a front for a sinister plan.[24] "Mr Gulen was planning to use the young people whom he brainwashed at his own schools to set up his Islamic state," the indictment maintains.[25]

Since his arrival in Pennsylvania, US State Department officials have made numerous attempts to deport him. But in 2008 a federal court ruled that Gulen was a person of "extraordinary ability in the field of education" who merits permanent residency status in the United States.[26] This ruling has struck many as odd, since Gulen reportedly lacks a high school education and speaks little or no English. Odder still is the fact that many individuals who offered testimony on Gulen's behalf were former CIA officials, including Graham Fuller and George Fidas.[27]

A PRIVATE ARMY

At his mountain fortress, Gulen is guarded by a small army of followers who obey the orders of their *hocaefendi* (master lord) and refrain from marrying until age fifty per his instructions. The guards wear suits and ties rather than the traditional Turkish Islamic attire of cloaks and turbans. Yet, when they marry, their spouses are obliged to dress in the Islamic manner, as dictated by Gulen himself.[28]

The Saylorsburg property consists of a massive chalet surrounded by a recreational center, dormitories, a helicopter pad, and firing ranges. Sentries are stationed at a small hut at the main entranceway that is identified as the "Golden Generation Worship and Retreat Center." Within this sentry post are plasma television screens that project high-resolution images from the security cameras throughout the twenty-eight-acre compound. Gulen purportedly lives on the third floor of the chalet and rarely makes himself available to visitors or reporters.[29]

Local residents complain of the sounds of gunfire—including fully automatic weapons—coming from the Gulen property and speak of a low-flying helicopter that circles the area in search of all intruders.[30] The FBI reportedly has been called to the scene, but no action has been taken to curtail what neighbors allege to be "paramilitary activity."

GULEN EXPOSED

Who is this mysterious Turkish pasha and why is he sheltered in Pennsylvania?

In his public statements, Gulen espouses a liberal version of Sunni/Hanafi Islam, and promotes the Muslim notion of *hizmet*, or altruistic service to the common good. He has condemned terrorism and called for interfaith dialogue. He has met with Pope John Paul II, the Greek Orthodox patriarch Bartholomeos, and Israeli Sephardic head rabbi Eliyahu Bakshi-Doron. Prominent US officials have lavished praise on

Author Paul L. Williams at the al-Farooq Mosque on Atlantic Avenue in Brooklyn, one of the nation's most notorious hotbeds of Islamic terrorism. The plans for the 1993 bombing of the World Trade Center were hatched at this place of worship. *Photo courtesy of Patrick Walsh.*

A security guard at Masjid al-Taqwa in Bedford-Stuyvesant, where Siraj Wahhaj serves as imam and tourists with cameras are hauled off for interrogation. *Photo courtesy of the the author.*

A Muslim woman reading Nabokov on a park bench in Brooklyn on a warm summer day. *Photo courtesy of the author.*

Author Williams at Islamberg, a paramilitary compound that has been created in the rural outskirts of Hancock, New York, by Jamaat ul-Fuqra. *Photo courtesy of Patrick Walsh.*

A colonial church in Washington, DC, that has been transformed into an Islamic house of worship. *Photo courtesy of the author.*

A fresh grave in Islamberg, where many bodies—unbeknownst to local law enforcement officials—are buried. *Photo courtesy of the author.*

A sign at the entrance to the ul-Fuqra compound in Red House, Virginia. *Photo courtesy of the author.*

Author Williams at the sentry post of the Gulen fortress in Saylorsburg, Pennsylvania. Gulen's movement has been labeled one of "the most dangerous Islamic movements" on the planet by Ursula Suler-Stegemann, an Islamic scholar in the western German university city of Marburg. *Photo courtesy of Patrick Walsh.*

The National Mosque in Washington, DC. *Photo courtesy of the author.*

Inscription in gold at the $20 million King Fahad Mosque in Culver City, California. *Photo courtesy of Pat Williams.*

Author Williams at a mosque in Lodi, California, where thousands of Muslims have recently settled. *Photo courtesy of Pat Williams*.

Author Williams at the United Muslim Mosque in Philadelphia, at the heart of an Islamic enclave that has been created by Kenny Gamble (Luqman Abdul Haqq) of the Universal Company. *Photo courtesy of Pat Williams*.

Muslim protestors taking to the streets in New York City. *Photo courtesy of the author.*

Muhammad Mosque no. 7, a Nation of Islam house of worship in New York City. *Photo courtesy of the author.*

Author Williams received the Quran as a gift from members of the King Fahad Mosque in Culver City, California. *Photo courtesy of Pat Williams.*

A "Jesus Saves" sign placed on a catty-corner to the King Fahad Mosque. *Photo courtesy of Pat Williams.*

A street scene in New York City. *Photo courtesy of the author.*

An Islamic store in Brooklyn, New York, selling scents, souvenirs, and books. *Photo courtesy of the author.*

A new storefront in Brooklyn, New York. *Photo courtesy of the author.*

A worker adjusts the Islamic flag at Dar al-Hijrah in Falls Church, Virginia. The mosque gained notoriety by sheltering 9/11 operatives. *Photo courtesy of the author.*

A trailer in Islamberg that is inhabited by a family of eight. It does not appear to be connected to a power source or a septic system. *Photo courtesy of the author.*

FBI officials attending a picnic in Islamberg. *Photo courtesy of the Federal Bureau of Investigation.*

Protestors in support of Hamas in New York City. *Photo courtesy of the author.*

The Shabaaz Mosque, a Nation of Islam house of worship in Harlem. *Photo courtesy of the author.*

A sentry hut within Fethullah Gulen's mountain fortress in Saylorsburg, Pennsylvania. *Photo courtesy of the author.*

A McDonald's restaurant in Brooklyn that appears to have been uprooted from Islamabad, Pakistan. *Photo courtesy of the author.*

A newly constructed mosque that buttresses the campus of the University of Southern California in Los Angeles. *Photo courtesy of Pat Williams.*

A public street in Red House, Virginia, that has been named in honor of Sheik Mubarak Gilani, the founder of Jamaat ul-Fuqra, an officially designated terrorist group in the 1999 Patterns of Global Terrorism report. *Photo courtesy of the author.*

Police protecting Muslim protestors in New York City. *Photo courtesy of the author.*

Muslims on the lookout for unwelcome visitors to Masjid al-Taqwa in Brooklyn. *Photo courtesy of the author.*

the Turkish pasha, claiming that he is a leading voice of moderation in the Islamic world. On September 25, 2008, former president Bill Clinton greeted an audience of Gulen's disciples at the third annual Friendship Dinner of the Turkish Cultural Center (one of Gulen's nonprofit organizations) by saying: "You're contributing to the promotion of the ideals of tolerance and interfaith dialogue inspired by Fethullah Gulen and his transnational social movement."[31]

In private, Gulen has said that "in order to reach the ideal Muslim society every method and path is acceptable, [including] lying to people."[32] In a sermon aired on Turkish television, he announced to his legion of followers his plan to create a New Islamic World Order:

> You must move in the arteries of the system without anyone noticing your existence until you reach all the power centers . . . until the conditions are ripe, they [the followers] must continue like this. If they do something prematurely, the world will crush our heads, and Muslims will suffer everywhere, like in the tragedies in Algeria, like in 1982 [in] Syria . . . like in the yearly disasters and tragedies in Egypt. The time is not yet right. You must wait for the time when you are complete and conditions are ripe, until we can shoulder the entire world and carry it. . . . You must wait until such time as you have gotten all the state power, until you have brought to your side all the power of the constitutional institutions in Turkey. . . . Until that time, any step taken would be too early—like breaking an egg without waiting the full forty days for it to hatch. It would be like killing the chick inside. The work to be done is [in] confronting the world. Now, I have expressed my feelings and thoughts to you all—in confidence . . . trusting your loyalty and secrecy. I know that when you leave here—[just] as you discard your empty juice boxes, you must discard the thoughts and the feelings that I expressed here.[33]

He continued:

> When everything was closed and all doors were locked, our houses of isik [light] assumed a mission greater than that of older times. In the past, some of the duties of these houses were carried out

> by madrasahs [Islamic schools], some by schools, some by tekkes [Islamist lodges]. . . . These isik homes had to be the schools, had to be madrasahs, [had to be] tekkes all at the same time. The permission did not come from the state, or the state's laws, or the people who govern us. The permission was given by God . . . who wanted His name learned and talked about, studied, and discussed in those houses, as it used to be in the mosques.[34]

In another sermon, Gulen proclaimed:

> Now it is a painful spring that we live in. A nation is being born again. A nation of millions [is] being born—one that will live for long centuries, God willing. . . . It is being born with its own culture, its own civilization. If giving birth to one person is so painful, the birth of millions cannot be pain-free. Naturally we will suffer pain. It won't be easy for a nation that has accepted atheism, has accepted materialism, a nation accustomed to running away from itself, to come back riding on its horse. It will not be easy, but it is worth all our suffering and the sacrifices.[35]

And, in yet another sermon, he told his followers:

> The philosophy of our service is that we open a house somewhere and, with the patience of a spider, we lay our web to wait for people to get caught in the web; and we teach those who do. We don't lay the web to eat or consume them but to show them the way to their resurrection, to blow life into their dead bodies and souls, to give them a life.[36]

Assessing such statements, Ariel Cohen, a Middle East analyst with the Heritage Foundation, says: "It's not just a religious movement; it's the Fethullah Gulen movement. They call themselves that. So it is, you can say, a cult. It is a highly personalized movement." Cohen, who has spent years tracking the Gulen movement, adds: "This is clearly the world according to the Koran, the world according to Islam, the world according to Fethullah Gulen. But what he's talking about is not the caliphate, is not the sharia state—he calls it the New World Islamic Order."[37]

CREATING THE NEW ORDER

Gulen, according to the *Middle East Quarterly*, was a student and follower of Sheikh Sa'id-i Kurdi (1878–1960), also known as Sa'id-i Nursi, the founder of the Islamist *Nur* (light) movement. After Turkey's war of independence, Kurdi demanded, in an address to the new parliament, that the new republic be based on Islamic principles. Gulen advanced these principles and helped to create the Justice and Democratic Party (*Adalet ve Kalkinma*, or AKP), which now controls the Turkish government.[38] Abdullah Gul, Turkey's first Islamist president, is a Gulen disciple, as are Prime Minister Recep Tayyip Erdogan and Yusuf Ziya Ozcan, the head of Turkey's Council of Higher Education.[39]

Under the AKP, Turkey has transformed from a secular state into a nation with eighty-five thousand active mosques—one for every 350 citizens—the highest number per capita in the world, ninety thousand imams—more imams than teachers and physicians—and thousands of state-run Islamic schools.[40] In recent years, Turkey has witnessed a reign of terror with the random arrests of opponents of the AKP, including a dozen middle-aged liberal women who worked for the Society for Contemporary Life, an organization that provided educational services and scholarships to poor teenage girls. Hundreds of others were taken into custody during midnight raids, including army officers, renowned journalists, and artists. According to *Newsweek*, the arrests illustrate the power of Gulen's *tarikat* (Islamic order), which now controls the government.[41]

THE GULEN SCHOOLS

According to Bayram Balci, one of Gulen's leading proponents and a spokesman for the movement, the Gulen schools have been established throughout the world to expand "the Islamization of Turkish nationality and the Turkification of Islam" in order to bring about a universal caliphate ruled by Islamic law.[42] Such a caliphate, Balci maintains, cannot be created without the cultivation of members of an educated elite who will advance Turkish and Islamic interests in their native countries. This task, he adds, may be accomplished only by the adoption of stealthy techniques, since the open promotion of religion is prohibited in the public schools of many countries, including the United States. Such techniques, Balci contends, mandate that the teachers and administrators of the Gulen schools indoctrinate students in the tenets of militant Islam by *temsel* (becoming role models) rather than *teblig* (open proselytism).[43]

Several countries have outlawed the establishment of Gulen schools and *cemaats* (communities) within their borders, including Russia and Uzbekistan. Even the Netherlands, a nation that embraces pluralism and tolerance, has opted to cut funding to the Gulen schools because of their threat to the social order.[44]

Over 130 "Gulen-inspired" schools have been established throughout the United States. They are staffed with Turkish administrators and Turkish educators who come to the United States with "H-1B" visas—visas reserved for highly skilled foreign workers brought to fill a need in the US workforce. A partial listing of the Gulen schools, all of which are operated with public funding, follows.

Arizona (7)

Charter holder: Daisy Education Corporation
Management organization:
Accord Institute for Education Research

1. Sonoran Science Academy, Tucson
   http://www.sonoranacademy.org/tucson/
2. Sonoran Science Academy—Broadway
   http://www.sonoranacademy.org/broadway/
3. Sonoran Science Academy—Phoenix
   http://www.sonoranacademy.org/phoenix/
4. Sonoran Science Academy—Davis Monthan Air Force Base
   http://www.sonoranacademy.org/davis-monthan/
5. Sonoran Science Academy—Ahwatukee
   http://www.sonoranacademy.org/ahwatukee/
6. Sonoran Science Academy—Phoenix Metro
7. Paragon Science Academy
   http://www.paragonscience.org/

Arkansas (5)

Management organization:
Cosmos Foundation/Harmony Public Schools

1. Lisa Academy
   http://www.lisaacademy.org/
2. Lisa Academy High School
   http://www.lisaacademy.org/
3. Lisa Academy-North Elementary
   http://www.lisanorth.org/
4. Lisa Academy-North Middle
   http://www.lisanorth.org/
5. Lisa Academy-North High
   http://www.lisanorth.org/

California (13)

Management organization:
Accord Institute for Education Research
Charter holder: Magnolia Foundation,
http://magnoliacharterschools.org/

1. Magnolia Science Academy 1—Reseda
   http://reseda.magnoliascience.org/
2. Magnolia Science Academy 2—Valley
   http://valley.magnoliascience.org/
3. Magnolia Science Academy 3—Carson
   http://gardena.magnoliascience.org/
4. Magnolia Science Academy 4—Venice
   http://venice.magnoliascience.org/
5. Magnolia Science Academy 5—Hollywood
   http://hollywood.magnoliascience.org/
6. Magnolia Science Academy 6—Palms
   http://palms.magnoliascience.org/
7. Magnolia Science Academy 7—Van Nuys
   http://vannuys.magnoliascience.org/
8. Magnolia Science Academy 8—Bell
   http://bell.magnoliascience.org/
9. Magnolia Science Academy—San Diego
   http://sandiego.magnoliascience.org/
10. Magnolia Science Academy—Santa Clara
    http://santaclara.magnoliascience.org/
11. Pacific Technology School—Orangevale
    http://ov.ptscharter.org/
12. Pacific Technology School—Orange County
    http://oc.ptscharter.org/
    Charter holder: Willow Education
13. Bay Area Technology School
    http://www.baytechschool.org/j/index.php

Colorado (1)

1. Lotus School for Excellence—Aurora
   http://www.lotusschool.org/

Florida (5)

Organization: Grace Institute

1. Stars Middle School—Tallahassee
   http://starsmiddleschool.org/
2. Sweetwater Branch Academy, Middle School
   http://swbacademy.org/
3. River City Science Academy, Middle School—Jacksonville
   http://www.rivercityscience.org/
4. Orlando Science Middle School
   http://orlandoscience.org/
5. New Springs Middle School—Tampa
   http://newspringsschools.org/

Georgia (3)

Organization: formerly Grace Institute

1. Fulton Science Academy High School (formerly TEACH—Technology Enriched Accelerated High School)
   http://fsahigh.org
2. Fulton Science Academy, Middle School
   http://www.fultonscience.org/
3. Fulton Sunshine Academy, Elementary School
   http://www.fultonsunshine.org/

Illinois (2)

Organization: Concept Schools, Inc.

1. Chicago Math and Science Academy
   http://cmsaonline.net/newwebsite/
2. Quest Charter Academy
   http://www.questpeoria.org/

Indiana (2)

Organization: Concept Schools, Inc.,
http://www.conceptschools.org/

1. Indiana Math and Science Academy—West
   http://www.imsaindy.org/
2. Indiana Math and Science Academy—North
   http://north.imsaindy.org/

Louisiana (1)

Charter holder: Pelican Educational Foundation
Management Organization:
Cosmos Foundation/Harmony Public Schools

1. Kenilworth Science and Technology—Baton Rouge
   http://www.kenilworthst.org/

Maryland (3)

1. Baltimore IT Academy
   http://www.bitacademy.org/
2. Chesapeake Math and IT Academy
   http://cmitacademy.org/

3. Chesapeake Science Point—Hanover
   http://www.mycsp.org/index.php

Massachusetts (2)

1. Pioneer Charter School of Science
   http://www.pioneercss.org/
2. Hampden Charter School of Science
   http://www.hampdencharter.org/

Michigan (1)

Management organization: Concept Schools, Inc.

1. Michigan Math and Science Academy
   http://www.mmsaonline.org/

Minnesota (1)

Management organization: Concept Schools, Inc.

1. Minnesota School of Science
   http://www.mssonline.org/

Missouri (3)

Charter holder: Frontier Schools
Management organization:
Cosmos Foundation/Harmony Public Schools

1. Frontier School of Excellence, also known as Brookside-Frontier Math and Science School
   http://www.bfmass.org/
   http://www.kcfse.org/

2. Frontier School of Innovation
   http://www.kcfsi.org/
3. Gateway Science Academy of St. Louis
   http://www.gsastl.org

Nevada (3)

Charter holder: Coral Education Corporation
Management organization:
Accord Institute for Education Research

1. Coral Academy of Science—Reno Elementary
   http://coralacademy.org/elementary/
2. Coral Academy of Science—Reno Midde High
   http://www.coralacademy.org/middle
   http://www.coralacademy.org/high
3. Coral Academy of Science—Las Vegas
   http://www.coralacademylv.org/

New Mexico (1)

Management organization:
Cosmos Foundation/Harmony Public Schools

1. Albuquerque School of Excellence
   http://www.abqse.org/

New York (3)

1. Syracuse Academy of Science
   http://www.sascs.org/
2. Buffalo Academy of Science
   http://www.bascs.org/

3. Rochester Academy Science School
   http://www.rochester-academy.org/

New Jersey (5)

1. Bergen Arts and Science Charter School Middle High
   http://bergencharter.org/middlehigh/
2. Bergen Arts and Science Charter School Elementary
   http://bergencharter.org/elementary/
3. Central Jersey College Prep
   http://njcollegeprep.com/
4. Passaic Arts and Science Charter School, Elementary
   http://passaiccharter.org/elementary/
5. Paterson Charter School for Science And Technology
   http://www.pcsst.org/

North Carolina (1)

1. Triad Math and Science Academy
   http://www.tmsacharter.org/

Ohio (19)

Management organization: Concept Schools, Inc.

1. Horizon Science Academy Cincinnati
   http://www.horizoncincy.org/
2. Horizon Science Academy Cleveland
   http://www.hsas.org/
3. Horizon Science Academy Cleveland Middle School
   http://www.hsacms.org/
4. Horizon Science Academy Cleveland Elementary School
   http://es.horizoncleveland.org/

5. Horizon Science Academy Columbus High School
   http://www.horizoncolumbus.org/
6. Horizon Science Academy Columbus Middle School
   http://www.horizoncolumbus.org/ms/
7. Horizon Science Academy Columbus Elementary School
   http://es.horizoncolumbus.org/
8. Horizon Science Academy Dayton Elementary School
   http://es.horizondayton.org
9. Horizon Science Academy Dayton
   http://www.horizondayton.org/
10. Horizon Science Academy Dayton Downtown
    http://dt.horizontoledo.org
11. Horizon Science Academy Denison Middle School
    http://www.horizondenison.org/
12. Horizon Science Academy Denison Elementary School
    http://www.denisonelementary.org/
13. Horizon Science Academy Lorain
    http://www.horizonlorain.org/
14. Horizon Science Academy Springfield
    http://www.horizonspringfield.org/
15. Horizon Science Academy Toledo
    http://www.horizontoledo.org/
16. Horizon Science Academy Toledo Downtown
    http://dt.horizontoledo.org
17. Horizon Science Academy Youngstown
    http://www.horizonyoungstown.org/
18. Noble Academy—Columbus
    http://www.noblecolumbus.org/index.php
19. Noble Academy—Cleveland
    http://www.noblecleveland.org/

Oklahoma (4)

Charter holder: Sky Foundation
Management organization:
Cosmos Foundation/Harmony Public Schools

1. Discovery School of Tulsa
   http://www.discoveryok.org/
2. Dove Science Academy—Oklahoma City
   http://www.dsaokc.org/
3. Dove Science Academy Elementary School
   http://www.dsaelementary.org/
4. Dove Science Academy—Tulsa
   http://dsatulsa.org/

Pennsylvania (3)

1. Truebright Science Academy, Philadelphia
   http://www.truebright.org/
2. Young Scholars of Central Pennsylvania
   http://www.yscp.org/
3. Young Scholars of Western Pennsylvania
   http://www.yswpcs.org/

Tennessee (1)

Management organization:
Cosmos Foundation/Harmony Public Schools

1. Memphis School of Excellence
   http://www.sememphis.org/

Texas (42)

Charter holder/management organization:
Cosmos Foundation/Harmony Public Schools

Austin area

1. Harmony School of Science—Austin
   http://hssaustin.org/
2. Harmony Science Academy—North Austin
   http://hsana.org/
3. Harmony School of Excellence—Austin
   http://hseaustin.org/
4. Harmony Science Academy—Austin
   http://hsaaustin.org/
5. Harmony School of Political Science and Communication
   http://hspaustin.org

Brownsville

1. Harmony Science Academy—Brownsville
   http://hsabrownsville.org/

Dallas area

1. Harmony Science Academy—Waco
   http://hsawaco.org/
2. Harmony Science Academy—Garland
   http://hsagarland.org/
3. Harmony Science Academy—Dallas
   http://hsadallas.org/
4. Harmony Science Academy—Dallas Middle School
5. Harmony Science Academy—Dallas Elementary School
6. Harmony School of Innovation—Dallas (formerly Harmony School of Innovation Carrollton)
   http://hsacarrollton.org/

El Paso

1. Harmony Science Academy—El Paso
   http://hsaelpaso.org/
2. Harmony School of Innovation—El Paso
   http://hsielpaso.org/

Fort Worth area

1. Harmony Science Academy—Fort Worth
   http://hsafortworth.org/
2. Harmony Science Academy—Grand Prairie
   http://hsagp.org/
3. Harmony Science Academy—Euless
   http://hsaeuless.org/
4. Harmony School of Nature and Athletics—Dallas
   http://hsnature.org/

Houston north area

1. Harmony School of Endeavor—Houston
   http://hsendeavor.org/default.asp
2. Harmony Science Academy—Bryan/College Station
   http://hsabcs.org/
3. Harmony Science Academy—Houston Northwest
   http://hsanw.org/
4. Harmony School of Excellence—Houston
   http://hsehouston.org/
5. Harmony School of Advancement High
   http://hsadvancement.org/
6. Harmony School of Discovery
   http://hsdhouston.org/

Houston south area

1. Harmony School of Ingenuity
   http://hsingenuity.org/default.asp
2. Harmony Science Academy—Beaumont
   http://hsabeaumont.org/
3. Harmony Science Academy—Houston
   http://hsahouston.org/default.asp
4. Harmony Science Academy High School—Houston
   http://hshigh.org/
5. Harmony School of Innovation—Houston
   http://hsihouston.org/default.asp
6. Harmony School of Art (and Technology)—Houston
   http://hsart.org

Houston west area

1. Harmony School of Science—Houston
   http://hsshouston.org/
2. Harmony Science Academy—West Houston
   http://hsawh.org
3. Harmony School of Science High—Sugarland
   http://hsshigh.org

Laredo

1. Harmony Science Academy—Laredo
   http://hsalaredo.org/

Lubbock area

1. Harmony Science Academy—Lubbock
   http://hsalubbock.org/
2. Harmony Science Academy—Odessa
   http://hsaodessa.org/

San Antonio area

1. Harmony Science Academy—San Antonio
   http://hsasa.org/
2. Harmony School of Innovation—San Antonio
   http://hsisa.org/

Charter holder: SST Schools (formerly Riverwalk Education Foundation, Inc.)

http://www.ssttx.org/

1. School of Science and Technology Discovery—Leon Valley
   http://www.sstdiscovery.org/
2. School of Science and Technology—San Antonio
   http://www.ssttx.org/default.asp
3. School of Science and Technology—Corpus Christi
   http://www.sstcc.org/
4. School of Science and Technology—Alamo
   http://www.sstalamo.org/default.asp

Utah (1)

1. Beehive Science and Technology Academy
   http://www.beehiveacademy.org

Wisconsin (2)

Management organization: Concept Schools, Inc.

1. Milwaukee Math and Science Academy
   http://www.mmsacademy.org/
2. Wisconsin Career Academy
   http://www.wiscca.org/

Schools closed or removed from Gulenist control:

California (1)

1. Magnolia Science Academy—San Diego 2

Louisiana (1)

1. Abramson Science and Technology—New Orleans
http://www.abramsonst.org/

COMPLAINTS AND PROTESTS

Nationwide, complaints have been raised about hundreds of teachers and administrators imported from Turkey: in Ohio and Illinois, the US Department of Labor is investigating union accusations that the schools have abused a special visa program in bringing in their expatriate employees. "I think they have a preference for these H-1B workers," Dr. Ronil Hira, a professor at the Rochester Institute of Technology who has studied the visa program, told the *New York Times*. "It may be a preference for a variety of reasons—lower wages or a network where they've got family or friends and connections and this is a stepping stone for them to get a green card."[45]

Despite the fact that the Gulen schools are public, virtually all the construction and renovation work at these institutions is conducted by Turkish-owned contracting firms. Several established local companies said they had lost out even after bidding several hundred thousand dollars lower. "It kind of boils my blood a little bit, all the money that was spent, when I know it could have been done for less," said Deborah Jones, an owner of daj Construction, one of four companies that provided lower bids yet failed to win a recent school-renovation contract in the Austin area.[46]

At the Harmony Schools, which have spread throughout Texas, students are immersed in Turkish culture, customs, religion, history, and language. They allegedly are taught that the Ottoman Empire represented the golden age of global civilization and that the Armenian Holocaust never occurred. In keeping with the Gulen agenda, students are not indoctrinated in the tenets of Islam by religious example but rather by *temsel* (spiritual example). The top students each year are sent to Turkey to compete for prizes in the Turkish Olympiad by singing Turkish songs and reciting Turkish poetry. The event, which is sponsored by the Gulen Movement, has been established to make Turkish the new international language.[47]

TAQIYYA—THE PRACTICE OF ISLAMIC DECEPTION

The thirty-four "Gulen-inspired" Harmony Schools throughout the Lone Star State have been established at an annual expense to Texas taxpayers of $68 million. The schools are operated by the Cosmos Foundation, a mysterious nonprofit corporation with headquarters in Houston. In an interview with the author of this book, Sonar Tarim, the superintendent of the schools and a member of the Cosmos Foundation, said: "We have no ties to Fethullah Gulen or his movement."[48] While Tarim admitted that the schools participate in the Turkish Olympiad, he expressed surprise that all his schools were constructed by Turkish construction companies that reportedly are affiliated with Gulen and his movement.

Tarim insisted that very few teachers in Harmony Schools hail from Turkey. Yet the Cosmos Foundation has obtained H-1B visas for more than 1,136 Turks to come to Texas to teach in the Harmony Schools.[49] He maintained that the Harmony Schools are not related in any way to the Bluebonnet Learning Centers, which represent yet another chain of Gulen charter schools in Texas. Yet the Bluebonnet Learning Centers were located within the Harmony Schools and information about the centers remained posted on the Harmony website until the conclusion of the interview. Tarim stated that he and all Harmony teachers are certified by the Texas Board of Educators. Yet Tarim himself is not certified for his position as a school administrator.[50] He further said that Turkish nationals are not in control of the Cosmos Foundation and the Harmony Schools. Yet every member of the board of directors for the Cosmos Foundation is a Turkish national and all members of the board of directors for the Harmony schools, save one, are Turks.[51]

THE CIA CONNECTION

Osman Nori, the retired head of Turkish intelligence, recently alleged that the Gulen movement has served as a front for US intelligence by sheltering 130 CIA agents in its schools throughout Kyrgyzstan and Uzbekistan.[52] This claim collaborates the testimony of Sybil Edmonds, a former FBI translator and celebrated whistle-blower. Ms. Edmonds says that Gulen and his movement began to receive vast sums of money from the CIA in the wake of the collapse of the Soviet Union, when US officials realized that they could not obtain control of the massive energy resources of the newly created Russian republics because of a deep-seated suspicion of American motives. The CIA, she insists, came to view Turkey as a perfect "proxy" for US interests because it was a NATO ally that shared the same language, culture, and religion as the other central Asian countries. But centralized control of these republics, she points out, could only be actualized by the creation of the Pan-Turkish nationalism and religion envisioned by Gulen and his followers.[53] And so, according to Ms. Edmonds, the CIA became Gulen's partner in the creation of the New Islamic World Order. The money for the pasha's schools and settlements, she says, came not from congressionally approved funding, but rather from covert CIA operations, including narcotics trafficking, activities on the nuclear black market, weapons smuggling, and terrorist activities.[54]

Although Gulen and his defenders have refuted this testimony, a Department of Justice inspector general's report called Ms. Edmonds's allegations "credible," "serious," and warranting a full and complete review. Ranking Senate Judiciary Committee members Pat Leahy (D-VT) and Chuck Grassley (R-IA) have offered her public backing. The CBS news program *60 Minutes* launched an investigation of her statements only to find them truthful and substantial. No one has ever disputed any of Ms. Edmonds's revelations, which she says can be verified by FBI investigative files.

THE PROBLEM

Despite Gulen's global ambitions, he continues to be presented as a moderate Muslim who champions the causes of tolerance, peace, and goodwill. Dalia Mogahed, the first Muslim woman to serve as a member of the White House Advisory Council on Faith-Based and Neighborhood Partnerships, says that the Gulen movement "offers people a model of what is possible if a dedicated group of people work together for the good of society."[55] Such praise serves to illustrate the complexity of Islam in America and the problem of distinguishing a moderate from a militant Islamist.

CHAPTER 17

THE FLAWED FINDINGS

American Muslims do not consist of a homogeneous body with shared beliefs and cultural practives. They rather represent a hodgepodge of ethnic and racial groups from Africa, the Middle East, Central Asia, Indonesia, and the Balkan states. Many are incredibly poor and without formal education. Others possess vast wealth and prestigious degrees. Some, most notably eastern Europeans and Arabs, experience little difficulty in assimilating within American society. Others, most notably Somalis, continue to retain their tribal identities and to remain hostile to Western values. Most appear to be moderate in their religious stance; others are extreme. The fact that American Muslims are not united in faith is witnessed by the animosity that exists between immigrant Arab Muslims and indigenous African American Muslims.[1] Since most surveys and polls fail to make a distinction between the varying Islamic ethnic groups for the sake of consensus, their findings are almost irredeemibly skewed.

THE PEW POLL

According to the Pew Research Group, 61 percent of American Muslims are highly religious, with 57 percent of Muslim men saying they attend mosque at least once a week; 48 percent recite all five salah prayers daily; and 18 percent say some salah daily. The same survey shows that 14 percent of American Muslims report a household income of $100,000 or more and that 26 percent have graduated from college. It further reports that 82 percent express complete satisfaction with their lives in America and that 79 percent rate their communities as excellent or good places to live. The Pew study was conducted in 2010 with 1,033 participants who had Muslim-sounding first names or surnames and a telephone number.[2]

THE CAIR CLAIMS

A previous poll conducted by the Research Center of the Council on American-Islamic Relations on a similar amount of participants displays radically different findings. According to this poll, only 31 percent of America's Muslims are deeply religious, while 22 percent are somewhat religious and 27 percent never attend religious services. The CAIR survey further shows that 62 percent of America's Muslims have a bachelor's degree or higher (more than twice the national average) and that 50 percent are white-collar workers (physicians, dentists, engineers, college professors, administrators, and educators).[3]

THE GALLUP SURVEY

To further complicate matters, a 2009 Gallup poll reported findings that conflicted with both the Pew and the CAIR surveys. According to Gallup, American Muslims are no more religious than evangelical Protestants and Catholics, with 41 percent attending mosque on a weekly basis. Gallup further maintains that 40 percent of the Muslims in the United States have a college degree or higher and that only 28 percent report incomes of $50,000 or higher. The Muslims in this study were more dissatisfied with the standard of living than other Americans, 35 percent compared to 22 percent of Protestants, 25 percent of Catholics, and 23 percent of Jews; and the Muslims were considerably more pessimistic about the country's future, 56 percent compared to 39 percent of Protestants, 45 percent of Catholics, and 50 percent of Jews.[4]

ALL WITHIN 3 PERCENT OF ERROR

This disparity in these studies attests to the outdated methods that are employed by present-day statisticians and demographers. All three surveys relied on individuals who had landline telephone service or listed cell-phone numbers; they failed to take into consideration the vast number of American Muslims, particularly immigrants and students, whose names do not appear in telephone books. At present, one out of four American households does not have landline service, and the vast majority of young people (twenty-five years or younger) communicate by cell phones without listed numbers.[5] The problem of uncovering reliable data on the country's Islamic population is compounded by the fact that the US Census Bureau is prohibited from gathering information concerning the religious beliefs and preferences of the American people.

WHO ARE AMERICA'S MUSLIMS?

But the combined findings of all three surveys may be used to affirm the following about Muslims in America:

1. They have more children than American Protestants, Catholics, and Jews. American Muslim women have an average of 2.8 children; other American women have an average of 2.01 kids (slightly below the required replacement fertility rate of 2.1).
2. They have the highest proportion of young adults in the eighteen to twenty-nine age bracket. More than 36 percent of the country's Muslims fall within this age category, compared to

9 percent of Protestants and 20 percent of the members of other faiths.

3. They boast the highest proportion of individuals in the thirty to forty-four age category, versus 19 percent of Protestants, 28 percent of Catholics, and 26 percent of Americans overall.
4. Between 68 and 70 percent were born overseas. Most—between 62 percent and 65 percent—have lived in this country for less than twenty years. Only 28 to 29 percent were born in the United States.
5. Nearly 40 percent come from the Arab world, 33 percent from Central Asia (Pakistan, India, Bangladesh, Afghanistan), 6 percent from Africa, 5 percent from Iran, and 4 to 6 percent from the Balkan states, Turkey, and Russia.
6. Between 87 and 89 percent of US Muslims marry Muslims within their own ethnic groups.
7. Approximately 65 percent are Sunni, 11 to 12 percent are Shia; and 15 percent describe themselves as "just Muslims."
8. About 55 percent of Muslims are male and 45 percent are female.
9. Over a third of Muslim women (34 percent to 36 percent) wear hijabs when they go out in public; 40 percent say they never wear a head covering.
10. Most (51 to 52 percent) believe that men and women should be separated at the mosque.
11. About 40 percent are employed in full-time jobs, while about one in five are self-employed or own their own businesses. This finding mirrors that of the general public.
12. About 55 percent say their situation has become more difficult since the attacks of 9/11; 37 percent say things have remained virtually unchanged.
13. About 20 percent cite discrimination as being the biggest problem confronting the US Muslim community.
14. About 30 percent are white, 23 percent black, 21 percent Asian, 6 percent Hispanic, and 19 percent of mixed race.

15. About 70 percent identify with the Democratic Party or lean Democratic in local, state, and national elections. Less than 10 percent say they are Republicans or lean toward the Republican Party. The remaining 20 percent say they are independents and do not lean toward any political party.
15. Most radical Muslims are African Americans. Only 44 percent express a very unfavorable view of al-Qaeda, and 40 percent say there is a fair to great amount of support for extremism within their community.[6]
16. Nearly half believe that Muslim leaders in the United States have not done enough to condemn the radical teachings of jihadists and advance the moderate teachings of their faith.

This last claim raises the pressing question: Why are prominent Muslim spokesmen for moderate Islam so immoderate in their personal pronouncements?

CHAPTER 18
THE FLAWED SPOKESMEN

IMMODERATE MODERATE MUSLIM NO. 1: SIRAJ WAHHAJ

An African American convert to Islam, Siraj Wahhaj serves as the imam of Masjid Al-Taqwa in the Bedford-Stuyvesant neighborhood of Brooklyn. The mosque was an abandoned clothing store, which Wahhaj and his followers purchased at an auction in 1979 for $30,000 with cash from the Saudis.[1] The interior is divided into large, windowless rooms that have been painted green and beige.

At Friday afternoon prayers the meeting room is crammed with hundreds of congregants. Some show up in do-rag stocking caps and Sean John® sweatshirts; others wear finely embroidered, authentic-looking Muslim caps and flowing robes of crimson and gold. More than half the attendees are African American. The others are immigrants from the Middle East, South Asia, and Africa. The congregants range from Brooklyn street bums to local celebrities, such as former heavyweight champion Mike Tyson.[2]

The imam has received commendations from the NYPD for eradicating crime from the Bedford-Stuyvesant area. In 2003, Siraj Wahhaj Day was celebrated in Brooklyn in recognition of a "lifetime of outstanding and meaningful achievement."[3] The Reverend Herbert Daughtry, pastor of the Pentecostal House of the Lord Church in Brooklyn, says that Wahhaj is "very effective, particularly within the Muslim community and very respected in the community at large."[4]

The imam and his congregation have been credited by Community Affairs officer Steven Ruffin and other NYPD officials with ridding Bedford-Stuyvesant of several crack houses.[5]

Wahhaj is also a well-known and welcome figure in Washington, DC. He became the first Muslim cleric to offer the invocation at the opening session of Congress. In 1999, former secretary of state Madeleine Albright hosted Wahhaj at a State Department banquet serving lamb, lentils, and saffron rice to commemorate the end of Ramadan.[6]

Born Jeffrey Kearse and raised as a Baptist, this prominent Muslim became a Black Panther and member of the Nation of Islam, where he assumed the name Jeffrey 12X, before making his way to mainstream Islam and renaming himself Siraj Wahhaj ("bright light" in Arabic). He now serves on a slew of national Islamic advocacy boards, including the American Muslim Council, the Council on American-Islamic Relations (CAIR), the North American Islamic Trust (which owns almost 80 percent of the mosques in America),[7] and the Islamic Society of North America. In the wake of 9/11, Imam Wahhaj appeared on national television to offer these consoling words to his fellow Americans: "I now feel responsible to preach, actually to go on a jihad against extremism."[8]

But Wahhaj himself often appears as a proponent of extremism. In one sermon, he proclaimed that the "real terrorists" are the Federal Bureau of Investigation and the Central Intelligence Agency. In another, he said, "In time, this so-called democracy will crumble, and there will be nothing. And the only thing that will remain will be Islam." In a third, he held that a society governed by strict Islamic law, in which adulterers are stoned to death and apostates beheaded, would be vastly superior to American democracy.[9]

To an audience in New Jersey, Wahhaj advocated the idea of Muslims forming a coup to take control of the federal government. "If we are united and strong," he said, "we'd elect our own emir [leader] and give allegiance to him. Take my word for it, if six to eight million Muslims united in America, the country will come to us."[10] He went on to expresses his belief that the imposition of sharia in the United States "appears to be approaching fast."[11]

Wahhaj also has been far from "moderate" in his interpretation of Islamic law. On one occasion, he said: "If Allah says 100 strikes, 100 strikes it is. If Allah says cut off their hand, you cut off their hand. If Allah says stone them to death, through the Prophet Muhammad, then you stone them to death, because it's the obedience of Allah and his messenger—nothing personal."[12]

On another occasion, the imam informed an audience of Muslim women that Islam condones a man's marrying up to four wives, and that this rule, when introduced in the seventh century, served as a restriction on previous arrangements involving even more wives per husband.[13] Wahhaj admits that he regularly performs polygamous weddings at his mosque.[14]

And then there is the matter of Wahhaj's appearance in federal court as a character witness for Clement Rodney Hampton-El, Siddig Ibrahim Siddig Ali, and Ibrahim El-Gabrowny, who were involved in the 1993 bombing of the World Trade Center.[15] He offered testimony to the good character of blind sheikh Omar Abdel Rahman, a frequent guest speaker at Masjid al-Taqwa.[16] Rahman, now under lock and key at the Butner Medical Center (part of the Butner Federal Correctional Institution) in North Carolina, served as the chief architect of the 1993 bombing and drafted plans for future attacks that included blowing up the United Nations, the Lincoln and Holland Tunnels, the George Washington Bridge, and buildings throughout Manhattan.[17] In a February 2, 1995, letter to defense lawyers in the landmarks-bombing case, then US attorney Mary Jo White named about 170 people, including Wahhaj, as "un-indicted persons who may be alleged as co-conspirators" in the World Trade Center bombing.[18]

Other infamous characters have made their way to Wahhaj's Brooklyn mosque, such as Imam Gulshair el-Shukrijumah, whose son Adnan has been singled out by the FBI as a "single-cell"—a lone agent capable of launching a solo nuclear or radiological attack on a major metropolitan area.[19] Gulshair served a stint as imam at another radical Brooklyn mosque—the now-defunct Masjid Nur al-Islam, on Church Street. Another alleged visitor was Sheikh Gilani, the founder of Jamaat ul-Fuqra, who served as the imam of the Yasin Masjid on Saratoga Avenue.

All this may be well and good, save for the fact that Wahhaj and his mosque retains a small army not of brown shirts but black belts, led by convicted felon Ali Abdul Karim, who collar ordinary citizens from the sidewalk if they dare to photograph the masjid and haul them into the basement for interrogation.[20]

MODERATE MUSLIM NO. 2: MUZAMMIL H. SIDDIQI

Another celebrated spokesman for Islam in America is Harvard-educated Muzammil H. Siddiqi, who served as president of the Islamic Society of North America. This imam, who is not related to the Siddiqi mentioned in chapter 12, was called upon to represent the Muslim community at a prayer service for victims of 9/11 at the National Cathedral in Washington. At this solemn occasion, he quoted this passage from the Quran: "But those that lay the plots of evil, for them is a terrible penalty." This caused some to wonder if the Islamic scholar was referring to the terrorist or their infidel target. Following the ceremony, Siddiqi presented President Bush with a copy of the Muslim holy book. The gift caused Bush to gush: "He did a heck of a job and we are proud to have him here."[21]

One year before the prayer service, Siddiqi harshly criticized US support for Israel at a rally outside the White House by saying: "America has to learn, if you remain on the side of injustice, the wrath of God will come. Please, all Americans. Do you remember that Allah is watching everyone. God is watching everyone. If you continue doing injustice, and tolerate injustice, the wrath of God will come."[22]

In addition, Siddiqi has called for the imposition of sharia on the American populace: "By participating in a non-Islamic system, one cannot rule by that which Allah has commanded. But things do not change overnight. Changes come through patience, wisdom and hard work. I believe that as Muslims, we should participate in the system to safeguard our interests and try to bring gradual change for the right cause, the cause of truth and justice. We must not forget that Allah's rules have to be established in all lands, and all our efforts should lead to that direction."[23]

More troublesome, for many, is Siddiqi's endorsement of violent jihad. In one taped message, he says: "When people really carry on Jihad, they carry on Islam in its peak in its totality. And that's why in the hadith the Prophet (SAS) said (Arabic), 'No people have ever neglected Jihad except they became humiliated.' And people leave, renounce Jihad, they became humiliated. That means in order to gain the honor, Jihad is the path—Jihad is the way to receive the honor."[24] He goes on to praise the victory of the mujahadeen in Afghanistan, a victory that should encourage Muslims to engage in increased acts of violent aggression: "I can see that there is already some impact after Jihad in Afghanistan in the Intifada movement in Palestine. With this, more courage, more strength, more confidence and shall I even say that in a few years we will be celebrating with each other the victory of Islam in Palestine. Insh'allah, we shall be celebrating the coming of the Masjid al-Aqsa under the Islamic rule. We shall be celebrating insh'allah the coming of Jerusalem and the whole land of Palestine insh'allah and the establishment of the Islamic State throughout that area."[25]

White House officials later learned that Siddiqi not only opposed the US-led invasion of Afghanistan but also stood firm against Muslims serving in the US military or defending American interests. He proclaimed to his followers: "Islam will not allow a Muslim to be drafted by non-Muslims to defend concepts, ideologies, and values other than those of Islam. . . . A Muslim shall defend non-Muslim lands not."[26]

For two decades, Siddiqi served as a key American official for the Saudi-based Muslim World League (MWL). Several months after 9/11, the Washington offices of this organization were raided by federal counterterrorism agents when reports surfaced that the MWL had assisted in bankrolling bin Laden's international operations.[27] Siddiqi also stood as the spiritual leader of the Islamic Society of Orange County, an institution that Paul Sperry in his book *Infiltration* has singled out as a sanctuary of terror.[28] One of his converts at the mosque was Adam Gadahn, who went on to become known as the "American al-Qaeda."[29]

IMMODERATE MODERATE MUSLIM NO. 3: HAMZA YUSUF

Few American Muslims are more honored than Sheikh Hamza Yusuf, who teaches Arabic and Islamic studies in Northern California. He served as a White House advisor on Muslim affairs in the months after 9/11. On September 20, 2001, he met with President Bush at the White House—the only Muslim in a group of religious leaders invited to pray with him. After the prayer session, the ecumenical group broke out in a chorus of "God Bless America," and Yusuf intoned to the National Press Corps: "Hate knows no religion. Hate knows no country. Islam was hijacked on that September 11, 2001, on that plane as an innocent victim."[30]

Two days before 9/11, Yusuf appeared at a gathering of Muslims in Irvine, California, to protest the arrest of a Muslim cleric for the shooting of an Atlanta cop. On that occasion, Yusuf said: "This country is facing a very terrible fate. The reason for that is that this country stands condemned. It stands condemned like Europe stood condemned because of what it did. And lest people forget, Europe suffered two world wars after conquering the Muslim lands. . . . Europe's countries were devastated; they were completely destroyed. Their young people were killed."[31]

Raised by a Roman Catholic father and Greek Orthodox mother, Yusuf, since the time of his conversion to Islam, has displayed a long history of radical preaching that any government official with a computer or a library card could have quickly uncovered. At the twenty-first Annual Convention of the Islamic Circle of North America (ICNA), which was held at Valley Forge, Pennsylvania, in 1996, he said: "I am a citizen of this country not by choice but by birth. I reside in this country not by choice but by conviction in attempting to spread the message of Islam in this country. I became Muslim in part because I did not believe in the false gods of this society whether we call them Jesus or democracy or the Bill of Rights or any other element of this society that is held sacrosanct by the ill-informed peoples that make up this charade of a society. . . . There should be no voting or debate. . . . We have no room for ayes or nays."[32] The ICNA is allegedly not an Islamic version of the Mickey Mouse Club, but rather a front for the al-Qaeda-allied Jamaat-i-Islami movement in Pakistan.[33]

After the prayer meeting, Yusuf became an official advisor to the White House on Islamic affairs. He became such a frequent visitor to the Oval Office that staff members began to refer to Yusuf as "Bush's pet Muslim." When the president opted to call the US-led invasion of Afghanistan "Operation Infinite Justice," the imam immediately voiced his objection, informing the dumbstruck Bush that only Allah could provide infinite justice. The president immediately acquiesced and the name of the campaign was changed to "Operation Enduring Freedom."[34]

IMMODERATE MODERATE MUSLIM NO. 4: ABDURAHMAN M. ALAMOUDI

Few Muslims in America were more celebrated than Abdurahman M. Alamoudi, whose face appeared on the cover of Paul Findley's bestselling book *Silent No More: Confronting America's False Images of*

Islam. Alamoudi is the founder of the American Muslim Armed Forces and Veteran Affairs Council, an agency that became responsible for the appointment of Muslim chaplains to the US armed forces. In 1993, he presented Imam Abdul Muhammad with the US military's latest insignia: a silver crescent moon, which distinguished him as America's first full-fledged Muslim chaplain. For the next decade, no imam could receive this insignia without Alamoudi's imprimatur.[35]

Alamoudi's appointments became problematic when it was discovered that several of the Muslim chaplains were on the opposite side of the war on terror, including Captain James "Yousef" Lee, who was arrested for espionage while working among the detainees at Guantanamo Bay.[36] Another problem arose when the Pentagon became aware that Alamoudi's agency was funded not by the American Muslim community, but rather by radical Wahhabists from Saudi Arabia. Chairman of the Senate Judiciary Subcommittee on Terrorism, Technology, and Homeland Security, Republican senator Jon Kyl of Arizona held hearings on this source of financing. "It is remarkable that people who have known connections to terrorism are the only people to approve these chaplains," he quipped, calling the Pentagon's review of all its chaplains "the height of politically correct stupidity."[37]

In 1993, Alamoudi became an official goodwill ambassador to Islamic countries for the Clinton administration. In 1996, he organized the first Ramadan dinner for government officials and members of Congress. But his loyalty did not remain with the Democrats. In 2000, Alamoudi met with George W. Bush in Austin to offer him the political support of the Islamic community in the coming election. Upon assuming the oath of office, President Bush provided lucrative contacts to Ptech, Inc., an enterprise software and security firm that had been cofounded by Alamoudi. Ptech's roster of clients included several governmental and supragovernmental agencies, including the United States Armed Forces, NATO, Congress, the Department of Energy, the Department of Justice, the Federal Bureau of Investigation, Customs, the Federal Aviation Administration, the

IRS, the Secret Service, and the White House. On December 5, 2002, the Boston office of Ptech was raided by federal officials amid allegations that the firm was engaged in funding international terrorism. Despite the allegation, the company continued to obtain government contracts and to operate with a top-level military clearance.[38]

Alamoudi was also the founder of the American Muslim Council (AMC). A registered charity with national headquarters in Washington, DC, the goal of the AMC was "to serve for political and civil rights for all Americans."[39] FBI director Robert Mueller served as the keystone speaker at an AMC luncheon, hailing Alamoudi's charity as "the most mainstream Muslim group in the United States."[40] Indeed, Mueller became so enamored with Islam that he ordered all employees of the bureau to attend Muslim-sensitivity training sessions. In these sessions, taught by imams, FBI agents were taught that they must never show Muslims the soles of their shoes, must never touch them with their left hands, must avoid eye contact with them during interrogations, and must never blow their noses at Islamic gatherings.[41]

Mueller's endorsement of the AMC and his embrace of Alamoudi as a model Muslim speaks volumes about the sorry state of the American intelligence community. The FBI director apparently was completely unaware that the AMC had strong ties to Hamas and Hezbollah and that Alamoudi was engaged in plotting acts of terrorism on American soil. A few months after Mueller's appearance at the luncheon, British authorities arrested Alamoudi while he was engaged in smuggling $340,000 in sequentially numbered $100 bills from Libya to the United States. Alamoudi eventually pled guilty to plotting terrorist attacks with Libya. Federal prosecutors also managed to connect the celebrated Muslim moderate to Hamas, al-Qaeda, and seven known terrorist leaders whose names were found in his PalmPilot™.[42] To make matters worse, evidence presented in court showed that Alamoudi had complained to his fellow jihadis that the 1998 al-Qaeda attacks on the US embassies in Kenya and Tanzania were not effective because they killed Africans but no Americans.[43]

The founder of the American Muslim Council, whom the *Washington* Post described as "a pillar of the local Muslim community," will not be attending White House iftar dinners in the immediate future. He is serving a sentence of twenty-three years at a US penitentiary in McCreary, Kentucky.[44] He wears an orange jumpsuit and, according to prison guards, remains in good spirits. Over 30 percent of the inmates at McCreary are Muslim, and Alamoudi receives a steady diet of halal food.

IMMODERATE MODERATE MUSLIM NO. 5: SAMI AL-ARIAN

Sami al-Arian, who served as a professor of computer engineering at the University of Southern Florida (USF) in Tampa, played a key role in establishing such organizations as the Arab Muslim Youth League, the Islamic Center in Tampa (where he served as imam), the Florida Islamic Academy, the World Islamic Study Enterprise (WISE), and the Islamic Association for Palestine (also known as Islamic Concern).[45] In 2000, he became active in George W. Bush's campaign for the White House and later claimed responsibility for the Bush victory. Bush, in turn, became attached to al-Arian, visited his family in southern Florida, and gave Abdullah, the professor's six-foot-three-inch-tall son the nickname "Big Dude." After the election, "Big Dude" came to serve as an intern for US representative David E. Bonior.[46]

Al-Arian soon began to wear out the welcome mat at the White House. He claimed to have conferred with President Bush about the government's use of "secret evidence" in deportation proceedings against alleged terrorists, including his brother-in-law.[47] He occupied a front-row seat at the ceremony during which Bush unveiled his plan for a faith-based initiative. In June 2001, al-Arian met with Bush's political advisor Karl Rove in the Eisenhower Executive Office Building to discuss the state of affairs in the Palestinian territories.[48] He became the favorite Muslim of the month among the inner circle of Washington's elite. Basking in the limelight, he appeared on the *Today Show* and proclaimed: "I am a very moderate Muslim person" and lauded the freedoms that people of all faiths receive in the land of the free and the home of the brave.[49]

Few seemed aware that al-Arian was wearing a mask. In a sermon at a Cleveland mosque, the bald and bespectacled professor said: "Let's damn America, let's damn Israel, let's damn their allies unto death."[50] He maintained the same tone in a forty-page manifesto in which he described America as the "Great Satan which makes the wrong right and the right wrong."[51]

But al-Arian was guilty of far more than standard Muslim hate mongering. He was responsible for transferring large sums of money to the Palestinian Islamic Jihad (PIJ), a group responsible for the murder of more than one hundred civilians in Israel, including two young American girls.[52] Moreover, with the establishment of WISE, al-Arian created a ratline between New York and central Florida to coordinate attacks on America soil. Many prominent jihadis from the al-Farooq Mosque in Brooklyn and the al-Salaam Mosque in Jersey City scurried back and forth on the ratline. The list included blind sheikh Omar Abdel Rahman; Ramzi Yousef, the chief strategist of the 1993 bombing of the World Trade Center; José Padilla, who was later indicted for planning to blow up the Brooklyn Bridge with a radiological device; Mohammad Atta and other al-Qaeda operatives of 9/11; and Adnan el-Shukrijumah, who has been singled out to serve as the commander for the forthcoming American Hiroshima.

In July 2002, al-Arian received word that he was the target of an FBI investigation. This prompted him to seek out Special Agent Gamal Abdel Hafiz, a member of the FBI's elite International Terrorism Squad, at a law enforcement conference in Washington, DC. Al-Arian, knowing that Hafiz was a devout Muslim, believed that the special agent would inform him of the details of the probe. His judgment, as it turned out, wasn't misplaced. Hafiz was one of the many Muslims who had been recruited by the FBI. The agency, under the direction of Robert Mueller, embarked on a national campaign to hire Muslims born and raised in Islamic countries to serve on the front line in the war on terror. Hafiz, an Egyptian national who obtained US citizenship in 1990, was one of Mueller's "golden boys."[53]

Upon his return to FBI headquarters after the conference, Hafiz informed his colleagues that he had been approached by al-Arian. Sensing a unique opportunity to obtain information about the workings of Islamic terrorist groups within the United States, Barry Carmody, an FBI veteran of thirty-four years, asked Hafiz to follow-up his meeting with al-Arian with a bugged telephone call. Hafiz was outraged at the suggestion. "I do not record another Muslim," he said. "That is against my religion."[54] Since such bugging is standard FBI procedure, Carmody and the other special agents were dumbfounded by Hafiz's position. "That's outrageous," Carmody replied. "That defeats the whole purpose."[55] Special Agent John B. Vincent, who worked with Hafiz, later added: "He [Hafiz] wouldn't have any problems interviewing or recording anyone who wasn't a Muslim, but he couldn't record a Muslim."[56]

The case against al-Arian dragged on for years—thanks to Special Agent Hafiz and the USF students and faculty members who rallied to the radical jihadi's defense. When the board of trustees and USF president Judy Genshaft voted to dismiss al-Arian from his teaching position, the Coalition of Progressive Student Organizations at the university published a newsletter to express outrage at "an act of injustice against a tenured faculty professor" that represented a "violation of academic free speech."[57] The coalition represented members of the Africana Studies Club, Amnesty International, the Campus Greens, the College Democrats, Cuba Viva, Free the Planet, the Free Thinkers, the Muslim Student Alliance, the NAACP, NOW@USF, the Student Environmental Association, Students for International Peace and Justice, the PRIDE Alliance, and the Shanachie.[58] The Free Thinkers represented an interesting addition to the list, since no student organization on campus displayed sufficient free thought to decry al-Arian's terrorist ties or his anti-American remarks.

On April 14, 2006, al-Arian pled guilty to a single count of conspiracy to provide services to the PIJ and agreed to deportation upon the completion of a prison sentence of fifty-seven months. In return, federal prosecutors agreed to drop the remaining eight charges against him. At the conclusion of the trial, Judge James S. Moody said:

> Dr. Al-Arian, as usual, you speak very eloquently. I find it interesting that here in public in front of everyone you praised this country, the same country that in private you referred to as "the great Satan." You are a master manipulator. You looked your neighbors in the eyes and said you had nothing to do with the Palestinian Islamic Jihad. This trial exposed that as a lie. The evidence was clear in this case that you were a leader of the Palestinian Islamic Jihad. When Iran, the major funding source of the PIJ, became upset because the PIJ could not account for how it was spending its money, it was to your board of directors that it went to demand changes. Iran wanted its representative to have a say in how its money was spent. To stop that, you leaped into action. You offered to rewrite the bylaws of the organization. But when it came to blowing up women and children on buses, did you leap into action then? No. You lifted not one finger, made not one phone call. To the contrary, you laughed when you heard about the bombings, what you euphemistically call "operations." And yet, still in the face of your own words, you continue to lie to your friends and supporters, claiming to abhor violence and to seek only aid for widows and orphans. Your only connection to widows and orphans is that you create them, even among the Palestinians; and you create them, not by sending your children to blow themselves out of existence. No. You exhort others to send their children. . . . You are indeed a master manipulator.[59]

The master manipulator's stay in a federal slammer was extended by his refusal to testify against his former associates in the jihad group. On March 28, 2007, he was subpoenaed to testify before a grand jury. Al-Arian again refused to spill his guts, opting instead to embark on an extended hunger strike to protest "government harassment."[60]

Al-Arian was released from police detention upon posting bond in 2008. He, at this writing, remains under house arrest as he continues to await trial on a criminal contempt charge. Special Agent Gamal Abdel Hafiz was promoted to the post of deputy legal attaché in Riyadh, Saudi Arabia.[61] Within months of Hafiz's arrival, the FBI headquarters in Washington, DC, began receiving complaints about the failure of the Riyadh office to pursue leads regarding terrorist activities. Bureau chiefs were dispatched to ferret out the root of the problem. They discovered that Hafiz had shredded more than two thousand documents relating to al-Qaeda and the 9/11 attacks.[62] Several of these documents were not duplicated in FBI computer files, including letters from Saudi officials concerning terror suspects.[63]

A SCHOLARLY ANSWER

Why are moderate Muslims so immoderate? Muqtedar Khan, author of *American Muslims: Bridging Faith and Freedom*, provides the following answer:

> Muslims in general do not like using the term, understanding it to indicate an individual who has politically sold out to the "other" side. In some internal intellectual debates, the term moderate Muslim is used pejoratively to indicate a Muslim who is more secular and less Islamic than the norm, which varies across communities. In America, a moderate Muslim is one who peddles a softer form of Islam—the Islam of John Esposito and Karen Armstrong—is willing to co-exist peacefully with peoples of other faiths and is comfortable with democracy and the separation of politics and religion. Both, Western media and Muslims, do a disservice by branding some Muslims as moderate on the basis of their politics. These people should in general be understood as opportunists and self-serving. Most of the moderate regimes in the Muslim World are neither democratic nor manifest the softer side of Islam. That leaves intellectual positions as the criteria for determining who is a moderate Muslim, and especially in comparison to whom, since moderate is a relative term.[64]

CHAPTER 19
MOSQUES MACABRE

By 2000, 80 percent of the 1,206 mosques in America had been established with Sunni funding from the Arab Middle East.[1] This funding was funneled from agencies such as the Muslim Student Association (MSA) and the Islamic Society of North America (ISNA) to the American Muslim Mission and similar organizations. By 2005, the Arab sheikhs had committed over $90 billion to accomplish the Islamic conquest of North America.[2] Mosques now sprouted up in nearly every corner of the country. Some were small and squalid storefronts like the al-Fatima Masjid in Queens, New York, which was situated within the basement of a run-down retail outlet; others were opulent structures with towering minarets, such as the $24 million Islamic Society of Boston. "It is very difficult for American Muslims to collect enough money to build their own mosques and so they rely on these [Saudi Arabian] institutions," Ahmed al-Rahim, a professor of Arabic Language and Literature at Harvard University, recently told an Ethnic and Public Center Panel in Washington, DC.[3]

By 2011, the number of mosques stood at 2,106, an increase of 74 percent within eleven years, according to the American Mosque Study, which was sponsored by the Hartford Institute for Religious Research (Hartford Seminary), the Association of Statisticians of American Religious Bodies, the Council on American-Islamic Relations (CAIR), the Islamic Society of North America, the Islamic Circle of North America (ICNA), and the International Institute of Islamic Study.[4] The study failed to address the matter of Saudi support and funding and neglected to include the Islamic houses of worship without formal addresses. Moreover, it refused to include the mosques and temples of the Nation of Islam, which the researchers viewed as a separate religion. Nevertheless, it revealed these substantial findings:

- ✓ 76 percent of the mosques were built since 1980.
- ✓ Over two-thirds (77 percent) are dominated by one ethnic group (Arab, African American, Somali, Central Asian, etc.).
- ✓ The percentage of mosques in suburban areas of the country has increased from 16 percent in 2000 to 28 percent in 2011.
- ✓ Imams endorse Islamic involvement in American society; 98 percent agree that Muslims should be involved in American institutions, and 91 percent state that Muslims should be involved in politics.
- ✓ Only 25 percent of imams now believe that America is hostile to Islam, compared to 54 percent in 2000.
- ✓ The annual conversion rate per mosque remains rather constant: 15.3 new converts per mosque in 2011, compared to 16.3 in 2000 and 16.5 in 1994.
- ✓ Approximately 64 percent of the converts are African Americans; 22 percent are white Americans; and 12 percent are Latinos/Hispanics.[5]

Concerning the ethnic breakdown of mosque participants, the study held that 33 percent are Central Asian (Pakistani, Indian, Bangladeshi, and Afghani), 27 percent are Arab, 24 percent are African American, 9 percent are sub-Saharan African (primarily Somali), and 2 percent are eastern European (primarily ethnic Albanian). The states, according to the study, with the largest number of mosques were as follows:

- ✓ New York—257
- ✓ California—246
- ✓ Texas—166

- ✓ Florida—118
- ✓ Illinois—109
- ✓ New Jersey—109
- ✓ Pennsylvania—99
- ✓ Michigan—77
- ✓ Georgia—69
- ✓ Virginia—62[6]

The metropolitan areas with the largest number of mosques were listed in the following manner:

- ✓ Greater New York City—192
- ✓ Southern California—120
- ✓ Greater Chicago—90
- ✓ Greater Philadelphia—63
- ✓ Greater Detroit—62
- ✓ San Francisco/Bay Area—62
- ✓ Greater Atlanta—55
- ✓ Northern New Jersey—53
- ✓ Greater Houston—42
- ✓ Greater Dallas–Fort Worth—39[7]

The key revelation of the study was that 2.6 million American Muslims attended Eid prayers (the holy day after Ramadan and Hajj) in 2011, compared to 2 million in 2000. This finding serves to negate the claim of the Pew Research Group that America's Islamic population is 2.4 million and to substantiate the contention that this population now exceeds 7 million.[8]

SEEDBEDS OF SUBVERSION?

In 1998, Sheikh Hisham Kabbani, chairman of the Islamic Supreme Council of America, testified before a committee of the US Department of State that over 80 percent of the mosques in America were controlled by Muslim extremists who were committed to the destruction of the United States. He maintained that Muslim schools, youth groups, community centers, political organizations, professional associations, and commercial enterprises within the United States share the ideology of terrorist organizations such as al-Qaeda and remain extremely hostile to American culture, wanting to replace it with an Islamic order.[9]

In response to these remarks, the American Muslim Political Coordination Council (AMPCC), the American Muslim Alliance (AMA), the American Muslim Council (AMC), CAIR, Muslim Public Affairs Council (MPAC), ICNA, and the Muslim Students Association of the United States and Canada issued this joint press release:

> Mr. Kabbani has put the entire American Muslim community under unjustified suspicion. In effect, Mr. Kabbani is telling government officials that the majority of American Muslims pose a danger to our society. Additionally, Islamophobic individuals and groups may use these statements as an excuse to commit hate crimes against Muslims. . . . We therefore ask Mr. Kabbani to promptly and publicly retract his statements, to apologize to the American Muslim community, and to exert his utmost effort to undo the damage these statements have done. The issue is not that of a mere difference of opinion within an American religious community, but involves the irresponsible act of providing false information to government officials. This false information can jeopardize the safety and well-being of our community and hurt America itself by damaging its values of inclusiveness, fairness and liberty.[10]

Kabbani offered no evidence to support this assertion and has provided little evidence since. In 2001, he told the *New York Times* that he had visited 114 mosques in the United States and "ninety of them were mostly exposed, and I say exposed, to extreme or radical ideology"—through speeches, books, and board members. He said that a telltale sign of an extremist mosque was "a focus on the Palestinian struggle," the *Times* reported.[11]

While the 2011 Mosque Report mollifies fears that the majority of US mosques uphold radical doctrine, several Islamic houses of worship pose a very real threat to national security.

ALLAH'S HOUSES OF HORROR: A SHORT LIST

A short list of the most troublesome of these "houses of worship" would have to include Masjid al-Taqwa in Brooklyn, Bridgeview Mosque in Chicago, and the Best Street Complex in Buffalo, New York.

Masjid al-Taqwa remains surrounded by security cameras and a small army of watchmen who will haul wandering tourists into the basement for questioning if they dare to snap a photo of this religious establishment. Detective David Casey of the New York Police Department informed the author of this book that the mosque represents one of the most dangerous places in Brooklyn.[12] With its ten-foot-high concrete block walls topped by razor wire, the Best Street Complex in Buffalo, which consumes an entire city block, looks like a medieval fortress. In keeping with its appearance, the complex contains underground tunnels that are connected to bunker-style rooms. According to Buffalo Common Council member Charley Fisher, the facility is used not only as a house of worship but a place for paramilitary training, where jihadi wannabes scale walls, fire weapons, and practice martial arts. These charges were verified by private investigator Douglas Hagmann.[13] The Bridgeview Mosque in Chicago has raised millions for three terrorist-front groups—Benevolence International Foundation (a front for al-Qaeda), Global Relief Foundation (al-Qaeda), and the Holy Land Foundation (Hamas). All three maintain offices near the mosque, and two employ mosque officials. One of the honored guests to the Chicago masjid was Abdullah Azzam, founder of al-Qaeda. Members of Azzam's family are now prominent members of Bridgeview.[14] But two of the country's Islamic houses of worship merit special attention.

DAR AL-HIJRAH

Dar al-Hijrah, located in Falls Church, Virginia, on the outskirts of Washington, DC, was built with funds from the Saudi-backed North American Islamic Trust and the Saudi Embassy's Islamic Affairs Department.[15] Several of its founding members, including Samir Salah, are alleged members of the Muslim Brotherhood. Salah helped to found the Safa Trust, which federal officials raided after 9/11, and Bank al-Taqwa, which the US government banned as a conduit for al-Qaeda and Hamas. Salah also ran the Talibah International Aid Association, another banned al-Qaeda charity, which was incorporated in Virginia by Osama bin Laden's nephew, Abdullah.[16] Abdullah, before he fled to Saudi Arabia, was also one of Dar al-Hijrah's founding members and a fixture there for many years.[17]

HAMAS AND HANOOTI

From 1995 to 1999, the spiritual leader at Dar al-Hijrah was Mohammed al-Hanooti. Born in Haifa, British Mandate of Palestine, Hanooti came to national attention by tesifying for Mousa Mohammed Abu Marzook, who was deported in 1997 and indicted years later on charges of arranging financial support for Hamas.[18] In 1998, he gained headlines by decrying President Clinton for ordering US military strikes in Sudan and Afghanistan, saying there was not enough convincing evidence to justify such violence against Muslim people.[19] One year later, Hanooti took the stand in federal court in support of Ihab M. Ali, who refused to offer evidence against the terrorists involved in the 1998 United States embassy bombings, telling the judge that such testimony would be "a serious sin" and "a betrayal of our beliefs as Muslims." When queried about Ali's position, Hanooti told the judge that by Islamic law Ali possesses "the right to abstain from giving testimony in case it hurts him or it hurts any other Muslim."[20]

As an imam, Hanooti acquired the rare distinction of not only being named by prosecutors as an unindicted coconspirator in the Holy Land Foundation trial, the largest terror-finance case in American history, but also of being listed as a conspirator in the trial of the blind sheikh Omar Abdel Rahman for the 1993 World Trade Center bombing and for planning to attack New York City landmarks.[21]

Despite his reputation as a big supporter of Hamas, who raised more than $6 million for the group in 1993 alone, Hanooti's speeches for the US State Department have been featured overseas on the Voice of America network and he has been singled out by the mayor of Washington, DC, as one of the top clerics in the area.[22]

In a recent interview with the *Washington Post*, Hanooti said, "I love America." He continued, "I always say to Muslims in my speeches that 70 percent of the laws in America are in compliance with Islam, and that they should Americanize everything in their life except things that are not in compliance with their faith."[23]

ENTER AL-AWLAKI

Anwar al-Awlaki, who had served as the spiritual leader of Masjid Ar-Ribat al-Islami in San Diego, California, became Hanooti's replacement at Dar al-Hijrah. Born in New Mexico and raised in Yemen, al-Awlaki was a self-professed student of Sayyid Qutb, the founder of the anti-Western jihadist movement, claiming that every day he read over 150 pages of Qutb's writings.[24]

Fluent in English, the new imam at al-Hijrah gained renown for his eloquent lectures on Islam that attracted hundreds of listeners. Among his attentive audience were Nawaf al-Hazmi and Hani Hanjour, two young Muslims who had followed al-Awlaki to Virginia from San Diego. Hazmi and Hanjour were the two al-Qaeda hijackers who flew a jumbo jet into the Pentagon on 9/11.[25] Another young man in attendance at the lectures was Nidal Malik Hasan, who stands accused of killing thirteen soldiers in a rampage at Fort Hood, Texas.[26]

When police investigating the 9/11 attacks raided the Hamburg, Germany, apartment of Ramzi Binalshibh (the "20th hijacker"), al-Awlaki's telephone number was found among Binalshibh's personal contact information.[27] The FBI interviewed al-Awlaki four times in the eight days following the 9/11 attacks. One detective told the 9/11 Commission that he believed al-Awlaki "was at the center of the 9/11 story." An FBI agent said that "if anyone had knowledge of the plot, it would have been him," since "someone had to be in the U.S. and keep the hijackers spiritually focused."[28]

A MODEL MUSLIM?

After the 9/11 attacks, al-Awlaki was interviewed by *National Geographic*, the *New York Times*, and other major media outlets because he was one of the country's most eloquent imams. He condemned the attacks, stating, "There is no way that the people who did this could be Muslim, and if they claim to be Muslim, then they have perverted their religion." He presented himself as a moderate who could "bridge the gap between the United States and the worldwide community of Muslims." Taking him at his word, US military officials invited him to a luncheon at the Pentagon.[29]

Esam Omeish and other Dar al-Hijrah officials assured the *Washington Post* that al-Awlaki "has no inclination or active involvement in any events or circumstances that have to do with terrorism" and that his sermons at the mosque condemn terrorism because "it is absolutely contradictory to Islamic principles." Omeish said that while there is "condemnation of the indiscriminate killing of civilians" among the members of the mosque, there is also "sympathy for the Palestinian cause," which, Omeish added, is "a core value."[30]

In 2002, al-Awlaki became the Congressional Muslim Staffer Association's first imam to conduct a prayer service at the US

Capitol. A few weeks later, he posted an essay in Arabic titled "Why Muslims Love Death" on the Islam Today website, praising the work of Palestinian suicide bombers.[31]

AL-QAEDA'S REGIONAL COMANDEER

Al-Awlaki's name came up in a dozen terrorist plots and incidents in the United States, England, and Canada, including the 2005 London subway bombings, the 2006 Toronto plot to blow up Parliament and behead the prime minister, the plans to attack Fort Dix, the jihadist killing of a US army recruiter in Little Rock, the Fort Hood massacre, the Christmas Day appearance of the underwear bomber, and the 2010 Times Square bombing attempt. In each case, the suspects expressed their devotion to al-Awlaki and his recorded sermons.[32]

On April 7, 2010, President Barack Obama ordered the targeted killing of al-Awlaki—an unprecedented move against a US citizen.[33] Several months later, as the "regional comandeer of al Qaeda," al-Awlaki proclaimed from his headquarters in Yemen that jihadists don't need a *fatwa* (a special religious ruling) to kill US citizens. "Don't consult with anybody in killing the Americans," the imam said, while sitting at a desk with a dagger in his belt. "Fighting the devil doesn't require consultation or prayers seeking divine guidance. They are the party of the devils." He added that Americans and Muslims are "two opposites who will never come together" and that it is "either us or them."[34] On September 30, 2011, the troublesome cleric was finally stilled by an unmanned US drone attack on his Yemeni base.[35]

AL-HIJRAH'S DIRECTOR OF OUTREACH

In 2002, Johari Abdul Malik, a Brooklyn-born convert to Islam, became Dar al-Hijrah's director of outreach. Before his appointment to this position, Malik had voiced his support for Jamil al-Amin (the former H. Rap Brown), who had been convicted of murdering a sheriff's deputy and wounding another officer at his store in Fulton County, Georgia. "Someone has a vendetta against people like H. Rap Brown," he said, "because he stood up during a period of great repression in this country and said it mattered to him."[36]

On March 20, 2002, when FBI officials raided fourteen homes and offices of northern-Virginia Muslims for evidence against Sami al-Arian, the alleged leader of the Palestine Islamic Jihad (PIJ) in the United States, Malik said: "Now the witch hunt has expanded into homes and families."[37] In 2006, al-Arian (see previous chapter) pled guilty to conspiracy to help the PIJ, an officially designated terrorist organization, and was sentenced to fifty-seven months in prison.[38]

IN DEFENSE OF TERRORISM

Not knowing when to bite his tongue, Malik decried the arrest of Abdul Rahman Al-Almoudi, founder of the American Muslim Council and a fixture at Dar al-Hijrah, on charges that he engaged in illegal financial transactions with Libya. In court, Almoudi pled guilty to the charges and received a sentence of twenty-one years in federal prison.[39] He also came to the defense of Ahmed Omar Abu Ali, who taught Islamic studies at Dar al-Hijrah and was arrested for plotting with members of al-Qaeda to assassinate President George W. Bush. "Our whole community is under siege," Malik said when Abu Ali was taken into custody. "They don't see this as a case of criminality. They see it as a civil rights case. As a frontal attack on their community." He added: "The feeling I get here on a daily basis must be what it was like to be a member of Martin Luther King Jr.'s church following the case of Rosa Parks. People always ask, 'What is the latest from the courthouse?'"[40] Malik was not the only Dar al-Hijrah official who was appalled by the arrest of Abu Ali. Shaker El-Sayed, the new imam at the mosque, called the case "laughable." "They didn't have the evidence. They don't have the evidence. The fishing expedition continues,"

El-Sayed announced to CNN.[41] Despite such outcries, Abu Ali was convicted in 2005 of providing material support to the al-Qaeda terrorist network, attempting to hijack an airplane, and conspiracy to assassinate President Bush. He was sentenced to life in prison.[42]

Still foaming at the mouth, Malik went on to denounce the arrest in April 2005 of Ali al-Timimi, who was convicted of inciting followers to wage war against the United States just days after the terrorist attacks of September 11, 2001, and for recruiting for Lashkar-e-Taiba, the Pakistani militant group. The irate Dar al-Hijrah spokesman told the press: "There is a view many Muslims have when they come to America that you could not be arrested for something you say. But now they have discovered they are not free to speak their minds. And if our opinions are out of vogue in the current climate, we feel we are all at risk."[43] The risk, unfortunately for Malik, proved real: Al-Timimi was sentenced to life imprisonment.

A JOURNALIST'S NOTE

Regarding the Virginia mosque, Paul Sperry, a Washington-based investigative journalist and Hoover Institution media fellow, writes: "Dar al-Hijrah is a veritable magnet for militant Islamists. Over the years, it has attracted an alarming number of terror supporters, terror facilitators, terror fundraisers, terror co-conspirators, and actual terrorists—including at least two of the 9/11 hijackers who crashed the plane into the Pentagon. These are not just random members who come and go. Many are the very leaders and founders of the mosque."[44]

MASJID AL-FAROOQ

Established in 1976, Masjid al-Farooq on Atlantic Avenue in Brooklyn doesn't look like a house of worship. It rather resembles a poorly lit private club in Little Italy, where good fellows might gather to shoot pool, play cards, and plan the day's events. The only indication that it is a mosque comes from the Arabic inscription above the entranceway: *Ashadu an la ilaha illa Llah, wa ashhadu anna Mohammad rasulu Llah* ("There is no God but Allah and Muhammad is his prophet"). Its lobby walls, which are cracked and badly in need of painting, are decorated with travel posters of Mecca and advertisements for the Muslim Youth Center indoor basketball league. In the corner near the entranceway is a metal container the size of a kitchen trash can that is used for donations.

The first three floors have narrow rectangular prayer rooms covered in purple and green carpeting. Shelves outside each room fill up with worshipers' shoes during services. The upper floors house the Al-Aqsa Islamic School as well as offices furnished with beat-up, taped-up desks and chairs.

This Islamic house of worship has been responsible for sending hundreds of recruits to al-Qaeda training camps throughout the Middle East. One such recruit was Jamal Ahmad al-Fadl, who worked to secure nuclear weapons and materials for al-Qaeda during Osama bin Laden's stay in Sudan.[45]

Al-Farooq mosque first gained national attention on November 5, 1990, when El-Sayyid Nosair, a prominent member, murdered Rabbi Meir Kahane, the founder of the Jewish Defense League, in the ballroom of the Marriott East Hotel in Manhattan, where Kahane was speaking. The murder was a case of an Arab jihadi killing an American rabbi on US soil—the first indication that the world-wide jihad had reached our shores.[46]

HEADQUARTERS FOR AL-QAEDA

At the time of Kahane's death, the Brooklyn mosque served as the headquarters of the al-Kifah Refugee Center, a front for al-Qaeda, with branches in Atlanta, Boston, and Tucson, along with recruiting stations in twenty-six states.[47]

Founded in 1986 by Abdullah Azzam, bin Laden's mentor, the al-Kifah Refugee Center acted as a CIA front for transferring funds, weapons, and recruits to the anti-Soviet mujahadeen in Afghanistan. In exchange for this service, President Ronald Reagan's administration forked over more than $2 million a year to the mosque, making it a very wealthy institution.[48] Not many Christian churches, let alone Jewish synagogues, have received similar donations from Uncle Sam. During this time, Azzam spent a great deal of time in Brooklyn. In a 1988 videotape, he can be seen and heard telling a large crowd of African Americans that "blood and martyrdom are the only way to create a Muslim society."[49]

By 1992 al-Farooq Mosque had become a haven for Arabian veterans from the jihad in Afghanistan who were granted special passports by the CIA to enter the United States. A feud erupted between the older African American members of the mosque and the Arab newcomers, which resulted in the murder of Mustafa Shalabi, the fiery imam of the Brooklyn house of prayer, on March 1, 1991.[50] The crime has never been solved.

BLIND MAN'S VISION

In the wake of the murder of Shalabi, Sheikh Omar Abdel Rahman, the revered blind cleric who had provided the religious authorization for the assassination of Egyptian president Anwar el Sadat, became the new imam at al-Farooq. The blind sheikh had migrated to Brooklyn in July 1990 after the consular secretary of the US embassy in Egypt granted him a visa even though his name appeared at the top of a CIA high-alert watch list. Wadith el-Hage, who arrived in Brooklyn from Tucson the day after the hit on Shalabi, became the new head of the al-Kifah Refugee Center. El-Hage, a naturalized American citizen, later became Osama bin Laden's personal secretary. Neither Sheikh Omar Rahman nor el-Hage were intent upon mounting an Islamic version of the Billy Graham Crusade. Rather, they were focused on launching major attacks against the "Great Satan" (the blind sheikh's favored name for the Unitd States of America).

Knowing that the Brooklyn mosque had become a hive for terrorist activities, Neil Herman, a senior FBI agent, asked the Justice Department for permission to wiretap the mosque and the blind sheikh's office. The request was denied because the establishment on Atlantic Avenue represents a "house of worship."[51]

Within the house of worship, Sheikh Omar Rahman was preaching jihad and calling upon the congregants to fight the "Great Satan" with bullets and bombs. In one sermon, he proclaimed:

> There is no solution for our problems except jihad for the sake of God. There's no solution, there's no treatment, there's no medicine, there's no cure except with what was brought by the Islamic method which is jihad for the sake of God. . . . No, if those who have the right to have something are terrorists, then we are terrorists. And we welcome being terrorists. And we do not deny this charge to ourselves. And the Qu'ran makes it, terrorism, among the means to perform jihad in the sake of Allah, which is to terrorize the enemies of God and who are our enemies, too. . . . They say that he who has done his job during the day in order to go to the mosque has performed jihad. And he who listens to a religious lecture has performed jihad. Praying, listening, jihad? Coming to the mosques is a good work. And group praying is just praying. Jihad is fighting the enemies. Fighting the enemies for God's sake in order to raise them high in his word. . . . We don't fight the enemies unless we have guns, tanks, and airplanes equal to those of the Soviet Union.[52]

The attack came on February 26, 1993, at the World Trade Center, with the detonation of a bomb that killed six people and injured 1,042, producing more hospital casualties than any event in US history apart from the Civil War.[53] Three of the terrorists involved in the bombing—Mohammad Salameh, Mahmud Abouhalima, and Nidal Ayyad—were prominent members of the al-Farooq Mosque.

The leader of the attack was Ramzi Yousef, a Kuwaiti radical who had been summoned to Brooklyn by the blind sheikh to mastermind the bombing.[54]

Yousef had arrived at the al-Farooq Mosque in August 1992 with an Iraqi passport and the intent to kill a quarter million American civilians. The number, Yousef later explained, was not random. It represented the number of Japanese civilians who had been killed by the atomic bombs that were dropped on Hiroshima and Nagasaki at the close of World War II.[55]

Following the 1993 bombing of the World Trade Center, the members of the Brooklyn mosque sought new ways to mount further attacks. Under Sheikh Omar Rahman's direction, they made plans to bomb the Lincoln and Holland Tunnels, the United Nations, the FBI headquarters, and other federal buildings in Manhattan. To create the bombs, they began mixing hundreds of pounds of Scotts® Super Turf Builder® with 255 gallons of diesel fuel at a safe house in Queens.[56] Neighbors became suspicious of the strange comings and goings by bearded men in Islamic robes and skullcaps. Calls were made to federal, state, and local law enforcement officials, which resulted in a raid on June 23, 1993. Eleven Muslims were taken into custody, including Sheikh Omar Rahman, and charged as coconspirators in a terrorist plot.

IMAMS AND IMPS

At the ensuing trial, Gulshair el-Shukrijumah, the interim imam at al-Farooq, served as Sheikh Omar Rahman's interpreter and character witness. When Rahman was sent to the slammer, Gulshair el-Shukrijumah packed his bags and headed off with his family to sunny Florida, where he established (thanks to a few million from the Saudi Embassy) Masjid al-Hijrah, yet another hard-line Wahhabi sanctuary.

As the spiritual leader of the Florida mosque, Gulshair el-Shukrijumah counseled al-Qaeda dirty-bomb suspect José Padilla and met with several of the 9/11 hijackers.[57]

Adnan el-Shukrijumah, Gulshair el-Shukrijumah's eldest son, is proof positive that a bad apple doesn't fall far from a rotten tree. Known as "Jafer the Pilot," Adnan has been identified as the appointed commander of the next major attack by al-Qaeda on US soil—an event, known as the "American Hiroshima," which will entail the detonation of tactical nuclear bombs in major cities throughout the country.[58]

In 2003, Amin Awad, the new imam at al-Farooq, was prevented from counseling prisoners in New York's Rikers Island prison because of his ties to al-Qaeda and international terrorism.[59]

BUNDLES FOR BIN LADEN

The saga of the little shop of Islamic horror in Brooklyn continued in 2003 with the arrest of Mohammad Ali Hasan al-Moayad, a fund raiser from al-Farooq, who personally delivered $20 million to Osama bin Laden and another gift of $3.5 million to the al-Aqsa Society, the financial arm of Hamas. These gifts represented the amount that al-Moayad and other members of the mosque had collected since December 1999.[60]

THE AL-FAROOQ ARSENAL

In the course of their surveillance of the al-Farooq Mosque, members of the FBI Joint Terrorism Task Force noted that members entered the house of worship in the early morning to withdraw crates of weapons and boxes of ammunition that they hauled to the Calverton Shooting Range on eastern Long Island. At the range, the members received training with semiautomatic rifles, shotguns, 9 mm and .367 caliber handguns, and fully automatic AK-47 assault weapons. Many of these weapons had been provided to the mosque by Ali Mohamed, a former army sergeant at Fort Bragg and an al-Qaeda sleeper agent.[61] The surveillance proved that some US mosques—no less than the Red Mosque in Pakistan—serve as arsenals for jihadists.

CHAPTER 20
ISLAMOPHOBIA

"Islamophobia refers to unfounded fear of and hostility towards Islam. Such fear and hostility leads to discriminations against Muslims, exclusion of Muslims from mainstream political or social progress, stereotyping, the presumption of guilty by association, and finally hate crimes."

So says Human Rights First, a nonprofit human rights organization with headquarters in New York and Washington, DC.[1] This organization claims that this new psychological disorder among the American people has resulted in "the general and unquestioned acceptance" of the following beliefs:

- ✓ Islam is a monolithic faith that cannot adapt to present-day realities.
- ✓ Islam does not share common values with other major faiths.
- ✓ Islam is archaic, barbaric, and irrational.
- ✓ Islam is a religion of violence that supports terrorism.
- ✓ Islam is a violent political ideology.[2]

In support of this contention, a *Washington Post*/ABC News poll conducted in September 2010 showed that 49 percent of Americans share an unfavorable view of Islam, an increase from 39 percent in October 2002.[3] Providing similar support, a *Time* magazine poll conducted at the same time found that 28 percent of the country's registered voters do not believe that Muslims should be eligible to sit on the US Supreme Court and nearly one-third maintain that followers of Islam should be barred from running for president.[4]

EVIDENCE OF THE EPIDEMIC

The seriousness of this new American madness, according to the Council on American-Islamic Relations (CAIR) and other pro-Islamic organizations, has been crystallized by the following incidents:

- ✓ In February 2008, three white supremacists—Eric Ian Baker, thirty-two, Michael Corey Golden, twenty-three, and Jonathan Edward Stone, nineteen—were charged with firebombing and destroying the Islamic Center of Columbia, forty miles southwest of Nashville, Tennessee, after spray-painting the walls of the mosque with swastikas and the words "White Power."[5]
- ✓ In 2009, Jamaat Ibad Ar-Rahman, the largest mosque in Durham, North Carolina, was vandalized three times in six months. One incident involved several irate men hurling rocks at the Muslim house of worship and yelling, "Go to hell."[6]
- ✓ On May 12, 2010, a firebomb exploded during an evening prayer service at a mosque in Jacksonville, Florida. Ashrad Shaikh, vice chairman of the Islamic Center of Northeast Florida, said that about sixty people were inside at the time. "I thought we were making so much progress—that we had started getting beyond tolerance to friendship," Shaikh told the local press.[7]
- ✓ On August 25, 2010, New York City cabdriver Ahmed Sharif was stabbed multiple times by an intoxicated passenger who asked if the cabbie was a Muslim. Michael Enright, the twenty-one-year-old perpetrator, was charged with attempted murder and assault as hate crimes. After his arrest, Enright declared that he was a "patriot" and told the police officers who arrested him that "you allow them to blow up buildings in this country," according to authorities.[8]
- ✓ Three days later, a fire, later ruled as arson, broke out at the site of a planned Islamic center and mosque in the Nashville

suburb of Murfreesboro. When members of the mosque gathered the next day to inspect the damage, nine shots in two volleys allegedly were fired near the site. Camie Ayash, a spokesperson for the Islamic Center of Murfreesboro, called the fire an "arson attack" and an "atrocious act of terrorism."[9]

- ✓ In January 2011, Roger Stockham, sixty-three, was arrested for planning to blow up the Islamic Center of America in Dearborn, Michigan, where hundreds of Muslim mourners had gathered for a funeral service.[10]
- ✓ On New Year's Day, 2012, Ray Lazier Lengend, forty, allegedly threw a Molotov cocktail at the Al-Khoei Foundation in Queens—a building that housed a mosque and an Islamic school. Lengend later told police that his plan was "to inflict as much damage as possible" and "to take out as many Muslims and Arabs as possible." In an indictment, the US Attorney's Office charged Lengend with a hate crime through the use of fire and explosives and a hate crime through damaging religious property.[11]

"We see hate crimes generally go in spurts, and are often in relation to international or domestic events," Ibrahim Hooper, spokesman for the CAIR, told the press.[12] In 2008, 105 hate crime "incidents" against Muslims were reported nationwide, far fewer than such crimes against Jews, lesbians, gay men, and Caucasians.[13] In 2009, that number climbed slightly to 107. But in 2010, anti-Islamic crimes rose nearly 50 percent due to the public outcry over plans to construct an Islamic Center at ground zero—the site of the 9/11 attacks in New York City.[14]

ANTI-MOSQUE CAMPAIGNS

These incidents seemed to pale in comparison with the reported 887 crimes against Jews that took place throughout the country that year.[15] But according to Islamic apologists John L. Esposito and Sheila Lalwani, the FBI's report of crimes against Muslims failed to include the efforts of Americans in municipalities throughout the country to halt construction of new mosques and expansion of existing ones.[16] Some of the most notable of such efforts that took place in 2010 and 2011 are as follows:

- ✓ In Temecula, California, members of a local Tea Party group took dogs and picket signs to Friday prayers at a mosque that sought to build a new worship center on a vacant lot the Muslims had purchased in 2000.[17]
- ✓ In Sheboygan, Wisconsin, a few Christian ministers led a noisy fight against a Muslim group that sought permission to open a mosque in a former health-food store bought by a Muslim doctor.[18]
- ✓ In DuPage County, Illinois, the county board proposed a ban on the opening of new religious establishments in unincorporated residential areas following the submission of plans by the local Muslims to expand or build three mosques. After months of debate, the board finally approved the construction of the Muslim Educational Cultural Center of America but rejected plans for the addition of a dome and a minaret to the structure.[19]

ISLAMOPHOBIC FUNDING

The Center for American Progress, an Islamic advocacy agency, claims that Islamophobia has been fueled by funding from the following seven organizations that have spent $40 million to perpetuate negative information about Islam to the American public: (1) Donors Capital Fund, (2) Richard Mellon Scaife Foundation, (3) Lynde and Harry Bradley Foundation, (4) Newton and Rochelle Becker Foundation and Newton and Rochelle Becker Charitable Trust, (5) Russell Berrie

Foundation, (6) Anchorage Charitable Trust and William Rosenwald Family Fund, and (7) the Fairbrook Foundation.[20]

From 2007 to 2009, the Donors Capital Fund provided $21,316,600 to such alleged anti-Muslim groups as the Middle East Forum, the Investigative Project on Terrorism, and the David Horowitz Freedom Center. The primary "Islamophobic" recipient purportedly was the Clarion Fund, which received $17 million to distribute the film *Obsession: Radical Islam's War against the West* to more than 28 million swing-state voters to influence the 2008 presidential election.[21]

Between 2001 and 2009, the Richard Mellon Sciafe Foundation shelled out $7,850,000 to such alleged anti-Muslim groups as the Center for Security Policy ($2,900,000), the Counterterrorism and Security Education and Research Foundation ($1,575,000), and the David Horowitz Freedom Center ($3,400,000).[22] During this same time span, the Lynde and Harry Bradley Foundation supported the "Islamophobic network" with its gifts to the Middle East Forum ($305,000), the Center for Security Policy ($815,000), and the David Horowitz Freedom Center ($4,250,000).[23]

Similarly, from 2001 to 2009, the Newton D. and Rochelle F. Becker Foundation, the Newton and Rochelle Becker Family Foundation, and the Newton and Rochelle Becker Charitable Trust purportedly furthered the cause of Islamophobia to the tune of $1,136,000 by granting $25,000 to the Investigative Project on Terrorism, $335,000 to the Middle East Forum, $405,000 to the Center for Security Policy, $15,000 to the Clarion Fund, $50,000 to ACT for America, and $86,000 to the David Horowitz Freedom Center,[24] while the Russell Berrie Foundation provided a total $3,109,016, with funding going to the Counterterrorism and Security Education and Research Foundation ($2,736,000), the Investigative Project on Terrorism ($100,000), and the Middle East Forum ($273,016.22).[25]

The Anchorage Charitable Fund and the William Rosenwald Family Fund, from 2001 to 2008, reportedly added $2,818,229 to the coffers of the anti-Muslim movement with grants of $2,320,229.33 to the Middle East Forum, $437,000 to the Center for Security Policy, $25,000 to the Clarion Fund, $15,000 to the Counterterrorism and Security Education and Research Foundation, $11,000 to the David Horowitz Freedom Center, and $10,000 to the Investigate Project on Terrorism.[26] And, finally, from 2004 to 2009, the Fairbrook Foundation added to the finances of the alleged Islamophobic network with donations of $125,000 to ACT For America, $66,100 to the Center for Security Policy, $618,500 to the David Horowitz Freedom Center, $25,000 for the Investigative Project on Terrorism, $253,250 to Jihad Watch, and $410,000 to the Middle East Forum.[27]

EMERSON'S COTTAGE INDUSTRY

Thanks to the largesse of these seven charitable organizations, Islamophobia has become a booming cottage industry. Steven Emerson made his name in the mid-1990s with his documentary film *Jihad in America*, which aired on PBS. Produced in the wake of the 1993 World Trade Center bombing, the film uncovered terrorists raising money in the United States. He capitalized on the success of the film with such books as *Jihad Incorporated: A Guide to Militant Islam in the U.S.* and *American Jihad: The Terrorists Living among Us.* In 1995, Emerson formed SAE Productions, a firm based in Washington, DC, to research the relationship between American Muslims and overseas terrorist groups. In 2008, the company raked in $3,390,000 for management services. Emerson remains the firm's sole officer.[28] In 2002 and 2003, despite lacking nonprofit status, Emerson received a total of $600,000 in grants from the Smith Richardson Foundation, a conservative public-policy shaper based in Connecticut.[29]

In 2006, Emerson formed the Investigative Project on Terrorism (IPT), a nonprofit entity that shares the same Washington address as SAE. In 2007 and 2008, IPT received $400,000 from Donors Capital Fund, $100,000 from the Becker Foundation, and $250,000 from the Middle East Forum.[30] In November 2010, large sums of money that had been contributed to IPT care of the Counterterrorism and Security Education and Research Foundation (CTSERF) were transferred to the International Association of Conterterrorism and Security professionals, a private for-profit agency. The Russell Berrie Foundation had given $2,736,000 to CTSERF, and the Richard Scaife Foundation had doled out $1,575,000.[31]

THE GAFFNEY THINK TANK

The Center for Security Policy (CSP), a think tank formed by Frank Gaffney, became another leading beneficiary of the burgeoning anti-Islam cottage industry. By 2009, CSP's annual revenue soared to $4 million and Gaffney's salary as head of the organization was set at $300,000. From 2002 to 2009, the CSP received about $20 million in revenue.[32] Gaffney's organization, which spearheads the anti-sharia movement throughout America, produced "Shariah: The Threat to America" in 2010. This report holds that Muslims advocate a "totalitarian ideology" and advance "legal-political-military doctrine."[33]

THE HOROWITZ FREEDOM CENTER

In 1988, David Horowitz and Peter Collier, his long-time collaborator, formed the David Horowitz Freedom Center, a private nonprofit charity, with funding from the Olin Foundation, the Bradley Foundation, and the Sarah Scaife Foundation. Twenty years later, the Freedom Center reported revenues of $5,466,103 and expenses of $5,994,547, including the annual compensation package of $480,162 to Horowitz and $228,744 to Collier.[34] The charity operates the Terrorism Awareness Program "to educate Americans on the threat to our freedom from terrorists, especially those engaged in jihadist campaigns"; Front Page Magazine, a website, "to deliver the news on the war at home and abroad; and Jihad Watch, another website, to disseminate information "regarding the jihadists worldwide, sharia law, and the threats to Western Civilization."[35] Horowitz has directed anti-Muslim campaigns such as "Islamo-Fascism Week," which brought speakers, such as former senator Rick Santorum, Ann Coulter, Robert Spencer, Nonie Darwish, and Wafa Sultan to more than one hundred college campuses throughout the country.[36]

PIPES AND THE PHOBIA

In 1990, Daniel Pipes, a prominent academician, formed the Middle East Forum (MEF) "to define and promote American interests in the Middle East and protect the Constitutional order from Middle Eastern threats."[37] By 2010, his nonprofit agency possessed more than $3,000,000 in revenue and published hundreds of articles by Pipes such as "CAIR: Islamist Fooling the Establishment." In this piece, Pipes argued that "the Wahhabi lobby" in Washington was involved in a stealth movement to take control of the government.

Since 2006, MEF has also run a project called "Islamist Watch," which bills itself as a watchdog group to combat "the ideas and institutions of nonviolent, radical Islam in the United States and other Western countries."[38] A 2008 press release on MEF's website states that "nonviolent radical Islam is more likely to alter the makeup of Western society over time than is terrorism" and quotes Daniel Pipes as saying, "Quietly, lawfully, peacefully, Islamists do their work throughout the West to impose aspects of Islamic law, win special privileges for themselves, shut down criticism of Islam, create Muslim-only zones, and deprive women and non-Muslims of their full civil rights."[39] The release lists the following examples of "lawful Islamism": (1) leading Muslim students in prayer at a public elementary school, (2) allowing cabdrivers to refuse service to people with guide dogs for reasons of religion, and (3) sponsoring Muslim lifeguard programs at public pools to ensure the modesty of Muslim women.[40]

CHRISTIAN CULPRITS

The long list of Islamophobes, according to the Center for American Progress, also includes prominent evangelical Christian spokesmen, such as John Hagee, Pat Robertson, Ralph Reed, and Franklin Graham. Hagee, the CEO of Global Evangelism Television, made the list for making the following pronouncements:

> Jihad has come to America. If we lose the war to Islamic fascism, it will change the world as we know it.[41]
>
> They are trained from the breast of their mother to hate us. Radical Islam is a doctrine of death. It is their desire, it is their hope, it is their ambition, it is their highest honor to die in the war against infidels. And you are "infidels" and there is nothing you can do to accommodate them.[42]
>
> Radical sects, which include about 200 million Islamists, believe they have a command from God to kill Christians and Jews.[43]

Robertson, the founder and head of the Christian Broadcasting Network, gained Islamophobic status by comparing Muslims to Nazis and labeling Islam "a violent political system bent on the overthrow of the governments of the world and world domination."[44] He also joined ranks with the anti-sharia league by asking, "Why can't we speak out against an institution [Islam] that is intent on dominating us and imposing *sharia* law and making us part of a universal Caliphate?"[45]

Reed, the head of the Faith and Freedom Coalition (FFC) made the cut for the list not for making anti-Islamic statements, but rather for inviting Frank Gaffney to give a talk titled "Defeating Terrorism and Jihad" at the annual convention of his organization. At the conference, Gaffney remarked that "it was certainly possible we'd have a Muslim flag flying over the White House" and urged the FFC to "take up the fight against shari'ah."[46]

Finally Franklin Graham, son of Billy Graham and the CEO of Samaritan's Purse, an international Christian relief organization, gained prominence as an Islamophobe by calling Islam "a very evil and wicked religion" in the wake of the 9/11 attacks.[47] His reputation as a leading spokesman against the Muslim religion was enhanced by his pronouncement that "true Islam" cannot be practiced in the United States for the following reasons: "You can't beat your wife. You can't murder your children if you think they've committed adultery or something like that, which they [Muslims] do practice in these other countries."[48]

IN DEFENSE OF ISLAMOPHOBIA

In defense of their anti-Muslim statement and positions, David Horowitz and bestselling author Robert Spencer say that Islamophobia is the "new favorite attack term of the Muslim Brotherhood, the Hamas-spinoff CAIR, and assorted Marxist groups" to silence critics "of Islamic terror, misogyny, and religious bigotry."[49] The bogus psychological condition, they maintain, represents a fabrication of Muslim apologists to silence critics of Islam through a direct assault on the Bill of Rights. The very real threat of Islam, they add, cannot be denied in light of Muslim attacks on the homeland that have resulted in 3,051 deaths since the dawn of the twenty-first century.[50] A synopsis of several such incidents follows:

December 5, 2009—Binghamton, New York

A forty-six-year-old graduate student at Binghamton University stabbed to death his Jewish professor and mentor because he was "persecuted as a Muslim." The slain professor was the author of several books, including *Understanding Fundamentalism: Christian, Islamic, and Jewish Movements.* The killer, who was writing his dissertation on early Arab culture, told one of his roommates, "I feel like destroying the world."[51]

November 5, 2009—Fort Hood, Texas

Major Malik Nadal Hasan, thirty-nine, a Muslim American psychiatrist, opened fire on American troops at Fort Hood, Texas, in a murderous rampage that left thirteen soldiers dead and thirty-eight wounded. The carnage began as approximately three hundred soldiers, in preparation for deployment to Afghanistan, lined up to get vaccinations and to have their eyes examined at a Soldier Readiness Center. Hasan, who worshipped at the Dar al-Hijrah mosque in Falls Church, Virginia, with several of the 9/11 operatives, screamed "Allahu Akbar" before opening fire with his semiautomatic pistol. Six months before the massacre, Major Hasan attracted the attention of law enforcement officials for his anti-American tirades and his statements of support for the global jihad. In an Internet posting, he equated suicide bombers to soldiers who throw themselves on a grenade to save the lives of their comrades. Reacting to the carnage, President Barack Obama said, "We don't know all the answers yet. And I would caution against jumping to conclusions until we have all the facts."[52]

November 2, 2009—Glendale, Arizona

A twenty-year-old woman died from injuries suffered when her Muslim father ran her down with his Jeep® Cherokee for becoming too Westernized. The father had taken his daughter to Iraq under the pretense of visiting relatives only to marry her off to a man nearly three times her age. The young woman managed to scrape up enough money to escape from her forced marriage and to make her way back to the United States. After killing his daughter, the Muslim father set fire to his house in Glendale. Nine people were inside the house when the fire broke out.[53]

October 29, 2009—Brighton, New York

A thirty-seven-year-old Muslim housewife slit the throat of her sleeping husband at the couple's home. She told police that she was forced to commit the crime because her husband was not a devout Muslim. She claimed that he pressured her to eat pork and gave her a drink that contained alcohol.[54]

June 1, 2009—Little Rock, Arkansas

A Muslim convert opened fire at a recruiting station in Little Rock, Arkansas, killing one young soldier and wounding another. The convert—Abdulhakim Mujahid Muhammed (formerly Carlos Bledsoe), twenty-four—said that he was "mad at the U.S. military" because of what American soldiers "had done to Muslims in the past." The killing, he claimed, was for the sake of Allah. "I do not feel I am guilty," he told police officers. "I don't think it was murder because murder is when a person kills another person without justified reason. U.S. soldiers are killing innocent Muslim men and women. We believe we have to strike back. We believe in an eye for an eye."[55]

February 14, 2009—Buffalo, New York

The founder of a Muslim TV station beheaded his wife in the hallway of his studio when he learned that she was seeking a divorce. Despite the heinousness of the crime, Muzzammil Hassan had been hailed by the Buffalo community as a model example of a moderate Muslim. Bridges TV—Hasan's television station—had been established "to fuse American culture with the values of Islam in a healthy, family-oriented way."[56]

January 1, 2008—Irving, Texas

An immigrant Muslim cabdriver shot and killed his two teenage daughters in his taxi upon discovering they had dated non-Muslim boys. He had planned for his eldest daughter to marry a man three times her age in Egypt. Discovering that she was no longer a virgin, he withdrew a 9 mm pistol and shot her twice at point-blank range in the chest, severing her spinal chord. Then he turned the pistol on Sarah, his younger daughter, who was sitting in the backseat. He pumped nine bullets into her body before abandoning the cab in the parking lot of the Omni Mandalay Hotel. He escaped arrest and remains at large. Many believe that he returned to Cairo.[57]

July 6, 2008—Jonesboro, Georgia

A distraught Muslim smashed his daughter's skull with an electric iron and strangled her to death with a bungee cord when she expressed her unhappiness over her arranged marriage. Ajay Nair, associate dean of multicultural affairs at Columbia University, explained the killing to CNN by saying, "I think there are ways that we can rationalize it and make sense of it particularly in thinking about new immigrant communities in the U.S. and thinking about some of the struggles that they face."[58]

February 12, 2007—Salt Lake City, Utah

An eighteen-year-old Bosnian Muslim refugee went on a shooting rampage at the Trolley Square Mall in Salt Lake City—targeting shoppers who were buying Valentine's Day cards. Five shoppers were killed and four others were critically wounded. Witnesses said that the shooter—Sulejman Talovic—cried out, "Allahu Akbar" every time he squeezed the trigger.[59]

October 6, 2006—Louisville, Kentucky

A Somali Muslim clubbed his estranged wife with a blunt object, leaving her for dead, and proceeded to murder their four children for adopting American lifestyles. The children ranged in age from eight to three. The youngest of the children—a boy and a girl—were stabbed to death while sleeping in their bedroom; the other two girls were killed in the kitchen—their bodies bearing defensive wounds on their hands and arms. The father told police officers that he was compelled to kill his family because his wife had treated him with disrespect.[60]

August 20, 2006—San Francisco and New Clips

An unemployed Muslim automobile worker used his black Honda® SUV to run down eighteen pedestrians through the streets of San Francisco—one was killed. When taken into custody, the Muslim said: "I am a terrorist. I don't care. Everyone needs to be killed."[61]

July 28, 2006—Seattle, Washington

A Muslim American, making use of a fourteen-year-old girl as a hostage, broke into a Jewish Center. He selected his target by researching "something Jewish" on the Internet and purchased two semiautomatic pistols from a local arms dealer. Upon entering the Jewish Center, he announced to the receptionist, "I'm a Muslim American and I'm angry at Israel," and then he shot her. He proceeded to walk down the hallway, firing at women as they sat at their desks. Three of the workers were struck in the abdomen, one in the chest, and another in the head. He fired another round at the stomach of an employee who was five months pregnant. The bullet missed and struck her arm, which she had raised for protection. The police managed to persuade the Muslim to surrender. In the wake of the carnage, six women were hospitalized—three in critical condition. One was paralyzed by a shot to the spine. Another was near dead from wounds to the liver, pancreas, kidney, and heart. A seventh victim—the director the center—was found dead at the scene.[62]

July 25, 2006—Denver, Colorado

A Muslim warehouse worker in Denver, announcing it was "Allah's Choice," shot four of his coworkers and a police officer with a long-barreled handgun. One was killed and the others were critically injured before a SWAT team arrived to take out the shooter, who greeted them with a hail of gunfire. The Muslim's sister later explained to police that her brother was upset because people at the warehouse were making fun of his religion.[63]

March 3, 2006—Chapel Hill, North Carolina

An Iranian Muslim, experiencing sudden-jihad syndrome, pressed the pedal of his SUV to the metal and mowed down nine students on the campus of the University of North Carolina. After striking each victim, he shouted, "Allahu Akbar." The Iranian later explained his actions by writing this note from his jail cell: "The U.S. government is responsible for the deaths and torture of countless followers of Allah, my brothers and sisters. My attack on Americans at UNC-CH March 3, was in retaliation for similar attacks orchestrated by the U.S. government on my fellow followers of Allah in Iraq, Afghanistan, Palestine, Saudi Arabia and other Islamic territories. I did not act out of hatred for America but out of love for Allah instead. I live only to serve Allah by obeying all of his commandments of which I am aware by reading and learning the contents of the Koran."[64]

August 6, 2004—Houston, Texas

A Saudi college student, upon receiving a so-called religious awakening, slashed the throat of his Jewish roommate with a four-inch butterfly knife, nearly decapitating him. After committing the murder, the Saudi visited a mosque to give praise to Allah. No motive for the crime has ever been presented.[65]

September and October 2002—Greater Washington, DC, Area

Muslim snipers killed ten people and critically wounded three more for no apparent reason, save jihad. Previous to this, the so-called Beltway snipers were responsible for additional murders in California, Georgia, Alabama, and the state of Washington. Upon his arrest, John Allen Muhammad, the lead sniper, persisted in making such statements as, "America got what it deserved on 9/11."[66] Lee Boyd Malvo, Muhammad's seventeen-year-old sidekick, provided even more telling evidence of the motive behind the murders. One of his jailhouse drawings depicted the White House in the crosshairs of the scope of a rifle with this caption: "You will weep and moan & MORN [*sic*]. You will bleed to death, little by little. Your life belongs to Allah. He will deliver you to us." To the side of the White House, another caption says, "Sept. 11 we will ensure will look like a picnic to you." A self-portrait of Malvo peering through the scope of a rifle while exclaiming, "Allahu Akbar" accompanies the following attempt at poetry: "Many more will have to suffer/Many more will have to die/Don't ask me why." Other sketches included Malvo and Muhammad together with the words: "We will kill them all. Jihad"; Osama bin Laden with the caption—"Servant of Allah"; Islamic luminaries such as Saddam Hussein and Muammar al-Qadhafi with this ditty: "Our minarets are our bayonets/Our mosques are our baracks [*sic*]/Our believers are our soldiers." Another doodle consisted of an illumination of these words from the Quran (Surah 2: 190): "Fight in the cause of Allah those who fight you and slay them wherever ye catch them."[67]

July 5, 2002—Los Angeles, California

An Egyptian Muslim living in Irvine, California, celebrated his forty-first birthday by going on a one-man jihad in order to gain martyrdom. He headed off to the Los Angeles International Airport, where he proceeded to shoot and kill a twenty-four-year-old ticket agent and a sixty-one-year-old diamond merchant. He critically wounded four more people before being gunned down and killed by security guards. Federal investigators later concluded that the killer had hoped to influence US government policy in favor of the Palestinians and that his attack met the definition of terrorism.[68]

September 11, 2001—New York City; Washington, DC; Shanksville, Pennsylvania

Muslim terrorists conducted coordinated attacks that resulted in 2,993 deaths.[69]

CHAPTER 21

CHRISLAM

On September 20, 2001, President George W. Bush addressed the Joint Session of Congress as follows:

> I want to speak tonight directly to Muslims throughout the world. We respect your faith. It's practiced freely by millions of Americans, and by millions more that America counts as friends. Its teachings are good and peaceful, and those who commit evil in the name of Allah blaspheme the name of Allah. The terrorists are traitors to their own faith, trying, in effect, to hijack Islam itself. The enemy of America is not our many Muslim friends; it is not our many Arab friends. Our enemy is a radical network of terrorists and every government that supports them.[1]

By these words, the chief executive officer of the United States came to serve as an Islamic apologist. Mr. Bush persisted in this role at a joint press conference with British prime minister Tony Blair when he proclaimed that Christians and Muslims worship the same God. "I do say that freedom is the Almighty's gift to every person," he told reporters, "and I condition it by saying that freedom is not America's gift to the world. It's much greater than that, of course. And I believe we worship the same God."[2] Mr. Bush went on to become the first president to mention the Quran in an Inaugural Address (January 20, 2005) and to celebrate Ramadan in the White House (November 19, 2001). He also issued an Islamic postal stamp, "Eid Mubarak" (August 1, 2001) and appointed a Muslim ambassador to the United Nations (Zalmay Khalizad, April 17, 2007).[3]

AN ISLAMIC DEMAND

A precedent had been set by the president for America in the twenty-first century. In 2003, Agha Saeed of the American Muslim Alliance issued a demand that "Judeo-Christian-Islamic" be used "in all venues where we normally talk about Judeo-Christian values, starting with the media, academia, statements by politicians, and comments made in churches, synagogues, and other places."[4] Muslim scholar Mohammed al-Hanooti added, "The Islamic contribution to [American] society is mounting, and we need to recognize this."[5] Several months later, in a nationally televised interview in 2003, Secretary of State Colin Powell described Iraq as "an Islamic country by faith, just as we are Judeo-Christian." Immediately after uttering these words, he corrected himself by adding "we are a country of many faiths now."[6]

STRANGE PRAYERS

Powell's words were reflected by the prominent involvement of imams within the public forum. In January 2008, Mohammed Khan, the imam of the Islamic Center of Des Moines, offered the opening prayer in the Iowa legislature at the request of Iowa state representative Ako Abdul-Samad, a former Iowa school board member with alleged ties to radical Islam. In his four-minute prayer, Khan made a plea for "victory over those who disbelieve" and "protection from the Great Satan" (militant Islam's label for the United States of America). Pastor Steve Smith of the Evangelical Free Church in Albert City took issue with Khan's invocation, explaining, "This is a request in the Iowa Legislature for God to grant the Muslims victory over every non-Muslim; not a request for salvation."[7]

Khan was far from the first imam to bless a gathering of state representatives. In April 2007, Imam Yusuf Kavakci of the Dallas Central Mosque and board member of the Wahhabist Society of

North America, was asked to open the Texas Senate with its first Islamic prayer. Kavakci read from the opening chapter of the Quran: "All praise is for Allah, our lord, the lord of the worlds, the compassionate, the merciful, Master of the day of judgments. Oh, God, Allah, you alone we worship, and you alone we call on for help. Oh, Allah, guide us to the straight path, the path of those whom you have favored, not of those who have earned your wrath or of those who have lost the way." There is only one "straight path" in Islam—the path to the throne of Allah. Robert Spencer, who has been accused of being a leading Islamophobe, argued that Imam Kavakci was praying that the members of the Texas State Senate become Muslims and abandon the faith of their Christian and Jewish forefathers. "Clearly," Spencer said, "this was a prayer that excluded Jews and Christians and was a prayer against them."[8]

During "Muslim Week," Representatives Lois McMahan and Cary Condotta left the floor of the assembly in the state of Washington when Imam Mohamed Joban of the Olympia Islamic Center was called upon to offer the opening prayer. Joban had made statements in support of Muslim chaplain Captain James Yee, who had pled guilty to acts of espionage at Guantanamo Bay. Following pressure from CAIR, the two state legislators apologized to Joban when he reappeared to offer yet another invocation before the assembly two days later. They stated their appreciation of the imam's God-given right for freedom of religious expression.[9]

In February 2007, Husham Al-Husainy, spiritual director of the Karbalaa Islamic Education Center in Dearborn, Michigan, gave the invocation before the Democratic National Committee. Al-Husainy had spoken at pro-Hezbollah rallies in Detroit, where he delivered speeches filled with anti-American and anti-Semitic rhetoric. At the gathering, he intoned, "In the name of God the most merciful, the most compassionate. We thank you, God, to bless us among your creations. We thank you, God, to make us as a great nation. We thank you God, to send us your messages through our father Abraham and Moses and Jesus and Mohammed. Through you, God, we unite. So guide us to the right path. The path of the people you bless, not the path of the people you doom. Help us, God, to liberate and fill this earth with justice and peace and love and equality. And help us to stop the war and violence, and oppression and occupation. Amen."[10] Commenting on the prayer, Robert Spencer wrote:

> In mentioning "Abraham and Moses and Jesus and Mohammed," Al-Husainy no doubt sounded as if he was expansive, broad-minded, and not narrowly sectarian to the assembled Democrats. But in fact, he was almost certainly invoking them in their capacity as Muslim prophets: it is mainstream Islam that all of these were prophets who taught Islam, and that the followers of Moses and Jesus corrupted their teachings to create Judaism and Christianity. The Qur'an says that Abraham was not a Jew or a Christian, but a Muslim (Surah 3: 67), and depicts Jesus denying his own divinity (Surah 5: 116)—and this, of course, is the Imam's frame of reference. So what seems to be a gesture of ecumenical generosity actually amounts to a declaration of religious supremacism and the delegitimization of other religions.
>
> What's more, if a Christian priest or minister had prayed at a DNC meeting that those attending be guided away from the path of those doomed by God, the outcry would have been swift and shrill. Those whom God dooms? Hardly a concept that fits comfortably into today's culture of non-accountability, but evidently it was acceptable to the Democrats when coming from a Muslim, although many of them would almost certainly [have] been among the first to condemn the same sentiment coming from a Christian.[11]

Two months after Al-Husainy delivered his invocation, Speaker of the House Nancy Pelosi submitted to Islamic law by covering her head with a hijad while attending a conference in Syria. First Lady Laura Bush and Secretary of State Condoleezza Rice followed her example. On January 4, 2007, Pelosi stood next to Keith Ellison, who placed his hand on the Quran to become the first Muslim US congressman.[12]

On June 3, 2009, President Barack Obama in an interview with Laura Haim on Canal Plus, a French television station, said that the United States was now "one of the largest Muslim countries in the world."[13]

One year later, Mr. Obama elaborated on this claim at the iftar dinner in the White House, which is now an annual event to commemorate the end of Ramadan. "Today," he said, "our nation is strengthened by millions of Muslim Americans. They excel in every walk of life. Muslim American communities—including mosques in all fifty states—also serve their neighbors. Muslim Americans protect our communities as police officers and firefighters and first responders. Muslim American clerics have spoken out against terror and extremism, reaffirming that Islam teaches that one must save human life, not take it. And Muslim Americans serve with honor in the military."[14]

In keeping with the emergence of Islam as a major factor in American society, Rick Warren, who offered the invocation at the inauguration of President Obama, established an outreach group called "King's Way." The purpose of the group is to heal divisions between evangelical Christians and Muslims by the establishment of common theological principles, including acknowledgement that they worship the same God. The effort caps years of meetings between Warren and Muslims. Warren has broken Ramadan fasts at a Mission Viejo mosque, met Muslim leaders abroad, and addressed eight thousand Muslims at a national convention in Washington, DC.[15]

Other Christians joined in the effort at rapprochement with Muslims. Over seventy-five churches under the rubric "Faith Shared" initiated a series of month-long sermons and Sunday school lessons on the teachings of the Prophet Mohammed to bring a common understanding between Christianity and Islam. Along with readings from the Old and New Testaments by Christian prelates, Islamic clerics were invited to recite surahs from the Quran.[16] The following is a list of the churches that participated in this ecumenical undertaking:[17]

John Stallsmith, the outreach minister at Grace Fellowship in Lilburn, Georgia, justified the participation of his church in Faith Shared by saying: "In 2001, like most Americans, we were pretty awakened to the true Islamic presence in the world and in the United States. Jesus says we should love our neighbors. We can't do that without having a relationship with them." He went on to maintain that a possible

Anchorage First Christian	Anchorage	AK
University Presbyterian Church	Tuscaloosa	AL
Federated Community Church	Flagstaff	AZ
First UMC Phoenix	Phoenix	AZ
All Saints Cathedral	Pasadena	CA
First United Lutheran	San Francisco	CA
Light of Christ Ecumenical Catholic Church	Longmont	CO
Park Hill Congregational	Denver	CO
Union Congregational	Nucla	CO
Temple Micah	Denver	CO
Riverfront Family Church	Hartford	CT
The National Cathedral	Washington	DC
Seekers Church	Washington	DC
North American Old Catholic Church	Washington	DC
National City Christian Church	Washington	DC
New Ark United Church of Christ	Newark	DE
Faith United Church of Christ	Clearwater	FL
Unitarian Universalist Church of Pensacola	Pensacola	FL
United Church of Christ at The Villages	The Villages	FL
Virginia Highland Church	Atlanta	GA
Decatur United Church of Christ	Decatur	GA
The Episcopal Church of St. John the Evangelist	College Park	GA
Cathedral of St. Andrew, the Episcopal Diocese of HI	Honolulu	HI
Collegiate United Methodist Church and Wesley Foundation	Ames	IA
Congregational United Church of Christ	Iowa City	IA
Urbandale UCC Church	Urbandale	IA
Hillview United Methodist	Boise	ID
Boise First UMC, Cathedral of the Rockies	Boise	ID
First United of Oak Park	Chicago	IL
St. Thomas Mission	Chicago	IL
The Chicago Temple First UMC	Chicago	IL
First Presbyterian Church of Fort Wayne	Fort Wayne	IN
Northminster Baptist Church	Monroe	LA
The Unitarian Universalist Society of Amherst	Amherst	MA
Grace Episcopal	Amherst	MA
Church of Our Savior	Arlington	MA
St. Paul's Cathedral	Boston	MA
Old Cambridge Baptist Church	Cambridge	MA
Hadwen Park Congregational Church	Worcester	MA
Veritas United Church of Christ	Hagerstown	MD
Trinity United Methodist	Mountain Grove	MO
St. Mary's Episcopal Church	Ely	MN
First Congregational	Great Falls	MT
Mountain View/Trinity United Methodist Parish	Butte	MT
Unitarian Universalist Ocean County Congregation	Toms River	NJ
Christ Episcopal Church	Toms River	NJ

Zion Methodist Church	Las Vegas	NV
The Sacred Center of New York	New York	NY
Cathedral Church of St. John the Divine	New York	NY
All Souls Bethlehem Church	Brooklyn	NY
Mayflower Church	Oklahoma City	OK
First Congregational United Church of Christ	Corvalis	OR
Spirit of Peace United Church of Christ	Sioux Falls	SD
Baha'i Faith Community Center	Nashville	TN
Saint John's United Methodist Church	Austin	TX
Hope for Peace & Justice Interfaith Peace Chapel	Dallas	TX
Cathedral of Hope	Dallas	TX
Wasatch Presbyterian Church of Salt Lake City	Salt Lake City	UT
Grace Episcopal Church	St. George	UT
United Church of Bellows Falls	Bellow Falls	VT
Cathedral of the Diocese of Vermont	Burlington	VT
Vermont Ecumenical Council & Bible Society	Burlington	VT
Dummerston Congregational Church UCC	Dummerston	VT
Memorial United Church of Christ	Fitchburg	WI
Trinity Episcopal Church	Janesville	WI
First Congregational Church UCC Casper	Casper	WY

union of beliefs can be achieved by the fact that Jesus is mentioned twenty-five times in the Quran. By identifying these supposed parallels, Stallsmith and others believe they are forging a spiritual sword to battle atheism and polytheism and solving a deadly conflict in the West.

King's Way and Faith Shared have been castigated by conservative Christians as manifestations of a religious phenomenon called "Chrislam," an attempted syncretism of the basic beliefs of Christianity and Islam. Tim Forsthoff, senior pastor of Cornerstone Church in Highland, Michigan, said: "We are not brothers with those who reject Christ. We are not part of the family of God with those who deny the death and resurrection of Jesus Christ."[18]

In June 2011, Jack Van Impe, a popular Christian television host, walked away from the Trinity Broadcasting Network (TBN) in the wake of a dispute over naming well-known ministers he claims are mixing Muslim and Christian beliefs. TBN decided to pull the broadcast. Van Impe cried censorship and ended the twenty-three-year relationship. "When I see heretical teaching leading to apostasy, I will speak out," Van Impe said.[19]

EPILOGUE

The future of the country—that was conceived by the pilgrims and Puritans as "the New Zion"—is now bound inextricably to Islam. The faith of the Prophet Mohammed will continue to impact and transform all aspects of American life: social, political, and economic. Save for a cataclysmic event that will shatter demographics, Islam by 2050 will emerge as the nation's dominant religion. Such a statement may seem hyperbolic, save for these findings:

- ✓ The US fertility rate is now below 2.1 children per woman, meaning Americans are no longer giving birth to enough children to keep the population from dwindling.[1] But this statistic does not hold true for the average Muslim American woman who displays a robust fertility rate of 2.8.[2]
- ✓ Muslims continue to pour into the country to occupy positions (vacated by aging Americans) as physicians, engineers, and scientists. Others arrive here to perform tasks that American workers are unwilling to perform in food-processing plants, agricultural facilities, and telecommunications. In addition to the Muslims who come here with employment visas, thousands more arrive with student visas to enroll in colleges throughout the country. Still others arrive with "diversity" visas to enrich America's racial composition. In 1992, nearly fifty thousand Muslims arrived in the United States and received permanent residency status. In 2009, that number soared to 115,000.[3] In truth, no one knows for certain how many Muslim immigrants are presently living in the country. A

Government Accountability Office report released to the press by Homeland Security and Governmental Affairs Committee Chairman Joe Lieberman (I-CT) and ranking member Susan Collins (R-ME) show that half of the 12 million US illegal immigrants have entered the country legally but have overstayed their visas. Many of those who overstay their visas are from Islamic countries. Five of the 9/11 hijackers overstayed their visas, and the Government Accountability Office found that thirty-six of the roughly four hundred people convicted of terrorism-related charges since September 2001 had overstayed their visas.[4] "Identifying individuals who overstay is a crucial component of securing our borders, and it is simply unacceptable that we are still unable to systematically identify people who overstay—some of whom may be terrorists waiting to attack innocent Americans. I am asking Secretary Napolitano to update the Committee on current efforts within the Department to close this dangerous vulnerability," said Lieberman.[5]

✓ In addition to the legal and illegal Muslim immigrants, eighty thousand refugees enter this country under resettlement programs. Nearly seventy-five thousand come from Islamic countries.[6]

✓ As the Christian Church militant is now defunct, America is witnessing the mosque militant. Muslims, unlike mainline denominational Christians, are fervent in their beliefs and eager to spread the faith. Islam, at present, is the most rapidly growing religion in the country, with outreach programs on college campuses, in prisons, and within the military.[7] The Muslim faith offers—particularly to inhabitants of America's inner cities—a place of belonging and a means of self-identification within a society without an autochthonous population.

✓ Islam provides an antithesis to secular America. It offers a return to the country's "traditional values" with a vengeance. The vast majority of US Muslims oppose abortion and same-sex marriage.

They call for a curtailment of women's rights and a return to "law and order" (as mandated by sharia). They are enterprising, hard working, and deeply devoted to their families.

✓ Unlike America's political leaders, Muslims do not recognize the legitimacy of all faiths. Their religion, according to Bernard Lewis, divides the world into two: the House of Islam (*dar al-Islam*), where Muslims rule and the law of Islam prevails, and the House of War (*dar ul-Harb*), comprising the rest of the world. "Between these two," Lewis writes, "there is a morally necessary, legally and religiously obligatory state of war, until the final triumph of Islam over unbelief."[8] For this reason, Muslims are unlikely to relinquish the cherished claims of their tradition before the prevailing zeitgeist.

The belief that America could be transformed into an Islamic state was first expressed by a small group of Muslim missionaries in 1922, who declared to a gathering of disgruntled city blacks in Syracuse, New York, "Our plan is: we are going to conquer America."[9] The audacity of this remark provoked the following commentary in the *Syracuse Sunday Herald*:

> To the millions of American Christians who have so long looked eagerly forward to the time the cross shall be supreme in every land and the people of the whole world shall have become the followers Christ, the plan to win this continent to the path of the "infidel Turk" will seem a thing unbelievable. But there is no doubt about its being pressed with all the fanatical zeal for which the Mohammedans are noted.[10]

Ninety years later, the remarks made by the early Islamic missionaries no longer seem audacious; instead, they seem prophetic. The transformation of America into an Islamic nation, Muslim scholars contend, is a matter of destiny. It is kismet (*quisma*). The words of the country's future have been written—and these words no mortal man may alter or erase.

NOTES

CHAPTER 1. THE SEA OF CHANGE

1. Leo Rosten, ed., *Religions of America: Ferment and Faith in an Age of Crisis* (New York: Simon and Schuster, 1975), p. 17.

2. Ibid., p. 380.

3. Ibid.

4. Ibid, p. 382.

5. Will Herberg, *Protestant, Catholic, Jew* (New York: Doubleday, 1960), p. 40.

6. Ibid., p. 39.

7. Mark Steyn, *America Alone* (Washington, DC: Regnery, 2006), p. 6.

8. Bob Smietana, "Muslims in USA Face Fears, Bias to Build, Expand Mosques," *USA Today*, August 3, 2010.

9. Ibid.; Rachel Zoll, "U.S. Muslim Study Finds Jump in American Mosques," *Miami Herald*, February 29, 2012.

10. Nisba Husain, "Michigan Has Largest U.S. Muslim Population," *Psychiatric News*, American Society of Psychiatrists 40, no. 2 (January 21, 2005), http://psychiatry online.org/newsarticle.aspx?articleid=103508 (accessed September 21, 2012).

11. Susan Headden, "Understanding Islam," *U.S. News & World Report*, April 7, 2008.

12. Paul M. Barrett, *American Islam: The Struggle for the Soul of a Religion* (New York: Faraar, Straus, and Giroux, 2008), pp. 8–9.

13. Kathleen Parker, "Pew Study of U.S. Muslims Isn't 'Largely' Reassuring," *Scranton Times-Tribune*, February 28, 2008.

14. Ihsan Bagby, Paul M. Perl, and Bryan T. Froehle, "The Mosque in America: A National Portrait," Council on American-Islamic Relations, Washington, DC, 2001, http://www.cair.com/Portals/0/pdf/The_Mosque_in_America_A_National_Portrait.pdf (accessed September 21, 2012). The most rigorous estimate was from the Mosque Study Project 2000, which combined seven lists of mosques, eliminated duplicates, and attempted to verify the existence of each place. This generated a final list of 1,209 mosques in 2000. The researchers then drew a sample of 631 and

were successful in obtaining information about 416 of the mosques. They found that 340 adults and children regularly participated in the average mosque and that 1,629 were "associated in any way with the religious life of the mosque." This converts to a national estimate of 1,969,000 mosque-associated Muslims nationally. The study supports the estimate of 6 to 7 million Muslims in the United States by assuming that for every Muslim associated with a mosque, three remain without association.

15. Jim West, "America's Muslim Capitals," *Daily Beast*, August 11, 2010, http://www.thedailybeast.com/articles/2010/08/11the-biggest-muslim-capitals-in-Armerica.html (accessed September 21, 2012).

16. IPP Digital, Bureau of International Information Programs, US Department of State, http://iipdigital.usembassy.gov/st/english/gallery/2011/06/20110629143232esiuol9.273708e-03.html#axzz1S81dW0y7 (accessed September 21, 2012).

17. Rachel Ehrenfeld, "Turning Off the Tap of Terrorist Funding," *Middle East Forum*, September 19, 2003, http://www.meforum.org/staff.php (accessed September 21, 2012).

18. Bagby et al., "The Mosque in America."

19. Adair Lummis, James Nieman, David Roozen, and Scott Thumma, "Fast Facts," Hartford Institute for Religion Research, http://hirr.hartsem.edu/research/fastfacts/fast_facts.html (accessed September 21, 2012).

20. Ray Suarez, *The Old Neighborhood* (New York: Simon and Schuster, 1999), p. 14.

21. Sarah Honig, "A Masjid Grows in Brooklyn," *Jerusalem Post*, July 3, 2008.

22. Sylvain Cypel, "Jews and Muslims Co-Exist Peacefully on the Streets of Brooklyn," *Guardian*, January 18, 2011, http://www.guardian.co.uk/world/2011/jan/18/judaism-islam-new-york-cypel (accessed September 12, 2012).

23. Jessica DuLong, "The Imam of Bedford Stuyvesant," *Saudi Aramco World*, May/June 2005, http://www.saudiaramcoworld.com/issue/200503/the.imam.of.bedford-stuyvesant.htm (accessed September 12, 2012).

24. Ibid.

25. Ibid.

26. Ibid.; Cypel, "Jews and Muslims Co-Exist."

27. Bagby et al., "The Mosque in America."

28. Tom Hayes, "Khat Comes to America, Prompting a Crackdown," Associated Press, April 23, 2000.

29. Ibid.

30. Alyson Zureick, "City, State Do Little to Address Female Genital Cutting," *Gotham Gazette*, March 2009.

31. John L. Esposito and Dalia Mogahed, *Who Speaks for Islam* (New York: Gallup, 2007), p. 68.

32. *The 9/11 Commission Report: Final Report of the National Commission on Terror Attacks upon the United States* (New York: W. W. Norton, 2004), p. 58.

33. Steven Emerson, "Terrorism Financing and US Financial Institutions," testimony before the House Committee on Oversight and Investigations of Financial Services, March 11, 2003.

34. John Miller, "A Decade of Warning: Did Rabbi's 1990 Assassination Mark Birth of Islamic Terror in America?" *20/20,* ABC News, August 16, 2002.

35. Terry Frieden, "FBI: Albanian Mobsters 'New Mafia,'" CNN, August 19, 2004.

CHAPTER 2. MUSLIM AMERICA

1. "Remarks by the President on a New Beginning," press release, White House, June 4, 2009, http://www.whitehouse.gov/the-press-office/remarks-president-cairo-university-6-04-09 (accessed September 12, 2012).

2. Barack Obama, quoted in Mathew Hay Brown, "Obama: Islam Has Always Been Part of America," *Baltimore Sun,* August 11, 2011, http://weblogs.baltimoresun.com/news/faith/2011/08/obama_islam_has_always_been_pa.html (accessed October 5, 2012).

3. George W. Bush, "Second Inaugural Address," January 20, 2005, American Presidency Project, http://www.presidency.ucsb.edu/ws/index.php?pid=58745#axzz1YRp5pdDA (accessed September 12, 2012).

4. Rayford W. Logan, "Estevanico, Negro Discoverer of the Southwest: A Critical Reexamination," *Phylon* 1, no. 4 (1940): 305–14, http://www.answers.com/topic/islam-in-the-united-states#ixzz1XBkYGoqM (accessed September 12, 2012).

5. Amadou-Mahtar M'Bow, cited in M. M. Ali, "Muslims in America," *Washington Report on Middle East Affairs,* May/June 1996.

6. N. Brent Kennedy with Robyn Vaughan Kennedy, *The Melungeons: The Resurrection of a Proud People—An Untold Story of Ethnic Cleansing* (Macon, GA: Mercer University Press, 1997), pp. 118–22.

7. Wayne Winkler, *Walking toward the Sunset: The Melungeons of Appalachia* (Macon, GA: Mercer University Press, 2005), pp. 40–45.

8. Melton J. Gordon, *Islam in North America: A Sourcebook* (New York: Garland, 1992), pp. 26–27.

9. Edward E. Curtis IV, "Five Myths about Mosques in America," *Washington Post,* August 29, 2010, http://www.washingtonpost.com/wp-dyn/content/article/2010/08/26/AR2010082605510.html (accessed September 12, 2012).

10. Thomas Bluett, "Some Memoirs of the Life of JOB, the Son of Solomon,

the High Priest of Boonda in Africa," National Humanities Council, http://national humanitiescenter.org/pds/becomingamer/growth/text5/diallo.pdf (accessed September 12, 2012).

11. Ibid.

12. Michael B. Oren, *Power, Faith, and Fantasy: America in the Middle East, 1776 to the Present* (New York: W. W. Norton, 2007), pp. 17–40.

13. Amir Muhammad, "A History of American Muslims," *Middle East Studies*, November 25, 2009, http://www.middle-east-studies.net/?p=2755 (accessed October 2, 2012).

14. Johari Abdul, "What Does It Mean to Be an American Muslim?" *Guest Voices* (blog), July 1, 2011, http://www.washingtonpost.com/blogs/guest-voices/post/the-fourth-of-july-what-does-it-mean-to-an-american-muslim/2011/07/01/AGr50ptH_blog.html (accessed September 12, 2012).

15. Amy Argetsinger and Roxanne Roberts, "But It's Thomas Jefferson's Koran," *Washington Post*, January 3, 2007.

16. Kevin J. Hayes, "How Thomas Jefferson Read the Qur'an," Council on American-Islamic Relations, http://www.cairchicago.org/doc/thomas_jefferson_quran.pdf (accessed September 12, 2012).

17. Oren, *Power, Faith, and Fantasy*, pp. 26–27.

18. Benjamin Franklin, *The Autobiography of Benjamin Franklin*, chap. 10, http://www.earlyamerica.com/lives/franklin/chapt10/ (accessed October 2, 2012).

19. Sheila Masaji, "Moriscos, Marranos, Columbus, and Islamophobes," *American Muslim*, September 5, 2012, http://theamericanmuslim.org/tam.php/features/articles/moriscos-marranos-and-columbus (accessed October 3, 2012).

20. Jonathan Curiel, "Muslim Roots of the Blues," *San Francisco Chronicle*, August 15, 2004.

21. Amir Muhammad, "Muslims in America: The Early Years—The 1700s," *Muslims in America*, http://muslims2america.blogspot.com/ (accessed October 3, 2012).

22. Ibid.

23. Ibid.

24. Jane I. Smith, *Islam in America* (New York: Columbia University Press, 1999), p. 51.

25. Robert Berg, "Camels West," *Saudi Aramco World*, May/June 2002, http://www.saudiaramcoworld.com/issue/200203/camels.west.htm (accessed September 12, 2012).

26. Edward Curtis IV, *Encyclopedia of Muslim American History* (New York: Infobase Publishing, 2010), p. xxiv.

27. Nicholas Said, *The Autobiography of Nicholas Said* (Memphis: Shotwell and

Company, 1873), p. 70, http://docsouth.unc.edu/neh/said/menu.html (accessed September 12, 2012).

28. Will Herberg, *Protestant, Catholic, Jew* (Garden City, NY: Doubleday, 1960), p. 8.

29. Smith, *Islam in America*, p. 52.

30. Roger Daniels, *Coming to America: A History of Immigration and Ethnicity in American Life*, 2nd ed. (New York: Harper Perennial, 2002), pp. 208–209.

31. Nina Totenberg, "High Court Weighs Legality of Memorial Cross," NPR, October 7, 2009, http://www.npr.org/templates/story/story.php?storyId=113532854 (accessed September 12, 2012).

32. Gordon England, "Remarks by Deputy Secretary Gordon England at the Islamic Prayer Center Dedication," US Department of Defense, June 6, 2006, http://www.defense.gov/Transcripts/Transcript.aspx?TranscriptID=14 (accessed September 12, 2012).

33. Karl Evanzz, *The Messenger: The Rise and Fall of Elijah Muhammad* (New York: Random House, 1999), p. 189.

34. Patrick J. Buchanan, *State of Emergency* (New York: St. Martin's Press, 2006), p. 229.

35. Editorial, *New York Times*, quoted in Otis J. Graham Jr., *Unguarded Gates: A History of America's Immigration Crisis* (Lanham, MD: Rowman and Littlefield, 2004), p. 47.

36. Buchanan, *State of Emergency*, p. 235.

37. Harry Truman, quoted in John F. Kennedy, *A Nation of Immigrants* (New York: Harper and Row, 1958), p. 236.

38. Kennedy, *Nation of Immigrants*, p. 80.

39. Robert Dannin, *Black Pilgrimage to Islam* (New York: Oxford University Press, 2002), p.36.

40. Smith, *Islam in America*, p. 74.

41. Kambiz Ghanea Bassir, *A History of Islam in America* (New York: Cambridge University Press, 2010), pp. 212–13.

42. Dannin, *Black Pilgrimage to Islam*, p. 37.

43. Ibid.

44. Ibid.

45. Nancy Haught, "Shunned by Main-Stream Muslims, Portland's Ahmadi Community Treasures Freedom to Worship Openly," *Oregonian*, July 11, 2010.

CHAPTER 3. THE FIRST AMERICAN MUSLIMS

1. Drew Ali, *The Holy Koran of the Moorish Science Temple*, p. 32, http://hermetic.com/bey/7koran.html (accessed October 4, 2012).

2. Ibid., chap. 46, "The Beginning of Christianity," pp. 2–4.

3. Ibid., chap. 7, "The Friendship of Jesus and Lamass—Jesus Explains the Meaning of Truth," p. 13.

4. Ibid., chap. 16, "Pilate's Final Effort to Release Jesus Fails—He Washes His Hands in Feigned Innocence—Delivers Jesus to the Jews for Execution—the Jewish Soldiers Drive Him to Calvary," pp. 1–3.

5. Sheik Ra Saadi, "Who Is Noble Drew Ali?" Moorish Science Temple of America, http://www.themoorishsciencetempleofamerica.org/about_our_prophet_drew_ali.html (accessed September 12, 2012).

6. Ibid.

7. James Williams, interview with the author, September 30, 1980.

8. Karl Evanzz, *The Messenger: The Rise and Fall of Elijah Muhammad* (New York: Random House, 1999), p. 64.

9. "Prophecies and Hadiths of Prophet Nobel Drew Ali (as transcribed in 1972 from Dr. Rufus German-Bey to Divine Minister N. Pleasant-Bey, Swift Angel no. 1)," http://www.sevensealspublications.com/1600873.html (accessed September 12, 2012).

10. Brigitte Gabriel, *They Must Be Stopped: Why We Must Defeat Radical Islam and How We Can Do It* (New York: St. Martin's Press, 2008), p. 82. Also see Abdullah al-Araby, "Neither Black nor African," *Islam Review*, http://www.islamreview.com/articles/neitherblacknorafrican.shtml (accessed September 12, 2012).

11. Federal Bureau of Investigation, document 32701, Moorish Science Temple.

12. Federal Bureau of Investigation, document 11249, Moorish Science Temple.

13. Ibid.

14. "Prophecies and Hadiths of Prophet Noble Drew Ali."

15. Evanzz, *Messenger*, p. 64.

16. FBI document 32701, Moorish Science Temple.

17. Ibid.

18. Debra Washington Mubashshir, "Forgotten Fruit of the City: Chicago and the Moorish Science Temple of America," *Cross Currents*, Spring 2001.

19. FBI document 11249, Moorish Science Temple.

20. "Birthday of Moorish Leader Is Celebrated," *Chicago Defender*, January 12, 1929.

21. Ibid.

22. "Prophecies and Hadiths of Noble Drew Ali."

23. Ibid.

24. Adrian Morgan, "Nation of Islam—What Is It?" *Family Security Matters*, March 5, 2007, http://www.fsmarchives.org/article.php?id=782248 (accessed September 12, 2012).

25. Noble Drew Ali, "Letter from Prison," *Early Studies in Black Nationalism*, Muslim Historical Society, http://www.oocities.com/Heartland/Woods/4623/moors.htm (accessed September 12, 2012).

26. Ibid.

27. "Birthday of Moorish Leader Is Celebrated."

28. WPA Study of the Moorish Science Temple, *Early Studies in Black Nationalism*, Muslim Historical Society, http://www.oocities.org/heartland/Woods/4623/moors.htm (accessed September 12, 2012).

29. Ibid.

30. Wendy Murray Zoda, "Islam, U.S.A.," *Christianity Today*, April 3, 2000, http://www.christianitytoday.com/ct/2000/april3/1.40.html (accessed September 12, 2012).

CHAPTER 4. THE MYSTERY OF MASTER FARD

1. Karl Evanzz, *The Messenger: The Rise and Fall of Elijah Muhammad* (New York: Random House, 1999), p. 73.

2. Federal Bureau of Investigation, ONI Rating Report 100-9129-63, May 15, 1957.

3. Evanzz, *Messenger*, pp. 405–406.

4. Federal Bureau of Investigation, search slip (ID-160), May 15, 1957.

5. C. Eric Lincoln, *Black Muslims in America* (Boston: Beacon Press, 1961), p. 17.

6. Claude Andrew Clegg III, *An Original Man: The Life and Times of Elijah Muhammad* (New York: St. Martin's Griffin, 1997), p. 21.

7. Anna Bontemps and Jack Conroy, *They Seek a City* (New York: Doubleday, Doran, 1945), p. 180.

8. *Early Studies in Black Nationalism: Cults and Churches in Chicago by the WPA* (Chicago: Muslim Historical Society of Chicago, 1994), p. 34.

9. Adrian Morgan, "Nation of Islam—What Is It?" pt. 1, *Family Security Matters*, February 13, 2007, http://www.familysecuritymatters.org/homeland.php?id

=782248 (accessed September 12, 2012). See also Federal Bureau of Investigation, "The Nation of Islam," n.d., p.18.

10. Clegg, *Original Man*, p. 42.

11. Ibid., p. 45.

12. Ibid., pp. 46–47.

13. Elijah Muhammad, *Message to the Blackman in America* (New York: Secretarius Memps, 1997), pp. 100–22.

14. Malcolm X and Alex Haley, *The Autobiography of Malcolm X* (New York: Grove Press, 1965), pp. 179–81.

15. Erdmann Doane Beynon, "The Voodoo Cult among Negro Migrants," *American Journal of Sociology* 43, no. 6 (May 1938): 898.

16. Ibid.

17. Evanzz, *Messenger*, p. 451.

18. Mattias Gardell, "The Sun of Islam Will Rise in the West: Minister Farrakhan and the Nation of Islam in the Latter Day," in *Muslim Communities in North America*, ed. Yvone Yazbeck Haddad and Jane Idleman Smith (Albany: State University of New York Press, 1994), p. 16.

19. Evanzz, *Messenger*, p. 451. See also *Early Studies in Black Nationalism*, Muslim Historical Society, http://www.oocities.org/heartland/woods/4623/moors.htm (accessed September 12, 2012).

20. Federal Bureau of Investigation, document 25-206-21, "Testimony of Colonel Alexander T. McCone, Fifth Army."

21. "Head of Cult Admits Killing," *Detroit News*, November 21, 1932, http://www.mythicdetroit.org/index.php?n=Main.VoodooMurdersCoverage (accessed August 22, 2012).

22. Evanzz, *Messenger*, p. 85.

23. "Leader of Cult Called Insane," *Detroit News*, November 22, 1932, http://www.mythicdetroit.org/index.php?n=Main.VoodooMurdersCoverage (accessed August 22, 2012).

24. "Voodoo Slayer Admits Plotting Death of Judges," *Detroit Free Press*, November 22, 1932, http://www.mythicdetroit.org/index.php?n=Main.VoodooMurdersCoverage (accessed August 22, 2012). See also Bontemps and Conroy, *They Seek a City*, p. 182.

25. "Raided Temple Bares Grip of Voodoo in City," *Detroit Free Press*, November 23, 1932, http://www.mythicdetroit.org/index.php?n=Main.VoodooMurdersCoverage (accessed August 22, 2012).

26. Federal Bureau of Investigation, document 100-26256-3, August 29, 1957.

27. Ibid.

28. "500 Join March to Ask Voodoo Kings' Freedom," *Detroit Free Press*,

November 25, 1932, http://www.mythicdetroit.org/index.php?n=Main.Voodoo MurdersCoverage (accessed August 22, 2012).

29. Federal Bureau of Investigation, file 00299, August 12, 1974.

30. Evanzz, *Messenger*, pp. 81–82.

31. Clegg, *Original Man*, pp. 37–38.

32. Evanzz, *Messenger*, p. 96.

33. Ibid.

34. Ibid., p. 96.

35. Ibid., p. 35.

36. Eric Pement, "Louis Farrakhan and the Nation of Islam: Part 1," *Cornerstone* 26, no. 111 (1997), http://www.cornerstonemag.com/features/ iss111/islam1.htm (accessed September 12, 2012).

CHAPTER 5. THE RISE OF THE NATION OF ISLAM

1. Claude Andrew Clegg III, *An Original Man: The Life and Times of Elijah Muhammad* (New York: St. Martin's Griffin, 1997), p. 95.

2. Ibid., p. 65.

3. Karl Evanzz, *The Messenger: The Rise and Fall of Elijah Muhammad* (New York: Vintage Books, 2001), p. 96.

4. "Voodoo Cult Revived in City: Negro Children Found in Islam School," *Detroit Free Press*, April 27, 1934.

5. Ibid. Syndicalism represents a doctrine by which radicals seize control of the government by direct means, including violence.

6. "U.S. May Fight Voodoo in City: Syndicalism Charges May Be Brought," *Detroit Free Press*, April 18, 1934.

7. Ibid.

8. Ibid.

9. "Police Hurt Battling Voodoo Band: Cult Backers March on Headquarters to Protest Arrests," *Detroit Free Press*, April 19, 1934.

10. Evanzz, *Messenger*, p. 100.

11. Federal Bureau of Investigation, document 1426, n.d.

12. Satohata Takahashi, quoted in Ernest Allen, "When Japan Was the 'Champion of the Darker Races': Satohata Takahashi and the Flowering of the Black Messianic Nationalism," *Black Scholar* 24, no. 1 (Winter 1994): 23–46.

13. "Cultists Riot in Court, One Dead, 41 Hurt," *Chicago Tribune*, March 6, 1935.

14. "Moors Battle in Court: 40 Hurt," *Chicago Defender*, March 9, 1935.

15. Elijah Poole, quoted in Evanzz, *Messenger*, p. 114.

16. Ibid.

17. Ibid., p. 120.

18. Ibid.

19. Federal Bureau of Investigation, file 351980. See also Erdmann Doane Beynon, "The Voodoo Cult among Negro Migrants," *Journal of Sociology* 43, no. 6 (May 1938): 898.

20. Federal Bureau of Investigation, file on Takahashi, n.d.

21. Evanzz, *Messenger*, p. 123.

22. Clegg, *Original Man*, p. 95.

23. Evanzz, *Messenger*, p. 151.

24. Malcolm X and Alex Haley, *The Autobiography of Malcolm X* (New York: Ballantine Books, 1977), p. 198.

25. Evanzz, *Messenger*, pp. 157–59.

26. Federal Bureau of Investigation, file 105-24822 on Elijah Muhammad, January 28, 1955, microfilm roll 003-0102.

27. X and Haley, *Autobiography of Malcolm X* (1977), p. 203.

CHAPTER 6. MALCOLM X

1. Malcolm X and Alex Haley, *The Autobiography of Malcolm X* (New York: Ballantine Books, 1977), p. 223.

2. Ibid

3. Ibid., p. 222.

4. Federal Bureau of Investigation, file 105-24822 on the Nation of Islam, January 31, 1956, microfilm roll 003-0102.

5. Federal Bureau of Investigation, files on the Nation of Islam, November 19, 1958, and May 17, 1961, microfilm roll 0204-0336. See also FBI Correlation Summary, August 22, 1961, and Supplementary Correlation Summary, September 25, 1963.

6. Malcolm X, quoted in Caesar E. Farrah, *Islam*, 7th ed. (Hauppauge, NY: Barron's, 2003), p. 329.

7. Thurgood Marshall, quoted in Karl Evanzz, *The Messenger: The Rise and Fall of Elijah Muhammad* (New York: Vintage Books, 2001), p. 199.

8. Claude Andrew Clegg III, *An Original Man: The Life and Times of Elijah Muhammad* (New York: St. Martin's Griffin, 1997) p. 139.

9. Federal Bureau of Investigation, files on the Nation of Islam, July 24, 1959, microfilm roll 0337-0472.

10. Clegg, *Original Man*, p. 154.

11. Kambiz Ghanea Bassiri, *A History of Islam in America* (New York: Cambridge University Press, 2010), p. 288. C. E. Lincoln's *The Black Muslims in America* (New York: Beacon Press) was published in May 1961.

12. Clegg, *Original Man*, p. 156.

13. Yusuf Nuruddin, "The Five Percenters: A Teenage Notion of God and Earth," in *Muslim Communities in North America*, ed. Yvonne Yazbeck and Jane Idleman Smith (Albany: State University of New York Press, 1994), p. 109.

14. Ibid.

15. Clegg, *Original Man*, pp. 159–65.

16. Federal Bureau of Investigation, file 100-399321, n.d.

17. Evanzz, *Messenger*, p. 252.

18. X and Haley, *Autobiography of Malcolm X* (1969), p. 305.

19. Ibid., p. 307.

20. Evanzz, *Messenger*, p. 295.

21. Federal Bureau of Investigation, file on Muslim Mosques, Inc. See also Evanzz, *Messenger*, p. 301.

22. X and Haley, *Autobiography of Malcolm X* (1969), p. 347.

23. Federal Bureau of Investigation, "Foreign Travel of Malcolm X," n.d.

24. X and Haley, *Autobiography of Malcolm X* (1969), p. 349.

25. Ibid.

26. Federal Bureau of Investigation Teletype, August 7, 1964.

27. FBI, File on Muslim Mosques, Inc., memo dated March 13, 1965. See also Evanzz, *Messenger*, p. 318.

28. "Minister Who Knew Him Best Rips Malcolm's Treachery, Defection," *Muhammad Speaks*, December 4, 1964.

29. Federal Bureau of Investigation Teletype, February 14, 1965.

30. Federal Bureau of Investigation Teletype, February 21, 1965.

31. Alex Haley, "Epilogue," *The Autobiography of Malcolm X* (New York: Random House, 1969), p. 459.

32. Evanzz, *Messenger*, p. 308.

CHAPTER 7. THE OPENING OF THE FLOODGATES

1. Lyndon B. Johnson, *Public Papers of the Presidents of the United States* (Washington, DC: US Government Printing Office, 1966), pp. 1037–40.

2. Otis Graham, "A Vast Social Experiment: The Immigration Act of 1965," Negative Population Growth Forum, October 2005. See also Stephen T. Wagner,

"The Lingering Death of the National Origins Quota System," PhD diss., Harvard University, 1986, pp. 8–19.

3. Ibid.

4. Ibid.

5. *Congressional Record*, August 25, 1965, pp. 217–83.

6. Ibid, pp. 217–65.

7. Center for Immigration Studies, "Three Decades of Mass Migration: The Legacy of the 1965 Immigration Act," September 1965, http://www.cis.org/articles/1995/back395.html (accessed September 12, 2012).

8. US Senate, Subcommittee on Immigration and Naturalization of the Committee on the Judiciary, Washington, DC, February 10, 1965, pp. 1–3.

9. Ibid., p. 8.

10. Ibid.

11. Ibid.

12. US Senate Report 748, 89th Cong., 1st sess., 1965.

13. Ibid.

14. Malcolm X and Alex Haley, *The Autobiography of Malcolm X* (New York: Random House, 1969), pp. 376–77.

15. Alia Malek, *A Country Called Amreeka: U.S. History Retold through Arab-American Lives* (New York: Free Press, 2009), p. 24.

16. Benny Morris and Ian Black, *Israel's Secret Wars* (New York: Grove Press, 1991), p. 327.

17. Ken Karson, "Palestinian Americans," *Middle East Monitor*, http://www.everyculture.com/multi/Pa-Sp/Palestinian-Americans.html (accessed August 21, 2012). See also "Population Estimates of Americans of Palestinian Ancestry," Arab American Institute, October 17, 2006; Malek, *Country Called Amreeka*, pp. 50–51.

18. Ken Kurson, "Palestinian Americans: An Overview," Countries and Their Cultures, http://www.everyculture.com/multi/Pa-Sp/Palestinian-Americans.html (accessed August 22, 2012).

19. Ibid.

20. "Palestinian Immigration," *Encyclopedia of Immigration*, February 24, 2011, http://immigrationonline.org/230-palestinian-immigration.html (accessed August 22, 2012).

21. Will Herberg, *Protestant, Catholic, Jew* (Garden City, NY: Doubleday, 1960), pp. 7–11.

22. Diana L. Eck, *A New Religious America* (New York: HarperCollins, 2002), p. 262.

23. Steven Emerson, *Jihad Incorporated* (Amherst, NY: Prometheus Books, 2006), pp. 236–63.

24. State of Texas, Holy Land Foundation for Relief and Development, Form 900, Income Report, 2000.

25. *USA v. Holy Land Foundation for Relief and Development et al.*, 04-CR-240, indictment (ND, TX, 2004).

26. "Who Are Hamas?" BBC News, January 4, 2009, http://news.bbc.co.uk/2/hi/1654510.stm (accessed August 22, 2012).

27. "Hamas Fact Sheet," Anti-Defamation League, January 30, 2006, http://www.adl.org/main_israel/hamas_facts.htm (accessed September 12, 2012).

28. Wayne Baker, Sally Howell, Amaney Jamal, Ann Chih Lin, Andrew Shryock, Ron Stockton, and Mark Tessler, "Preliminary Findings from the Detroit Arab American Study," University of Michigan, July 4, 2004.

29. Loukia K. Sarroub, *All American Yemeni Girls: Being Muslim in Public School* (Philadelphia: University of Pennsylvania Press, 2005), pp. 32–38.

30. Geneive Abdo, *Mecca and Main Street: Muslim Life in America after 9/11* (New York: Oxford University Press, 2006), p. 38.

31. Ibid.

CHAPTER 8. BEFORE THE FLOOD

1. Kambiz Ghanea Bassiri, *A History of Islam in America* (New York: Cambridge University Press, 2010), p. 264.

2. Data compiled from *Open Doors: Report on International Educational Exchange: 1948–2004*, CD-ROM, Institute of International Education.

3. Steve Emerson, "Report on the Roots of Violent Islamic Extremism and the Efforts to Counter It," Senate Committee on Homeland Security and Governmental Affairs, July 10, 2008, http://www.investigativeproject.org/documents/testimony/353.pdf (accessed August 22, 2012).

4. Robert Siegel, "Sayyid Qutb's America," *All Things Considered*, NPR, May 6, 2003, http://www.npr.org/templates/story/story.php?storyId=1253796 (accessed August 22, 2012).

5. Ismail al-Faruqi, quoted in Daniel Pipes, "It Matters What Kind of Islam Prevails," *Los Angeles Times*, July 22, 1999.

6. Ismail Raji al-Faruqi, "Islamic Ideals in North America," in *The Muslim Community in North America*, ed. Baha Abu-Laban, Regula B. Qureshi, and Earle H. Waugh (Edmonton: University of Alberta Press, 1983), p. 268.

7. Behrooz Ghamari-Tabrizi, *Loving America and Longing for Home: Isma'il al-Faruqi and the Emergence of the Muslim Diaspora in North America* (Malden, ME: Blackwell, 2004), p. 75.

8. Paul Kramer, "International Students and U.S. Global Policy in the Long

20th Century," *Asia Pacific Journal*, January 18, 2010, http://www.japanfocus.org/-Paul_A_-Kramer/3289 (accessed August 22, 2012).

9. Bassiri, *History of Islam in America*, p. 264.

10. Seyyed Vali Reza Nasr, *Mawdudi and the Making of Islamic Revivalism* (New York: Oxford University Press), p. 83.

11. Sayeed Abdul A'la Maudidi, *Jihad in Islam* (Beirut: Holy Koran Publishing House, 2006), pp. 6–7, http://www.muhammadanism.org/Terrorism/jihah_in_islam/jihad_in_islam.pdf (accessed Aygyst 22, 2012).

12. Ibid., p. 266.

13. "The Message of the M.S.A.," *al-Ittihad*, March 1968.

14. Bassiri, *History of Islam in America*, p. 268.

15. Emerson, "Report on the Roots of Violent Islamic Extremism."

16. Yvonne Yazbeck Haddad, *The Muslims of America* (New York: Oxford University Press, 1991), p. 15. See also Leila Ahmed, *A Quiet Revolution: The Veil's Resurgence from the Middle East to America* (New Haven, CT: Yale University Press, 2012), p. 166.

17. Ibid.; Haddad, *Muslims of America*.

18. Marc Ferris, "Immigrant Muslims in New York City," in *Muslim Communities in North America*, ed. Yvonne Yazbeck Haddad and Jane Idleman Smith (Albany: State University of New York Press, 1994), p. 215.

19. Yusuf Nuruddin, "The Five Percenters: A Teenage Notion of Gods and Earth," in *Muslim Communities in North America*, ed. Yvonne Yazbeck Haddad and Jane Idleman Smith (Albany: State University of New York Press, 1994), p. 129.

20. Robert Dannin, *Black Pilgrimage to Islam* (New York: Oxford University Press, 2002), p. 66. See also B. Ramn, "Focus on Pakistan's Tablighi Jamaat," *Tariq Jamil*, http://www.tariqjamil.org/articles/nonmuslims/index.php?display=pakistans_tablighi _jamaat (accessed August 22, 2012).

21. Statement of Dr. Ibrahim Al-Assaf, as reported by Saudia Online, January 2, 2003, http://www.saudia-online.com/news2003/newsjan03/news2.shtml (accessed August 22, 2012).

22. "Saudi Aid to the Developing World," November 2002, http://www.saudinf.com/main/1102.htm (accessed September 12, 2012). See also Alex Alexiev, "Wahhabism: State Sponsored Extremism Worldwide," testimony before the US Senate Subcommittee on Terrorism, Technology, and Homeland Security, June 26, 2003, http://kyl.senate.gov/legis_center/subdocs/sc062603_alexiev.pdf (accessed September 12, 2012). In this book, Salafism and Wahhabism are used interchangeably.

CHAPTER 9. THE NIGHT OF THE NOI

1. Karl Evanzz, *The Messenger: The Rise and Fall of Elijah Muhammad* (New York: Random House, 1999), pp. 188–89.

2. Malu Halasa, *Elijah Muhammad: Religious Leader* (New York: Chelsea House, 1990), p. 67. See also Claude Andrew Clegg III, *An Original Man: The Life and Times of Elijah Muhammad* (New York: St. Martin's Griffin, 1997), p. 243.

3. Ibid.

4. Prentice Earl Sanders and Bennett Cohen, *The Zebra Murders: A Season of Killing, Racial Madness, and Civil Rights* (New York: Arcade, 2006), p. 1.

5. Ibid., p. 16.

6. Stephanie Salter, "S.F.'s Own Time of Terror," *San Francisco Chronicle,* October 13, 2002.

7. Sanders and Cohen, *Zebra Murders,* pp. 81–83.

8. Ibid., p. 97.

9. Ibid., p. 183.

10. Nicholas Stix, "Lest We Forget: Remembering the Zebra Victims," Men's News, October 20, 2005, http://thezebraproject.blogspot.com/2006/12/lest-we-forget-remembering-zebra.html (accessed October 8, 2012).

11. Ken Raymond, "Black Muslim Killings Gain New Attention," *Oklahoman,* September 7, 2008.

12. Stix, "Lest We Forget."

13. Duffy Jennings, "7 Blacks Arrested in Zebra Killings," *San Francisco Chronicle,*" May 1, 1974.

14. Julia Scheeres, "The Zebra Killers," *Crime Library* (blog), http://www.trutv.com/library/crime/notorious_murders/mass/zebra_murders/15.html (accessed August 23, 2012).

15. Sanders and Cohen, *Zebra Murders,* p. 107.

16. Ibid., p. 215.

17. Ibid., p. 232; Nicholas Stix, "Domestic Terrorism: The Nation of Islam and the Zebra Murders," *Nicholas Stix Uncensored* (blog), October 22, 2006, http://nicholasstixuncensored.blogspot.com/2006_10_01_archive.html (accessed August 22, 2012).

18. Stix, "Lest We Forget"; Stix, "Domestic Terrorism."

19. Ibid.

20. Stix, "Domestic Terrorism."

21. Randy Jurgenson and Robert Cox, *Circle of Six: The True Story of New York's Most Notorious Cop-Killer and the Cop Who Risked Everything to Catch Him* (New York: Disinformation Company, 2006), pp. 6–18.

22. Evanzz, *Messenger*, p. 381.

23. Adrian Morgan, "Nation of Islam—History," pt. 4, *Family Security Matters*, March 9, 2007.

24. Stix, "Domestic Terrorism."

25. C. Gerald Fraser, "Elijah Muhammad Dead; Black Muslim Leader, 77," *New York Times*, February 26, 1975.

26. Mattias Gardell, *In the Name of Elijah Muhammad* (Durham, NC: Duke University Press, 1996), p. 242.

27. Daniel Pipes, "How Elijah Muhammad Won," *Commentary*, June 2000, http://www.danielpipes.org/article/341 (accessed August 22, 2012).

28. Askia Muhammad, "Col. Muammar Qadhafi Speaks to the American People," *Final Call Newspaper*, December 1997, http://worldfriendshiptour.noi.org/qadhafi-press.html (accessed August 22, 2012).

29. Wallace Deen Muhammed, *Mohammad Speaks*, May 23, 1975.

30. Richard Brent Turner, *Islam in the African American Experience*, 2nd ed. (Bloomington: Indiana University Press, 2004), p. 226.

31. Robert Dannin, *Black Pilgrimage to Mecca* (New York: Oxford University Press, 2002), p. 73.

32. Turner, *Islam in the African American Experience*, p. 226.

33. Caesar E. Farah, *Islam*, 7th ed. (Hauppauge, NY: Barron's, 2003), p. 328.

34. Mattias Fardell, "The Sun of Islam Will Rise in the West: Minister Farrakhan and the NOI in the Latter Days," in *Muslim Communities in North America*, ed. Yvonne Yazbeck Haddad and Jane Idleman Smith (Albany: State University of New York Press, 1994), p. 22.

35. Jane I. Smith, *Islam in America* (New York: Columbia University Press, 1999), p. 93.

36. Ibid.

37. Louis Farrakhan, "Who Is God?" Christ Universal Temple, Chicago, IL, February 24, 1991, videotape.

38. Aminah Beverly McCloud, *African American Islam* (New York: Routledge, 1995), p. 79.

CHAPTER 10. DAWAH AND THE DAR

1. Lisa Curtis and Raymond Ibrahim, "Tablighi Jamaat," *The World Almanac of Islamism*, http://almanac.afpc.org/tablighi-jamaat (accessed August 22, 2012).

2. Jenny Taylor, "What Is the Tablighi Jamaat?" *Guardian*, September 8, 2009.

3. News Report, "Tablighi Jamaat: *Azizi in hasbe hal*," http://www.youtube.com/watch?v=c_96QSTce9E (accessed August 22, 2012).

4. Alex Alexiev, "Tablighi Jamaat: Jihad's Stealthy Legion," *Middle East Quarterly* 12, no. 1 (Winter 2005), http://www.meforum.org/686/tablighi-jamaat-jihads-stealthy-legions (accessed August 22, 2012).

5. Nicholas Howenstein, "Islamic Networks: The Case of Tablighi Jamaat," United States Institute for Peace, October 2006.

6. Jane I. Smith, *Islam in America* (New York: Columbia University Press, 1999), p. 161.

7. Ibid.

8. "Tablighi Sets Goal," *Dawn* (Karachi, Pakistan), January 14, 1996. See also Alexiev, "Tablighi Jamaat."

9. News Report, "Adress [*sic*] Jemaah Tabligh in the World," September 13, 2009, http://adressmarkazjemaahtabligh.blogspot.com/ (accessed August 22, 2012). See also M. K. Hermansen, "The Muslims of San Diego," in *Muslim Communities in North America*, ed. Yvonne Yazbeck Hadad and Jane Idleman Smith (Albany: State University of New York Press, 1994), pp. 183–84.

10. Curtis and Ibrahim, "Tablighi Jamaat."

11. Muhaafiz Khan, "The Islamic Party: A History Unknown," Muslim Link, March 1, 2008, http://www.muslimlinkpaper.com/index.php/community-news/community-news/1340-The%20Islamic%20Party-%20A%20History%20Unknown.html (accessed August 22, 2012).

12. Aminah Beverly McCloud, *African American Islam* (New York: Routledge, 1995), p. 21.

13. Steven Emerson, *Jihad Incorporated: A Guide to Militant Islam in the US* (Amherst, NY: Prometheus Books, 2006), p. 290.

14. Ibid. See also US Department of State fact sheet, October 11, 2005.

15. Robert Dannin, *Black Pilgrimage to Islam* (New York: Oxford University Press, 2002), p. 64.

16. Ibid., p. 66.

17. R. M. Mukhtar Curtis, "Urban Muslims: The Formation of the Dar ul-Islam Movement," in *Muslim Communities in North America*, ed. Yvonne Yazbeck Hadad and Jane Idleman Smith (Albany: State University of New York Press, 1994), p. 56.

18. Laura Grossman, "The Dar ul-Islam in the United States," Foundation for the Defense of Democracies, November 20, 2009, http://www.defenddemocracy.org/media-hit/the-darul-islam-movement-in-the-united-states/ (accessed August 22, 2012).

19. Dannin, *Black Pilgrimage to Islam*, p. 67.

20. Sheikh Mahmoud Andrake Ibrahim Al Amreeki, *The Dar Ul Islam Movement: An American Odyssey Revisited* (New York: Strange Land, 2010), p. 56.

21. Patrick Dunleavy, "Jihadist out on Parole," Front Page Magazine, June 8, 2010, http://frontpagemag.com/2010/06/08/jihadist-out-on-parole/ (accessed August 22, 2012).

22. John T. McQuistan, "Four Die in Brooklyn Mosque in Shootout by Two Factions," *New York Times,* February 5, 1974.

23. Robert Dannin, "Island in a Sea of Ignorance: Dimensions of the Prison Mosque," in *Making Muslim Space in North America and Europe,* ed. Barbara Daly Metcalf (Berkeley: University of California Press, 1996), UC Press E-Books Collection, 1982–2004, University of California Press, http://publishing.cdlib.org/ucpressebooks/view?docId=ft2s2004p0&chunk.id=d0e7161&toc.id=d0e7161&brand=ucpress (accessed August 22, 2012).

24. Ibid.

25. Dannin, *Black Pilgrimage to Islam,* p. 172.

26. Dunleavy, "Jihadist out on Parole."

27. Daniel Pipes, *Militant Islam Reaches America* (New York: W. W. Norton, 2003), p. 236.

28. Jamil al-Amin, quoted in Steven Barboza, *American Jihad: Islam after Malcolm X* (New York: Image/Doubleday, 1994), p. 49.

29. Justin Bochman, "Who Is Al-Amin?" Associated Press, May 12, 2000.

30. Beverly McCloud, *African American Islam,* p. 70.

31. Al Amreeki, *Dar Ul Islam Movement,* p. 50.

32. R. M. Mukhtar Curtis, "Urban Muslims: The Formation of the Dar ul-Islam Movement," in *Muslim Communities in North America,* ed. Yvonne Yazbeck Haddad and Jane I. Smith (Albany: State University of New York Press, 1994).

33. Ibid.

34. Ibid., p. 61.

35. Gutbi Mahdi Ahmed, "Muslim Organizations in the United States," *The Muslims of America* (New York: Oxford University Press, 1991), p. 20.

36. Al Amreeki, *Dar Ul Islam Movement,* pp. 53–54.

37. Ibid, pp. 46–48.

38. Sulayman S. Nyang, *Islam in the United States of America* (Chicago: KAZI, 1999), p. 147.

39. Ibid., pp. 144–45.

40. *Al-Jihadul Akbar,* the DAR newsletter, cited in Nyang, *Islam in the United States,* p. 147.

41. Ibid.

42. Zachary Crowley, "Jamaat al-Fuqra Dossier," Center for Policing Terrorism, March 16, 2005, http://www.cpt-mi.org/pdf/JAMAATAL-FUQRA2.pdf (accessed August 22, 2012).

43. Ibid.

44. Anti-Defamation League, "Al Fuqra: Holy Warriors of Terrorism," *Anti-Defamation League*, November 4, 2002, http://www.adl.org/extremism/moa/al-fuqra.pdf (accessed August 22, 2012).

45. George E. Jordan and M. P. McQueen, "Pakistani Sheik Swayed NY Sect," *Newsday*, June 29, 1993.

46. Dannin, *Black Pilgrimage to Islam*, p. 76.

47. Ibid., pp. 75–77.

48. Ibid.

49. Jamil al-Amin, *Revolution by the Book* (Beltsville, MD: Writers' Inc., 1993), p. xvi; Dannin, *Black Pilgrimage to Islam*, p. 77.

50. "Eleven Members of Ummah Charged with Federal Violations," press release, Federal Bureau of Investigation, Detroit Division, October 28, 2009, http://www.fbi.gov/detroit/press-releases/2009/de102809.htm (accessed August 22, 2012).

51. Beila Rabinowitz, "Muhammad and Mrs. Jones—Kenny Gamble's Philadelphia Muslim Enclave," *Pipeline News*, January 1, 2008, http://www.pipelinenews.org/index.cfm?page=gamble01.01.08.htm (accessed August 22, 2012).

52. Daniel Pipes, "Is Kenny Gamble Building a Muslims-Only Enclave in Philadelphia?" *Daniel Pipes Blog*, November 1, 2007, http://www.danielpipes.org/blog/2007/11/is-kenny-gamble-building-a-muslim-only.html (accessed August 22, 2012).

53. "Ex Black Panther Convicted of Murder," CNN, March 9, 2002, http://edition.cnn.com/2002/LAW/03/09/al.amin.verdict/index.html (accessed August 22, 2012).

54. Frank J. Gaffney, "The Enemy Within," Front Page Magazine, August 19, 2005, http://archive.frontpagemag.com/readArticle.aspx?ARTID=7541 (accessed August 22, 2012).

55. Ibid.

56. Safraz Mohammed, "Fatwa about Tablighi Jamaat," Tabligh and Ahbab Jamaat Site, February 6, 2012, http://en.aljawlah.com/noname/49-fatwa.html (accessed August 22, 2012).

57. Steve Denny, quoted in Alexiev, "Tablighi Jamaat."

CHAPTER 11. WELCOME TO ISLAMBERG

1. Robert Dannin, *Black Pilgrimage to Islam* (New York: Oxford University Press, 2002), pp. 75–77.

2. Robert Young Pelton, *The World's Most Dangerous Places*, 6th ed. (New York: HarperCollins, 2003), pp. 327–28.

3. The author of this work paid numerous visits to Islamberg and other Jamaat ul-Fuqra compounds throughout the country. He reported his findings to the FBI and other law enforcement agencies.

4. Paul L. Williams, "Springtime in Islamberg," *Canada Free Press*, May 11, 2007.

5. Ibid.

6. Gordon Gregory and Donna Williams, "Jamaat ul-Fuqra," Special Research Report, Regional Organized Crime Information Center, 2006.

7. Ibid.

8. "Afghanistan Update," *Daily Telegraph* (London), August 5, 1983; *Los Angeles Times*, August 5, 1983.

9. Ibid.

10. ICM, "JMT UL-Fuqra: Terror Group of Pakistan," Institute of Contact Management, 2001, http://www.satp.prg/satorgtp/pakistan/terroristoutfits/jamaatul-fuqra.htm (accessed August 23, 2012).

11. Mira L. Boland, "Sheikh Gilani's American Disciples," *Weekly Standard*, March 18, 2002.

12. ROIC Publications Unit, "Jamaat ul-Fuqra: Gilani's Followers Conducting Paramilitary Training in U.S.," Regional Organized Crime Information Center, 2006, http://info.publicintelligence.net/ROCICjamaatulfuqra.pdf (accessed November 8, 2012).

13. Boland, "Sheikh Gilani's American Disciples." See also "Jamaat Ul-Fuqra: Gilani's Followers Conducting Paramilitary Training in U.S.," Regional Organized Crime Information Center, 2006.

14. Zachary Crowley, "Jamaat al-Fuqra Dossier," Center for Policing Terrorism, March 16, 2005, http://www.terroracts.com/index.php?option=com_phocadownload&view=category&id=2:terrorist-group-information&download=10:jamaat-al-fuqra-dossier&Itemid=58 (accessed August 23, 2012).

15. Colorado Attorney General, "Information Regarding Colorado's Investigation and Prosecution of Members of Jamaat Ul-Fuqra," Colorado Department of Law, 2008, http://www.investigativeproject.org/documents/case_docs/1260.pdf (accessed August 23, 2012).

16. Anti-Defamation League, "Al Fuqra: Holy Warriors of Terrorism," Anti-Defamation League Newsletter, November 4, 2002.

17. Boland, "Sheikh Gilani's American Disciples."

18. Crowley, "Jamaat al-Fuqra Dossier."

19. Ibid.

20. Boland, "Sheikh Gilani's American Disciples."

21. Sean Wibby and Brandon Bailey, "The Mysterious Saga of Sister Khadijah," *Mercury News*, February 11, 2007.

22. Crowley, "Jamaat al-Fuqra Dossier."

23. Patrick Briley, "Islamic Terror Network Protected by US Gov't Agencies," NewsWithViews, July 29, 2006, http://www.newswithviews.com/Briley/Patrick28.htm (accessed August 23, 2012).

24. Ibid.

25. Richard Reid, quoted in Terence Neilan, "Shoe Bomber Admits He Tried to Blow-Up Trans-Atlantic Jet," *New York Times*, October 4, 2002.

26. Farah Stockman, "Bomb Probe Eyes Pakistan Links," *Boston Globe*, January 6, 2002.

27. Sultan Mubarik Ali Gilani, *Pillar of Lies* (Islamberg, NY: Muslims of the Americas, n.d.), chap. 7, http://www.iqou-moa.org/sheikh_jilani/pillar_of_lies1.htm (accessed August 23, 2012).

28. "Sheik Gilani: CBS' Man in Pakistan Tracks Him Down," *60 Minutes*, CBS News, March 13, 2002.

29. Ibid.

30. Ibid.

31. James Langton, "U.S. Sniper Linked to Terror Cult," *Weekly Standard*, October 14, 2003.

CHAPTER 12. THE PAKISTANI'S VISION

1. Adil Najam, *Portrait of a Giving Community: Philanthropy by the Pakistani-American Diaspora* (Cambridge, MA: Global Equity Initative, Harvard University, 2006), pp. 36–38.

2. Marc Ferris, "Immigrant Muslims in New York City," in *Muslim Communities in North America*, ed. Yvonne Yazbeck Haddad and Jane Idleman Smith (Albany: State University of New York Press, 1994), p. 217

3. Ibid., p. 221.

4. Ibid., p. 226.

5. Ibid., p. 222.

6. Carrie Loewenthal Massey, "American Pakistan Foundation Ready to Engage Pakistani Diaspora," press release, Embassy of the United States, Islamabad, Pakistan, 2010, http://islamabad.usembassy.gov/pr-10061601.htm (accessed August 23, 2012).

7. Carol L. Stone, "Estimate of Muslims Living in America," in *The Muslims of America*, ed. Yvonne Yazbeck Haddad (New York: Oxford University Press, 1991), p. 32.

8. Ferris, "Immigrant Muslims," p. 226.

9. Chris Heffelfinger, *Radical Islam in America: Salafism's Journey from Arabia to the West* (Washington, DC: Potomac Books, 2011), p. 44.

10. Neil MacFarquhar, "Pakistanis Find U.S. an Easier Fit Than Britain," *New York Times,* August 21, 2006.

11. Leila Ahmed, *A Quiet Revolution: The Veil's Resurgence, from the Middle East to America* (New Haven, CT: Yale University Press, 2012), p. 158.

12. MacFaquhar, "Pakistanis Find U.S. an Easier Fit."

13. Karen Leonard, "South Asian Leadership of American Muslims," in *Muslims in the West,* ed. Yvonne Yazbeck Haddad (New York: Oxford University Press, 2002), p. 235.

14. Ibid.

15. Association of Physicians of Pakistani Descent of North America, APPNA Facebook page, http://www.facebook.com/pages/APPNA/305949531091?sk=info (accessed October 18, 2012).

16. Omar Sacirbey, "Muslims Launch Campaign to 'Understand' Shariah," *USA Today,* March 3, 2012, http://www.usatoday.com/news/religion/story/2012-03-02/shariah-campaign/53338008/1 (accessed August 23, 2012).

17. Akbar Ahmed, *Journey into America: The Challenge of Islam* (Washington, DC: Brookings Institution Press, 2010), pp. 272–73.

18. Shamim A. Siddiqi, *Dawah in the Americas* (New York: Forum of Islamic Work, 1993), p. 10.

19. Ibid., p. 25.

20. Shamim A. Siddiqi, *Methodology of Dawah Ilallah in American Perspective* (New York: Forum of Islamic Work, 1989), p. 45.

21. Ibid. See also Daniel Pipes, *Militant Islam Reaches America* (New York: W. W. Norton, 2003), pp. 113–15.

22. Saddiqi, *Methodology of Dawah,* pp. 28–90. See also Pipes, *Militant Islam Reaches America,* pp. 117–20.

23. Jane El Horr and Sana Saeed, "Campus Radicals: A New Muslim Student Group Tries to Rouse the Moderates," *Wall Street Journal,* June 29, 2008.

24. Hasan al-Banna, quoted in Brynjar Lia, *The Society of the Muslim Brothers in Egypt* (Ithaca, NY: Ithaca Press, 1998), p. 79.

25. Zeyno Baran, "The Muslim Brotherhood's US Network," Hudson Institute, February 27, 2008, http://www.futureofmiuslimworld.com/research/pubID.81/pub_detail.asp# (accessed August 23, 2012).

26. "Profile: Egypt's Muslim Brotherhood," BBC News, June 26, 2012, http://www.bbc.co.uk/news/world-middle-east-12313405 (accessed November 8, 2012).

27. Robert Hallett, *Africa since 1875* (Ann Arbor: University of Michigan Press, 1974), p. 138.

28. Baran, "Muslim Brotherhood's US Network."

29. Douglas Farah and Ron Sandee, "The Ikhwan in North America: A Short History," NEFA Foundation, 2008, http://www.nefafoundation.org/miscellaneous/nefafl0807.pdf (accessed August 23, 2012).

30. Ibid.

31. Mohamed Akram Adlouni, "An Explanatory Memorandum on the General Strategic Goal for the Group in North America," May 22, 1991, Government Exhibit 003-0085, *U.S. v. the Holy Land Foundation*, 2007.

32. Ibid. See also Sylvan Besson, "Revelations," *Le Temps* (Geneva), October 6, 2005.

33. Akram Adlouni, "An Explanatory Memorandum."

34. Ibid.

35. Ibid.

36. Ibid.

37. Ibid.

CHAPTER 13. SHIA SUNRISE

1. Edward E. Curtis IV, *Muslims in America: A Short History* (New York: Oxford University Press, 2009), pp. 84–85.

2. David Card and Thomas Lemieux, "Going to College to Avoid the Draft: The Unintended Legacy of the Vietnam War," *American Economic Review* 91, no. 2 (May 2001), pp. 97–102.

3. The author of this book was a key witness before a federal grand jury in Philadelphia Federal Court in May 1978 concerning the sale of student visas to Iranian students.

4. Akbar E. Torbot, "The Brain Drain from Iran to the United States," *Middle East Journal* (Spring 2002), http://www.jstor.org/discover/10.2307/4329755?uid=3739256&uid=2&uid=4&sid=21101169513057 (accessed August 23, 2012).

5. Abdulaziz A. Sachedina, "A Minority within a Minority: The Case of the Shi'a in North America," in *Muslim Communities in North America*, ed. by Yvonne Yazbeck Hahhad and Jane Idleman Smith (Albany: State University of New York Press, 1994), p. 6.

6. Shirin Hakimzadeh and David Dixon, "Spotlight on the Iranian Foreign Born," Migration Policy Institute, June 2006, http://www.migrationinformation.org/USfocus/display.cfm?ID=404 (accessed August 23, 2012).

7. Phyllis McIntosh, "Iranian Americans Reported among Highly Educated

in U.S.," Payvand Iran News, January 26, 2004, http://www.payvand.com/news/04/jan/1191.html (accessed October 10, 2012).

8. "SBA Report: Iranian-Americans with One of Highest Rates of Immigrant-Owned Businesses," Payvand Iran News, November 18, 2008, http://www.payvand.com/news/08/nov/1171.html (accessed August 23, 2012).

9. Sachedina, "Minority within a Minority," p. 5.

10. Liyakat Takim, "Multiple Identities in a Pluralistic World: Shiism in America," in *Muslims in the West: From Sojourners to Citizens*, ed. Yvonne Y. Haddad (New York: Oxford University Press, 2002), p. 221.

11. Jeff Stein, "FBI Hopes to Follow Falafel Trail to Iranian Terrorists," Investigative Project on Terrorism, November 6, 2007, http://www.investigativeproject.org/537/fbi-hoped-to-follow-falafel-trail-to-iranian-terrorists-here (accessed August 23, 2012).

12. M. K. Hermansen, "The Muslims of San Diego," in *Muslim Communities in North America*, ed. Yvonne Yazbeck Haddad and Jane Idleman Smith (Albany: State University of New York Press, 1994), p. 188.

13. Jeff Jacoby, "Hezbollah Is Our Enemy, Too," *Boston Globe*, July 30, 2006, http://www.boston.com/news/world/middleeast/articles/2006/07/30/hezbollah_is_our_enemy_too/ (accessed August 23, 2012).

14. Stein, "FBI Hopes to Follow Falafel Trail."

15. Shahryar Rouhani, quoted in Kambiz Ghanea Bassiri, *A History of Islam in America* (New York: Cambridge University Press, 2010), p. 322.

16. Ibid.

17. Yvonne Yazbeck Haddad, quoted in Bassiri, *History of Islam in America*, pp. 322–23.

18. Ibid.

19. "Festival of Ashura" (slideshow), *New York Daily News*, January 20, 2008, http://www.nydailynews.com/news/festival-ashura-gallery-1.6958 (accessed October 10, 2012).

20. Linda S. Walbridge, "The Shi'a Mosques and Their Congregations in Dearborn," in *Muslim Communities in North America*, ed. Yvonne Yazbeck Haddad and Jane Idleman Smith (Albany: State University of New York Press, 1994), p. 248.

21. Alia Malek, *A Country Called Amreeka: U.S. History Retold through Arab-American Lives* (New York: Free Press, 2009), pp. 101, 124.

22. "Demographics," Arab American Institute, http://www.aaiusa.org/pages/demographics (accessed August 23, 2012).

23. Kirk Semple, "Iraqi Immigrants Face Lonely Struggle in U.S." *New York Times*, August 12, 2003.

24. Margaret Talbot, "Baghdad on the Plains," *New Republic*, August 11, 1997.

25. Don Terry, "Cultural Tradition and Law Collide in Middle America," *New York Times*, September 24, 1997.

26. Kathleen M. Moore, "Representation of Islam in the Language of Law: Some Recent U.S. Cases," in *Muslims in the West: From Sojourners to Citizens*, ed. Yvonne Y. Haddad (New York: Oxford University Press, 2002), pp. 197–98.

27. Intelligence Strategy Report (Confidential), Office of the Commissioner, New York Police Department, Intelligence Division, Intelligence Analysis Unit, May 15, 2006, http://privacysos.org/sites/all/files/NYPD_racist.pdf (accessed August 23, 2012).

28. Adam Goldman, Chris Hawley, Eileen Sullivan, and Matt Apuzzo, "NYPD Document: Collect Intelligence on Mosques," Associated Press, February 2, 2012.

29. David Gloven, "Alavi Foundation Is Iran Front, U.S. Says in Lawsuit," *Bloomberg News*, December 30, 2004, http://www.bloomberg.com/apps/news?pid=newsarchive&sid=aA6SZIk_JW04 (accessed August 23, 2012).

30. Kenneth R. Timmerman, "Islamic Iran's American Base," *American Spectator*, December 1995, http://www.iran.org/news/AS_9512.html (accessed August 23, 2012).

31. Adam Goldman, "Alavi Foundation: Feds Move to Seize Four Mosques, Tower Linked from Organization to Iran," *Huffington Post*, November 12, 2009, http://www.huffingtonpost.com/2009/11/12/feds-move-to-seize-4-mosq_0_n_356080.html (accessed Sugust 23, 2012).

32. Timmerman, "Islamic Iran's American Base."

33. Ibrahim Hooper, quoted in "U.S. Alleges Company Laundered Money for Iran," CNN, November 13, 2009, http://edition.cnn.com/2009/US/11/12/mosque.seized/ (accessed August 23, 2012).

34. "Grant Programs—Islamic Organizations," Alavi Foundation, http://www.alavifoundation.org/programs/islamicorganizations.html (accessed August 23, 2012).

35. Harry Mount, "Islam's US Faithful Are Happy to Embrace the American Dream," *Daily Telegraph*, July 23, 2005.

36. "About Us," Muslim Congress, http://www.muslimcongress.org/content mc/organization/about-us.aspx (accessed August 23, 2012).

37. Rachel Zoll, "American Shi'as Struggle with Their Future," Associated Press, July 23, 2009.

38. Ibid.

39. Takim, "Multiple Identities in a Pluralistic World."

CHAPTER 14. RESETTLING SOMALIS

1. Annabel Lee Hoag, "Timeline: Somalia, 1991–2008," *Atlantic*, February 2008, http://www.theatlantic.com/magazine/archive/2008/12/timeline-somalia-1991-2008/7190/ (accessed August 23, 2012).

2. Erin Patrick, "The U.S. Refugee Resettlement Program," Migration Policy Institute, http://www.migrationinformation.org/feature/display.cfm?ID=229 (accessed August 23, 2012).

3. Abdulkadir Aden, "Letter to Business Owners," Somali-American Chamber of Commerce, http://www.soamcc.org/ (accessed October 20, 2012).

4. "Somali American Community Association Vision, Mission, and Values," Somali American Community Association, http://www.sacausa.org/about.html (accessed August 23, 2012).

5. David Kirby, "Minneapolis and the Somali Autism Riddle," *Huffington Post*, November 11, 2008, http://www.huffingtonpost.com/david-kirby/minneapolis-and-the-somal_b_143967.html (accessed August 23, 2012).

6. Andrea Elliott, "A Call to Jihad, Answered in America," *New York Times*, July 11, 2009.

7. Robert Young Pelton, *The World's Most Dangerous Places*, 4th ed. (New York: HarperResource, 2000), p. 835.

8. Elliott, "Call to Jihad."

9. Ibid.

10. Alyson Zureick, "City, State Do Little to Address Female Genital Cutting," *Gotham Gazette*, March 24, 2009, http://www.gothamgazette.com/index.php/city/archives/175-city-state-do-little-to-address-female-genital-cutting (accessed October 17, 2012).

11. Harvey Kushner with Bart Davis, *Holy War on the Home Front* (New York: Sentinel, 2004), p. 76.

12. Ibid., p. 78.

13. Ibid., p. 79

14. Sean Gardiner, "That Darned Khat," *Village Voice*, November 14, 2006.

15. Ibid.

16. "InfoFacts: Khat," National Institute on Drug Abuse, http://www.drugabuse.gov/publications/infofacts/khat (accessed August 23, 2012).

17. Amy Forliti, "Indictment: Somali Gangs Trafficked Girls for Sex," Associated Press, November 8, 2010.

18. Susan Sharon, "Ten Years after Somalis Began Arriving, Lewiston Looks Back," Maine Public Broadcasting Network, January 29, 2010.

19. Brian Mosely, "Somali Refugees Find Haven in Shelbyville," *Shelbyville Times*

Gazette, December 22, 2007, http://www.t-g.com/story/1299489.html (accessed August 23, 2012).

20. Brian Mosely, "Tyson Defends Hiring Practices, Works with Refugees," *Shelbyville Times Gazette*, March 28, 2008, http://www.t-g.com/story/1321194.html (accessed August 23, 2012).

21. Brian Mosely, "Tyson Drops Labor Day Holiday for Eid al-Fitr," *Shelbyville Times Gazette*, August 1, 2008, http://www.t-g.com/story/1449487.html (accessed August 23, 2012).

22. Erick Stakelbeck, "Somali Muslims Changing Small Town," CBN, May 19, 2009, http://www.cbn.com/cbnnews/566637.aspx?option=print (accessed August 23, 2012).

23. Jerry Gordon, "Somalis, Shelbyville, and Severe Culture Shock: An Interview with Brian Mosely," *New English Review*, February 2008, http://www.newenglishreview.org/Jerry_Gordon/Somalis,_Shelbyville_and_Severe_Culture_Shock/ (accessed August 23, 2012).

24. Ibid.

25. Ibid.

26. Roger D. McGrath, "The Great Somali Welfare Hunt," *American Conservative*, November 18, 2002.

27. Ibid.

28. Ibid.

29. Laurier Raymond, quoted in McGrath, "Great Somali Welfare Hunt."

30. David Paulin, "Somali Immigrants Remake Minneapolis," *American Thinker*, April 4, 2009.

31. Elizabeth Dunbar, "Survey: Nearly 1 in 3 US Somalis Live in Minnesota," Minnesota Public Radio (MPR), December 14, 2012, http://minnesota.publicradio.org/display/web/2010/12/14/american-community-survey-initial-findings/ (accessed August 23, 2012).

32. Ibid.

33. Issa Mansaray, "Renovating America's 'Little Mogadishu,'" *Africa Paper*, June 19, 2011, http://theafricapaper.com/2011/06/19/renovating-americas-little-mogadishu/ (accessed August 23, 2012).

34. Joan Neuhaus Schaan and Jessica Phillips, "Analyzing the Islamic Extremist Phenomenon in the United States: A Study of Recent Activity," James A. Baker III Institute for Public Policy, Rice University, http://bakerinstitute.org/publications/SEC-pub-USIslamicExtremist110411.pdf (accessed August 23, 2012).

35. "FBI Investigates Somalia in Minneapolis," MSNBC, March 10, 2009, http://www.msnbc.msn.com/id/29620604/ns/us_news-security/t/fbi-investigates-somalis-minneapolis/ (accessed August 23, 2012).

36. Jason Staziuso, Amy Forliti, and Julie Watson, "Al Shabbab's American Recruits in Somalia," *Huffington Post*, January 14, 2012, http://www.huffingtonpost.com/2012/01/14/americans-al-shabaab_n_1206279.html (accessed August 23, 2012).

37. "Al Shabaab's American Recruits," Anti-Defamation League, February 2012, http://www.adl.org/NR/exeres/D0E7DF5A-46A1-47F9-8252-784E6AFBB52C,DB7611A2-02CD-43AF-8147-649E26813571,frameless.htm (accessed August 23, 2012).

38. Ibid.

CHAPTER 15. THE MUSLIM MAFIA

1. Dennis L. Nagi, *The Albanian-American Odyssey: A Pilot Study of the Albanian Community of Boston, Massachusetts* (New York: AMS Press, 1989), p. 5.

2. Frances Trix, "Bektashi Tekke," in *Muslim Communities in North America*, ed. Yvonne Yazbeck Haddad and Jane Idleman Smith (Albany: State University of New York Press, 1994), p. 368.

3. Edward E. Curtis IV, *Muslims in America: A Short History* (New York, Oxford University Press, 2009), p. 56.

4. Ibid.

5. Audrey Singer and Jill A. Wilson, "Refugee Resettlement in Metropolitan America," Brookings Institution, March 2007.

6. Deborah Feyerick, "Fort Dix Speeds Up Relocation of Kosovo Refugees," CNN, June 6, 1999, http://articles.cnn.com/1999-06-06/US/9906_06_fort.dix_1_refugee-status-move-refugees-kay-bellor?_S-PM:US (accessed November 8, 2012).

7. Linda D. Kozaryn, "Today's Refugees Recall America's Past," Armed Forces Press Service, June 15, 1999.

8. Nadege Ragaru and Amilda Dymi, "The Albanian-American Community in the United States: A Diaspora Coming to Visibility," *Canadian Review of Studies in Nationalism* 31, no. 1–2 (2004), http://hal.archives-ouvertes.fr/docs/00/14/75/88/PDF/The_Albanian-American_Community_in_the_United_States.pdf (accessed August 23, 2012).

9. Jane Jurgen, "Albanian Americans," Countries and Their Cultures, http://www.everyculture.com/multi/A-Br/Albanian-Americans.html (accessed August 23, 2012).

10. Akbar Ahmed, *Journey into America: The Challenge of Islam* (Washington, DC: Brookings Institution Press, 2010), p. 280.

11. Kathleen M. Moore, "Representation of Islam in the Language of Law: Some Recent U.S. Cases," in *Muslims in the West: From Sojourners to Citizens*, ed. Yvonne Yazbeck Haddad (New York: Oxford University Press, 2002), p. 198.

12. Ibid.

13. Don Terry, "Cultural Tradition and Law Collide in Middle America," *New York Times*, December 2, 1996.

14. Ibid.

15. Ragaru and Dymi, "Albanian-American Community in the United States."

16. John Pappalardo, "War Torn: Dallas' Ethnic Albanians Grapple with Twin Dreams of American Assimilation and an Expanded Homeland in the Balkans," *Dallas Observer*, April 5, 2000, http://www.dallasobserver.com/content/printVersion/277920/ (accessed August 23, 2012).

17. Ibid.

18. Ahmed, *Journey into America*, p. 280.

19. Terry Frieden, "FBI: Albanian Mobsters 'New Mafia,'" CNN, August 19, 2004.

20. Ibid.

21. Jerry Capeci, "Zef's Got Staying Power Too," *Gangland*, September 4, 2003, http://www.ganglandnews.com/column346.htm#zef (accessed August 23, 2012).

22. Mike Brunker, "Alleged Mobsters Guilty in Vast Net, Phone Fraud," MSNBC, February 15, 2005.

23. Gus Xhudo, "Men of Purpose: The Growth of Albanian Criminal Activity," Ridgeway Center for International Security Studies, University of Pittsburgh, Spring 1996.

24. M. Bozinovich, "The New Islamic Mafia," *Serbianna*, February 21, 2005, http://www.serbianna.com/columns/mb/028.shtml (accessed August 23, 2012).

25. Anthony M. DeStefano, "The Balkan Connection," *Wall Street Journal*, September 9, 1985.

26. Ibid.

27. Kareem Fahim, "Beating Them at Their Own Game," *New York Times*, January 3, 2006.

28. Ibid.

29. Anemona Hartocollis, "Albanian Gang Portrayed as Aspiring Mafiosi," *New York Times*, December 20, 2005.

30. "Four Leaders of Violent Albanian Racketeering Enterprise Sentenced to 27 Years in Prison," press release, US Attorney's Office, Southern District of New York, June 16, 2006.

31. "Dozens of Albanians Charged in New York Case Related to Violent Drug Ring," CBS News/Associated Press, July 13, 2011, http://newyork.cbslocal.com/2011/07/13/dozens-of-albanians-charged-in-ny-case-related-to-violent-drug-ring/ (accessed August 23, 2012); "37 Alleged Members and Associates of an International Ethnic Albanian Crime Syndicate Arrested," press release, US

Department of Justice, Eastern District of New York, July 13, 2011, http://www.justice.gov/usao/nye/pr/2011/2011jul13.html (accessed August 23, 2012).

32. Bozinovich, "New Islamic Mafia."

33. Dusan Janic, quoted in ibid.

34. Agim Gashi, quoted in Roberto Ruscica, "The Albanian Mafia: This Is How It Helps the Kosovo Government," *Corriere della Sera* (Milan), October 17, 1998.

35. Wayne Parry, "6 Charged in Plot to Attack Army Post," *Washington Post*, May 8, 2007.

36. Anthony Faiola and Dale Russakoff, "The Terrorists Next Door," *Washington Post*, May 10, 2007.

37. Ahmed, *Journey into America*, p. 281.

CHAPTER 16. THE TURKS AND THE NEW ISLAMIC ORDER

1. Barbara Bilge, "Old Turkish Community of Detroit," in *Muslim Communities in North America*, ed. Yvonne Yazbeck Haddad and Jane Idleman Smith (Albany: State University of New York Press, 1994), p. 386.

2. Kemal Karpat, "The Turks in America," *Les Annales de l'Autre Islam* 3 (1995): 231–52.

3. Birol Akgun, "The Turkish Diaspora and Its Role in Promoting Turkish-American Relations," *Turkish Yearbook* 31 (2000), http://dergiler.ankara.edu.tr/dergiler/44/671/8546.pdf (accessed August 23, 2012).

4. "The Forgotten Holocaust: The Armenian Massacre That Inspired Hitler," *Daily Mail* (UK), October 11, 2007, http://www.dailymail.co.uk/news/article-479143/The-forgotten-Holocaust-The-Armenian-massacre-inspired-Hitler.html (accessed August 23, 2012).

5. Bilge, "Old Turkish Community of Detroit," p. 385.

6. Ibid., p. 386.

7. Bernard J. Rothwell et al., *Report of the Commission on Immigration on the Problem of Immigration in Massachusetts* (Boston: Wright and Potter Printing, 1914), pp. 66–67.

8. Bilge, "Old Turkish Community of Detroit," p. 391.

9. Karpat, "Turks in America."

10. Ibid.

11. Bilge, "Old Turkish Community of Detroit," p. 391.

12. Akgun, "Turkish Diaspora."

13. Donald Altschiller, "Turkish Americans," Countries and Their Cultures, http://

www.everyculture.com/multi/Sr-Z/Turkish-Americans.html (accessed August 23, 2012). See also Faruk Sen, "Being a Turk in California," *Turks in America the Movie Pre Production Research Blog*, January 3, 2009, http://turksinamericathemovie.blogspot.com/2009/01being-turk-in-california.html (accessed August 23, 2012).

14. Ryan Maye Handy, "New Mosque Welcomed in Brighton Beach," *Brooklyn Daily Eagle*, October 14, 2010.

15. Karpat, "Turks in America."

16. Ibid.

17. Paul Thomasch, "Irene Another Blow to Struggling New Jersey City," Reuters, September 1, 2011.

18. Guy Rodgers, "Fethullah Gulen: Infiltrating the U.S. through Our Charter Schools," Act for America, http://www.actforamerica.org/index.php/learn/email-archives/1069-fethulla-gulen-infiltrating-us-through-our-charter-schools/ (accessed August 23, 2012); Rachel Sharon-Krespin, "Fethullah Gulen's Grand Ambition," *Middle East Quarterly* 16, no. 1 (Winter 2009), http://www.meforum.org/2045/fethullah-gulens-grand-ambition (accessed August 23, 2012).

19. "Global Muslim Networks: How Far They Have Traveled," *Economist*, May 6, 2008, http://www.economist.com/node/10808408 (accessed August 23, 2012).

20. Chris Morris, "Turkey Accuses Popular Islamist of Plot against State," *Guardian* (UK), August 31, 2000, http://www.guardian.co.uk/world/2000/sep/01/1 (accessed August 23, 2012).

21. Edward Stourton, "What Is Islam's Gulen Movement?" BBC Newsworld, http://www.bbc.co.uk/news/world-13503361 (accessed August 23, 2012).

22. *Fethullah Gulen v. Michael Chertoff, Secretary, U.S. Department of Homeland Security, et al.*, Case 207-cv-02148-SD, US District Court for the Eastern District of Pennsylvania, http://www.novatv.nl/uploaded/ FILES/ Karin/IN%20THE%20UNITED%20STATES%20DISTRICT%20COURT.doc (accessed August 23, 2012).

23. Ibid. See also Suzy Hensen, "The Global Imam," *New Republic*, November 10, 2010, http://www.tnr.com/article/world/magazine/79062/global-turkey-imam-fethullah-gulen?page=0,2 (accessed August 23, 2012).

24. Morris, "Turkey Accuses Popular Islamist."

25. Ibid.

26. *Fethullah Gulen v. Michael Chertoff, Secretary, U.S. Department of Homeland Security, et al.*

27. Sharon-Krespin, "Fethullah Gulen's Grand Ambition."

28. Ibid.

29. Hensen, "Global Imam."

30. The author of this book has paid several visits to the Gulen compound on Mt. Eaton Road in Saylorsburg, PA, but was denied entrance into the compound by

Turkish sentries. He has conducted interviews with nearby residents who have complained of the gunfire and the surveillance helicopter.

31. "Bill Clinton on Fethullah Gulen's Contribution to the World," Hizmet Movement (the official website of the Gulen Movement), January 1, 2011, http://hizmetmovement.blogspot.com/2011/01/bill-clinton-on-fethullah-gulens.html (accessed August 23, 2012).

32. Arnold Ahlert, "Stealth Islamist Charter Schools under Investigation," Front Page Magazine, November 1, 2012, http://frontpagemag.com/2012/arnold-ahlert/stealth-islamist-charter-schools-under-investigation/ (accessed November 8, 2012).

33. Sermon aired on Turkish channel ATV (General Television Station), June 18, 1999. See also Sharon-Krespin, "Fethullah Gulen's Grand Ambition."

34. Ibid.

35. Second sermon aired on Turkish channel ATV, June 18, 1999. See also Sharon-Krespin, "Fethullah Gulen's Grand Ambition."

36. Ibid.

37. Ariel Cohen, quoted in Erick Stakelbeck, "The Gulen Movement: A New Islamic World Order," CBN, June 4, 2011, http://www.cbn.com/cbnnews/world/2011/May/The-Gulen-Movement-The-New-Islamic-World-Order/ (accessed August 23, 2012).

38. Sharon-Krespin, "Fethullah Gulen's Grand Ambition."

39. Ibid.

40. Ibid.

41. "Behind Turkey's Witch Hunt," *Newsweek*, May 15, 2009, http://www.thedailybeast.com/newsweek/2009/05/15/behind-turkey-s-witch-hunt.html (accessed August 23, 2012).

42. Bayram Balci, "Fethullah Gulen's Missionary Schools in Central Asia and Their Role in the Spreading of Turkism and Islam," *Religion, State, and Society* 31, no. 2 (2003), http://bloximages.chicago2.vip.townnews.com/azstarnet.com/content/tncms/assets/v3/editorial/6/13/613faab0-5159-11df-84f8-001cc4c03286/613faab0-5159-11df-84f8-001cc4c03286.pdf.pdf (accessed August 23, 2012).

43. Ibid.

44. Sharon-Krespin, "Fethullah Gulen's Grand Ambition."

45. "Gulen Movement an Inspiration for All, Says Obama's Muslim Advisor Mogahed," *Today's Zaman*, June 14, 2009, http://www.todayszaman.com/newsDetail_getNewsById.action?load=detay&link=177999 (accessed August 23, 2012).

46. Stephanie Saul, "Charter Schools Tied to Turkey Grow in Texas," *New York Times*, June 6, 2011.

47. "Turkish Olympiad Kicks Off with Glorious Opening at Dolmabahce

Palace," Fethullah Gulen: A Life Dedicated to Service (a Gulen website), June 17, 2011, http://www.fethullah-gulen.net/news/turkish-olympiad-dolmabahce/ (accessed August 23, 2012).

48. Paul L. Williams, "Gulen Movement Engulfs Lone Star State," *Family Security Matters*, June 22, 2010, http://www.familysecuritymatters.org/publications/detail/exclusive-gulen-movement-engulfs-lone-star-state (accessed November 8, 2012). Figures in the text have been adjusted to reflect more recent developments and taxpayer expenses as of 2011.

49. "Gulen Schools and Their Booming H-1B Visa Applications," *Charter School Sandals*, July 23, 2010, http://charterschoolscandals.blogspot.com/2010/07/gulen-schools-and-their-booming-h1b.html (accessed November 11, 2012). See also Ibrahim Sel, "Cosmos Foundation d.b.a. Harmony Science Academy," *MyVisaJobs.com*, 2012, http://www.myvisajobs.com/Visa-Sponsor/Cosmos-Foundation-dba/131451.htm (accessed November 11, 2012); Stephanie Saul, "Charter Schools Tied to Turkey Grow in Texas," *New York Times*, June 2, 2011.

50. Texas State Board for Educator Certification, Official Record of Educator Certificates, Educator Search Criteria, Houston, Texas, http://secure.sbec.state.tx.us/SBECONLINE/virtcert.asp (accessed November 11, 2012); Peyton Wolcott, "Cosmos Foundation—Questions Asked 2010–2011," *Peyton Wolcott* (blog), March 27, 2011, http://peytonwolcott.com/TX_CosmosFoundation_QueriesToCosmosSupeSonerTarim.html (accessed November 11, 2012). See also Donna Garner, "Thirteenth Harmony School in Houston Area Now Complete," ACT for America, September 24, 2011, http://actforamericahouston.wordpress.com/2011/09/24/thirteenth-harmony-school-in-houston-area-now-complete/ (accessed November 11, 2012).

51. "About Us—Board of Directors," Cosmos Foundation/Harmony Schools website, 2012, http://www.harmonytx.org/about/board-members/ (accessed November 11, 2012). See also Peyton Wolcott, "Cosmos Foundation—Turkish Education and Employment for Charter School Operator Applicants," http://peytonwolcott.com/TX_CosmosFoundation_BoardMembers_TurkishEducationEmploymt.html (accessed November 11, 2012).

52. Jeff Stein, "Islamic Group Is CIA Front, Ex-Turkish Intel Chief Says," *Washington Post*, May 7, 2011.

53. Sibel Edmonds, "Let Sibel Edmonds Speak: Court Documents Shed Light on CIA Illegal Operations in Central Asia Using Islam and Madrassas," July 11, 2008, http://letsibeledmondsspeak.blogspot.com/2008/07/court-documents-shed-light-on-cia.html (accessed August 23, 2012).

54. Ibid.

55. Ibid.

CHAPTER 17. THE FLAWED FINDINGS

1. Khaled A. Beydoun and Abed Ayoub, "Building African-Arab Connections during Black History Month," *Al Jazeera*, February 8, 2012, http://www.aljazeera.com/indepth/opinion/2012/02/201221103654119631.html (accessed October 22, 2012).

2. Pew Rearch Group, "Muslim Americans: No Sign of Growth in Alienation or Support of Extremism," Pew Research Center, August 30, 2011, http://www.people-press.org/2011/08/30/muslim-americans-no-signs-of-growth-in-alienation-or-support-for-extremism/?src=prc-headline (accessed August 23, 2012).

3. "American Muslim Voters: A Demographic Profile and Survey of Attitudes," Council on American-Islamic Relations, Research Center, October 24, 2006, http://www.cair.com/Portals/0/pdf/American_Muslim_Voter_Survey_2006.pdf (accessed August 23, 2012).

4. Gallup Research Group, "Muslim Americans: A National Portrait," Muslim West Facts Project, Gallup Research Center, December 31, 2009, http://www.slideshare.net/AlHaqqNetwork/american-muslim-report (accessed August 23, 2012).

5. Stephen J. Blumberg and Julian V. Luke, "Wireless Substitution: Early Release of Estimates from the National Health Interview Survey," Division of Health Interview Statistics, National Center for Health Statistics, July–December 2009, http://www.cdc.gov/nchs/data/nhis/earlyrelease/wireless201005.htm#wireless (accessed August 23, 2012).

6. This last finding is most clearly revealed by the Pew Research Group. See "Muslim Americans: No Sign of Growth in Alienation or Support of Extremism."

CHAPTER 18. THE FLAWED SPOKESMEN

1. Paul M. Barrett, "One Imam Traces the Path of Islam in Black America," *Wall Street Journal*, October 24, 2003.

2. Ibid.

3. Jessica DuLong, "The Imam of Bedford Stuyvesant," *Saudi Aramco World*, May/June 2005.

4. Herbert Daughtry, quoted in ibid.

5. DuLong, "Imam of Bedford Stuyvesant."

6. Paul Sperry, *Infiltration: How Muslim Spies and Subversives Have Penetrated Washington* (New York: Nelson Current, 2005), p. 20.

7. Steven Emerson, *Jihad Incorporated: A Guide to Militant Islam in the US* (Amherst, NY: Prometheus Books, 2006), pp. 432–33.

8. Robert Spencer, "A Good Moderate Muslim Is Hard to Find," Front Page

Magazine, November 29, 2004, http://www.frontpagemagazine.com/Articles/Read.aspx?GUID=C469EFD9-3253-4737-992A-C5F824DBA2E5 (accessed August 23, 2012).

9. Siraj Wahhaj, quoted in Barrett, "One Imam Traces the Path of Islam."

10. Transcript of videotaped speech by Siraj Wahhaj, "Muslim Community Building in America," International Institute of Islamic Research, Burlington, New Jersey.

11. Siraj Wahhaj, quoted in Daniel Pipes, *Militant Islam Reaches America* (New York: W. W. Norton, 2003), p. 122.

12. Wahhaj, quoted in Barrett, "One Imam Traces Path of Islam."

13. Ibid.

14. Paul M. Barrett, *American Islam: The Struggle for the Soul of a Religion* (New York: Farrar, Straus and Giroux, 2006), p. 116.

15. Ibid., p. 125.

16. Ibid.

17. Peter L. Bergen, *Holy War, Inc.: Inside the Secret World of Osama Bin Laden* (New York: Simon and Schuster, 2002), pp. 69–70.

18. Joe Kaufman, "Hosting Un-Indicted Co-Conspirators," Front Page Magazine, February 15, 2008, http://frontpagemag.com/articles/Read.aspx?GUID=6ACBCC4B-FAAE-41AB-8867-7AD089094A3F (accessed August 23, 2012).

19. Debka Intelligence, "One-Man 'Dirty Bomb Cell' Sought in US and Canada," *Debka*, no. 132, November 7, 2003, http://www.debka-net-weekly.com/issue.pl?username=iunumber-132 (accessed August 23, 2012).

20. Bos Smith, "Nabbed and Held Captive by Brooklyn Jihadis," *Canada Free Press*, April 28, 2008, http://www.canadafreepress.com/index.php/article/2795 (accessed August 23, 2012). The author of this book was escorted to the basement of Masjid al-Taqwa to snap photos of the mosque with private security investigator Patrick Walsh.

21. Marilyn Mellowes, "God in America Interviews: Muzammil Siddiqi," *Frontline*, PBS, October 11, 2010, http://www.pbs.org/godinamerica/interviews/muzammil-saddiqi.html (accessed November 8, 2012).

22. Hanna Rosin and John Mintz, "Muslim Leaders Struggle with Mixed Messages," *Washington Post*, October 2, 2001.

23. Michael Anastasio, "A Need to Distinguish Radical from Moderate Islam," *Yale Herald*, September 26, 2003.

24. Steven Emerson, "Muzammil the Moderate," *Counter-terrorism* (blog), July 30, 2007, http://counterterrorism.org/2007/07/muzammil_the_moderate.php (accessed August 23, 2012).

25. Ibid.

26. Erick Stakelbeck, "Islamic Radicals on Campus," Front Page Magazine,

April 23, 2003, http://archive.frontpagemag.com/readArticle.aspx?ARTID=18601 (accessed August 23, 2012).

27. Sperry, *Infiltration*, p. 106.

28. Ibid., pp. 105–106.

29. Ibid.

30. Ibid., p. 22.

31. Hamza Yusuf, quoted in Rosin and Mintz, "Muslim Leaders Struggle."

32. Stephen Schwartz, "Is Cat Stevens a Terrorist?" *Weekly Standard*, September 22, 2004.

33. Ibid.

34. "Infinite Justice Out—Enduring Freedom In," BBC, September 25, 2001.

35. Kate O'Beirne, "The Chaplain Problem: What Gives with Imams in the Military?" *National Review*, October 27, 2002.

36. Ibid.

37. Ibid.

38. "US-Terror Links Kept in the Dark as Former Bush Associate Refuses to Testify," *American Monitor*, November 24, 2006, http://americanmonitor06.blogspot.com/ (accessed August 23, 2012).

39. "American Muslim Council (AMC)," DiscoverTheNetworks.org, http://www.discoverthenetworks.org/groupProfile.asp?grpid-6146 (accessed November 8, 2012).

40. Frank Gaffney, "The Truth about the AMC," Fox News, June 28, 2002.

41. Sperry, *Infiltration*, pp. 3–4.

42. Ibid., p. 27.

43. Daniel Pipes, "United States of America vs. Abdurahman Muhammad Alamoudi," *Daniel Pipes Blog*, June 27, 2007, http://www.danielpipes.org/blog/2003/09/united-states-of-america-vs-abdurahman.html (accessed August 23, 2012).

44. "Abdurahman Alamoudi Sentenced to Jail," press release, Department of Justice, October 15, 2004.

45. Elaine Silvestrini, "Al Arian Gets Federal Subpoena," *Tampa Tribune*, March 4, 2008, http://www2.tbo.com/news/news/2008/mar/04/me-al-arian-gets-federal-subpoena-ar-145787/ (accessed August 23, 2012).

46. "Intern Removal Prompts Bush Apology," United Press International, June 29, 2001.

47. Michael Isikoff, "Hiding in Plain Sight: Did a Muslim Professor Use Activism as a Cloak for Terror?" *Newsweek*, March 3, 2003.

48. Ibid.

49. Transcript of *Today Show*, NBC, August 23, 2002.

50. Sami al-Arian, quoted in Sperry, *Infiltration*, p. 25.

51. Ibid.

52. "FBI Charges Florida Professor with Terrorist Activities," CNN, February 20, 2003.

53. Marlena Telvick, "Fixing the FBI: A Portrait of Gamal Abdul Hafiz," *Frontline*, PBS, October 16, 2003, http://www.pbs.org/wgbh/pages/frontline/shows/sleeper/fbi/gamal.html (accessed August 23, 2012).

54. Daniel Pipes, "The FBI Fumbles," *New York Post*, March 14, 2003.

55. Michael Fechter, "FBI Agent Who Refused to Tape al-Arian Is Suspended," *Tampa Tribune*, March 3, 2003.

56. Special Agent John B. Vincent, quoted in ibid.

57. Harvey Kushner and Bart Davis, *Holy War on the Homefront* (New York: Sentinel, 2004), p. 17.

58. Ibid.

59. "Judge Moody: 'You Are a Master Manipulator,'" *St. Petersburg Times*, May 1, 2006, http://www.sptimes.com/2006/05/01/State/Judge_Moody__You_are_.shtml (accessed August 23, 2012).

60. Amy Goodman and Juan Gonzalez, "Al-Arian Enters 19th Day of Hunger Strike in Protest of 'Government Harassment,'" *Democracy Now*, March 21, 2008, http://www.democracynow.org/appearances/laila_al_arian (accessed August 25, 2012).

61. Michael Isikoff and Mark Hosenball, "Reinstated," *Newsweek*, February 25, 2004.

62. Marlena Telvick, "The Story of Gamal Abdel-Hafiz: Former Agent in the FBI's International Terror Squad," *Frontline*, PBS, September 11, 2002.

63. Isikoff and Hosenball, "Reinstated."

64. Muqtedar Khan, "Who Are Moderate Muslims?" *Ijtihad*, http://www.ijtihad.org/moderatemuslims.htm (accessed August 25, 2012).

CHAPTER 19. MOSQUES MACABRE

1. Paul Sperry, *Infiltration: How Muslim Spies and Subversives Have Penetrated Washington* (New York: Nelson Current, 2005), p. 100.

2. Paul Sperry, "U.S.-Saudi Oil Imports Fund American Mosques," *World Net Daily*, April 22, 2002, http://www.worldnetdaily.com/news/article.asp?ARTICLE_ID=27327 (accessed August 25, 2012).

3. "Muslim American Politics after September 11," transcript of the Ethnic and Public Center's conversation with Ahmed H. al-Rahim, December 29, 2003.

4. Cathy Lynn Grossman, "Number of U.S. Mosques Up 74% since 2000," *USA Today*, February 29, 2012, http://www.usatoday.com/news/religion/story/2012-02-29/islamic-worship-growth-us/53298792/1 (accessed August 25, 2012).

5. Ihsan Bagby, "The American Mosque 2011: Basic Characteristics of the American Mosque, Attitudes of Mosque Leaders," Report Number 1 from the US Mosque Study 2011, http://faithcommunitiestoday.org/sites/faithcommunities today.org/files/The%20American%20Mosque%202011%20web.pdf (accessed August 25, 2012).

6. Ibid.

7. Ibid.

8. Ibid.

9. Sheikh Hisham Kabbani, "Islamic Extremism: A Viable Threat to U.S. National Security," report prepared by the US Department of State, January 7, 1999.

10. Richard H. Curtiss, "Dispute between U.S. Muslim Groups Goes Public," *Washington Report on Middle East Affairs*, April/May 1999, http://www.wrmea.com/backissues/0499/9904071.html (accessed August 25, 2012).

11. Laurie Goodstein, "A Nation Challenged: The Cleric, Muslim Leader Who Was Once Labeled an Alarmist Is Suddenly a Sage," *New York Times*, October 28, 2001.

12. The author of this book and photographer Patrick Walsh have been dragged into the Masjid for questioning after snapping photos from the sidewalk. Detective Casey also has made statements about the dangerousness of this mosque to Jonathan Wachtel, a producer for Fox News.

13. Douglas J. Hagmann, "Islamic Jihad Training in America," *Canada Free Press*, May 27, 2005, http://www.canadafreepress.com/2006/hagmann052206.htm (accessed August 25, 2012).

14. Sperry, *Infiltration*, p. 105

15. Caryle Murphy, "Facing New Realities as Islamic Americans," *Washington Post*, September 12, 2004.

16. Sperry, *Infiltration*, pp. 112–13.

17. Ibid., p. 114.

18. Pamela Constable and Karin Brulliard, "Iraq Strife Cuts Close for Va. Cleric," *Washington Post*, March 16, 2007, http://www.washingtonpost.com/wp-dyn/content/article/2007/03/15/AR2007031501768.htm (accessed August 25, 2012).

19. Peter Pae, "Muslim Residents Doubt, Decry American Action, U.S. Lacked Evidence to Support Retaliation, Many Say," *Washington Post*, August 22, 1998, http://pqasb.pqarchiver.com/washingtonpost/access/33295801.html?dids=33295801:33295801&FMT=ABS&FMTS=ABS:FT&type=current&date=Aug+22%2C+1998&author=Peter+Pae%3B+Bill+Broadway&pub=The+Washington+Post&desc=Muslim+Residents+Doubt%2C+Decry+American+Action%3B+U.S.+Lacked+Evidence+to+Support+Retaliation%2C+Many+Say&pqatl=google (accessed August 25, 2012).

20. Benjamin Weiser, "Theological Discussion on Testifying Emerges in Terrorism Case," *New York Times*, August 8, 1999.

21. Mary Jo White, "List of Unindicted Co-Conspirators in the 1993 World Trade Center Bombing," *Militant Muslim Monitor*, December 6, 2005, http://www.militantislammonitor.org/article/id/1369 (accessed August 25, 2012).

22. Sperry, *Infiltration*, p. 113.

23. Constable and Brulliard, "Iraq Strife Cuts Close for Va. Cleric."

24. Scott Shane, Squad Mekhennet, and Robert F. Worth, "Imam's Path from Condemning Terror to Preaching Jihad," *New York Times*, May 8, 2010; Sperry, *Infiltration*, pp. 117–18.

25. Ibid.

26. Spencer S. Hsu and Carrie Johnson, "Fort Hood Suspect's Links to Imam under Scrutiny," *Washington Post*, November 9, 2009.

27. Ahmed al-Haj and Donna Abu-Nasr, "U.S. Imam Wanted in Yemen over Al-Qaeda Suspicions," Associated Press, November 10, 2009.

28. Shane, Mekhennet, and Worth, "Imam's Path."

29. Sean Alfano, "Anwar Al-Awlaki, Radical Islamic Cleric Wanted by the CIA, Ate Lunch at Pentagon after 9/11: Report," *New York Daily News*, October 21, 2010, http://www.nydailynews.com/news/national/anwar-al-awlaki-radical-islamic-cleric-wanted-cia-ate-lunch-pentagon-9-11-report-article-1.190917 (accessed August 25, 2012).

30. Murphy, "Facing New Realities."

31. Susan Schmidt, "Imam from Va. Mosque Now Thought to Have Aided Al-Qaeda," *Washington Post*, February 26, 2008.

32. Scott Shane, "Born in U.S., a Radical Cleric Inspires Terror," *New York Times*, November 18, 2009.

33. Greg Miller, "Muslim Cleric Aulaqi Is First U.S. Citizen on List of Those CIA Is Allowed to Kill," *Washington Post*, April 7, 2010.

34. "Cleric Says American 'Devils' Must Die," United Press International, November 8, 2010, http://www.upi.com/Top_News/World-News/2010/11/08/Cleric-says-American-devils-must-die/UPI-61991289245343/#ixzz1smteo6Wu (accessed August 25, 2012).

35. "Islamic Cleric Anwar Al-Awlaki Killed in Yemen," BBC, September 30, 2011, http://www.bbc.co.uk/news/world-middle-east-15121879 (accessed August 25, 2012).

36. "Ex Black Militant Awaits Trial," *Black News*, http://www.blacknewsweekly.com/bin56.html (accessed August 25, 2012).

37. Mary Jacoby, "Muslims Renounce Raids Linked to Al Arian," *St. Petersburg Times*, March 22, 2002, http://www.sptimes.com/2002/03/22/Worldandnation/Muslims_denounce_raid.shtml (accessed August 25, 2012).

38. "Plea Agreement: USA v. Sami Amin Al-Arian," U.S. District Court, Middle

District of Florida, February 28, 2006, http://nefafoundation.org/miscellaneous/FeaturedDocs/U.S._v_Al-Arian_pleaagr.pdf (accessed August 25, 2012).

39. Mustafa El-Menshawy, "Fall from Grace," *al-Ahram* (Cairo), October 28–November 3, 2004, http://weekly.ahram.org.eg/2004/714/in3.htm (accessed August 25, 2012).

40. James Dao and Eric Lichtblau, "Case Adds to Outrage for Muslims in Northern Virginia," *New York Times*, February 27, 2005.

41. Terry Frieden, "Man Pleads Innocent to Al Qaeda Aid in Bush Plot," CNN, March 14, 2005, http://articles.cnn.com/2005-03-14/justice/abu.ali.plea_1_abu-ali-saudi-custody-saudi-authorities?_s=PM:LAW (accessed August 25, 2012).

42. "Jury Finds Abu Ali Guilty on Terrorism Charges," NPR, http://www.npr.org/templates/story/story.php?storyId=5024013 (accessed August 25, 2012).

43. James Dao, "Muslim Cleric Found Guilty in 'Virginia Jihad' Case," *New York Times*, April 27, 2005.

44. Sperry, *Infiltration*, p. 112.

45. *United States v. Usama Bin Laden et al.*, court transcript, Southern District of New York, February 6, 2001, http://cryptome.org/usa-v-ubl-02.htm (accessed August 25, 2012).

46. Andy Newman and Daryl Khan, "Brooklyn's Mosque Becomes Terror Icon," *New York Times*, March 9, 2003.

47. Carl Limbacher, "Mosque Linked to '93 World Trade Center Bombing Funded Bin Laden," *Newsmax Magazine*, November 26, 2003.

48. Peter Lance, *100 Years of Revenge* (New York: Regan Books, 2003), pp. 38–42.

49. Abdullah Azzam, quoted in Peter L. Bergen, *Holy War, Inc.: Inside the Secret World of Osama bin Laden* (New York: Simon and Schuster, 2002), p. 136.

50. Daniel Pipes, *Militant Islam Reaches America* (New York: Norton, 2003), p. 137.

51. John Miller, "A Decade of Warnings: Did Rabbi's 1990 Assassination Mark Birth of Islamic Terror in America?" *20/20*, ABC News, August 16, 2002.

52. Sheikh Omar Abdul Rahman, quoted in Simon Reeve, *The New Jackals: Ramzi Yousef, Osama Bin Laden, and the Future of Terrorism* (Boston: Northeastern University Press, 2002), p. 7.

53. Ibid., p. 24.

54. Ibid.

55. Daniel Benjamin and Steven Simon, *The Age of Sacred Terror* (New York: Random House, 2002), p. 7.

56. Ibid., p. 18.

57. Sperry, *Infiltration*, p. 109.

58. James Gordon Meek, "Officials Fear Al-Qaeda Nuclear Attack," *New York Daily News*, March 14, 2003.

59. Harvey Kushner and Bart Davis, *Holy War on the Home Front* (New York: Sentinel, 2004), p. 64.

60. Jason Williams and Andrew Brent, "The World Comes to Atlantic Avenue," *Street Level*, New York University School of Journalism, July 15, 2003, http://www.journalism.nyu.edu/publiczone/streetlevel/atlanticave/world/money.html (accessed August 26, 2012).

61. Miller, "A Decade of Warnings."

CHAPTER 20. ISLAMOPHOBIA

1. Elissa Massimino et al., "Violence against Muslims," 2011 Report, Human Rights First, http://www.humanrightsfirst.org/wp-content/uploads/pdf/3-2010-muslim-factsheet-update.pdf (accessed August 26, 2012).

2. Ibid.

3. *Washington Post*-ABC News Poll, September 2010, http://www.washingtonpost.com/wp-srv/politics/polls/postpoll_09072010.html (accessed August 26, 2012).

4. Alex Altman, "Time Poll: Majority Oppose Mosque, Many Distrust Muslims," *TIME*, August 19, 2010, http://www.time.com/time/nation/article/0,8599,2011799,00.html (accessed August 26, 2012).

5. "Feds Charge Three Suspected White Supremacists for Tennessee Mosque Burning," Associated Press, February 12, 2008, http://www.foxnews.com/story/0,2933,330504,00.html (accessed August 26, 2012).

6. Yonat Shimron, "Durham Mosque Vandalized," *News Observer*, November 4, 2009, http://www.newsobserver.com/2009/11/04/174919/durham-mosque-is-vandalized.html (accessed August 26, 2012).

7. "Mosque in Jacksonville, Fla., Firebombed," United Press Service, May 12, 2010 http://www.upi.com/Top_News/US/2010/05/12/Mosque-in-Jacksonville-Fla-firebombed/UPI-85931273693653/#ixzz1suTdmuVD (accessed August 26, 2012).

8. "Hate Crime Case in NYC Cabbie Slashing Upheld," CBS News, January 26, 2011, http://www.cbsnews.com/2100-201_162-7286721.html (accessed August 26, 2012).

9. Robert Mackey, "Fire and Gunshots at Tennessee Mosque Site Called Terrorism," *New York Times*, August 30, 2010.

10. Jeff Karoub, "Roger Stockham Arrested with Explosives outside Major U.S. Mosque," *Huffington Post*, January 30, 2011, http://www.huffingtonpost.com/2011/01/30/roger-stockham-arrested-explosives_n_815984.html (accessed August 26, 2012).

11. "Alleged Mosque Bomber Indicted on State, Federal Charges," *Queens Chronicle*, March 19, 2012, http://www.qchron.com/editions/eastern/eastern

-queens-alleged-mosque-bomber-indicted-on-state-federal-charges/article_1eea4350-71f0-11e1-b025-001871e3ce6c.html (accessed August 26, 2012).

12. Michael Doyle, "Hate Crimes against Muslims Rare, FBI Data Shows," *McClatchy Newspapers,* August 27, 2010, http://www.mcclatchydc.com/2010/08/27/99767/hate-crimes-against-muslims-rare.html#storylink=cpy (accessed August 26, 2012).

13. Ibid.

14. "FBI: Dramatic Spike in Hate Crimes Targeting Muslims," Southern Poverty Law Center, *Intelligence Report,* no. 145 (Spring 2012).

15. "Anti-Muslim Hate Crime up 50 Percent in US: FBI," America Free Press, November 14, 2011, http://www.google.com/hostednews/afp/article/ALeqM5jYDtVJ67MpEY_NjXVEVQw39B7QZg?docId=CNG.f8a1357252414e391fa429a67d8b9601.d41 (accessed August 26, 2012).

16. John L. Esposito and Sheila Lalwani, "The Reality of Islamophobia in America," *Los Angeles Times,* September 9, 2010.

17. Laurie Goodstein, "Across Nation, Mosque Plans Meet Opposition," *New York Times,* August 7, 2010.

18. Ibid.

19. Odette Yousef, "DuPage Denies Mosque's Request for Tall Minaret and Dome," WBEZ (Chicago), March 13, 2012, http://www.wbez.org/story/dupage-denies-mosque%E2%80%99s-request-tall-minaret-and-dome-97260 (accessed August 26, 2012).

20. Wayahat Ali, Matthew Duss, Lee Fang, Scott Keyes, and Faiz Shakir, "The Roots of the Islamophobia Network in America," Center for American Progress, August 2011, http://www.americanprogress.org/issues/2011/08/pdf/islamophobia.pdf (accessed August 26, 2012).

21. Ibid. See also Paul Martens, "The Far Right's Secret Slush Fund," *Counterpunch,* October 26, 2010, http://www.counterpunch.org/2010/10/26/the-far-right-s-secret-slush-fund-to-keep-fear-alive/ (accessed August 26, 2012).

22. Sarah Scarife Foundation 2009, Form 990, http://www.scaife.com/sarah08.pdf (accessed August 26, 2012).

23. "Bradley Foundation Grants since 2001," *Milwaukee Journal-Sentinel,* November 15, 2011, http://www.jsonline.com/watchdog/dataondemand/133910113.html (accessed August 26, 2012).

24. Newton D. and Rochelle F. Becker Foundation, 2009, Form 990, http://dynamodata.fdncenter.org/990s/990search/990.php?ein=954095134&yr=200912&rt=900&t9=A (accessed August 26, 2012).

25. Russell Berrie Foundation, 2009, Form 990, http://dynamodata.fdhcenter.org/990pf_pdf_archive_/222/222620908_20912_990PF.pdf (accessed August 26, 2012).

26. Anchorage Charitable Trust, 2008, Form 990, http://dynamodata,fdncenter

.org/990pf_pdf_archive/133/133202345/133202345_200904_990PF.pdf (accessed August 26, 2012); William Rosenwald Family Trust, 2009, Form 990, http://dynamodata.fdncenter.org/990s/990seach/990.php?ein=131635289&yr=200912&rt=990PF&t9=B (accessed August 26, 2012).

27. Fairbrook Foundation Charitable Fund, 2009, Form 990, http://dynamodata.fdncenter.org/990_pdf_archive/200/200993106/200993106_200412_990.pdf (accessed August 26, 2012).

28. Bob Smietana, "Anti-Muslim Crusaders Make Millions Spreading Fear," *Tennessean*, October 24, 2010, http://www.tennessean.com/article/20101024/NEWS01/10240374/The+price+of+fear (accessed August 26, 2012).

29. Ibid.

30. Wayahat Ali et al., "Roots of the Islamophobia Network in America."

31. Ibid.

32. Ibid.

33. Ibid.

34. David Horowitz Freedom Foundation, Form 990, 2008, http://www.tennessean.com/assets/pdf/DN1658821023.PDF (accessed August 26, 2012).

35. Ibid.

36. "Islamo-Fascism Awareness Week," Terrorism Awareness Project, 2007, http://www.terrorismawareness.org/islamo-fascism-awareness-week/ (accessed August 26, 2012).

37. Middle East Forum, http://www.meforum.org (accessed August 26, 2012).

38. "About the Middle East Forum," Middle East Forum, http://www.meforum.org/about.php (accessed November 8, 2012).

39. "Middle East Forum Launches 'Islamist Watch' Website," Middle East Forum, March 5, 2008, http://www.meforum.org/1869/middle-east-forum-launches-islamist-watch-website (accessed August 26, 2012).

40. Ibid.

41. Ron Brown, "John Hagee Warns against Radical Islam," *Religion News*, September 3, 2008, http://www.religionnewsblog.com/15816/john-hagee-warns-against-radical-islam (accessed August 26, 2012).

42. Ibid.

43. Ibid.

44. Kyle Mantyla, "Robertson: Muslims Should Be Treated Like 'Some Fascist Group,'" Right Wing Watch, November 10, 2009, http://www.rightwingwatch.org/category/organizations/anti-defamation-league (accessed August 26, 2012).

45. Brian Tashman, "Robertson: Fighting Muslims Is Just Like Fighting Nazis," Right Wing Watch, May 31, 2011, http://www.rightwingwatch.org/content/robertson-fighting-muslims-just-fighting-nazis (accessed August 26, 2012).

46. Sarah Posner, "Showdown over Shariah at Faith and Freedom Conference,"

Religion Dispatches, June 3, 2011, http://www.religiondispatches.org/dispatches/sarahposner/4707/showdown_over_shari (accessed August 26, 2012).

47. Carol Lee, "Rev. Franklin Graham: Islam 'Evil,'" *Politico*, October 3, 2010.

48. David Weigel, "Franklin Graham, Conservative Cause Celebre (Thanks to Sarah Palin)," *Washington Post*, April 23, 2010.

49. "Islamophobia: Thought Crime of the Totalitarian Future," Front Page Magazine, September 7, 2011, http://frontpagemag.com/2011/09/07/islamophobia-thought-crime-of-the-totalitarian-future/ (accessed August 26, 2012).

50. Ibid.

51. William Moyer, "Man Charged with Killing Binghamton University Professor Threatened Apartment-Mate," Press Connects, December 5, 2009, http://www.pressconnects.com/article/20091205/NEWS01/912050390/Man-charged-killing-Binghamton-University-professor-threatened-apartment-mate (accessed August 26, 2012).

52. David Johnson and Scott Shane, "U.S. Knew of Suspect's Tie to Radical Cleric," *New York Times*, November 9, 2009.

53. Dustin Gardiner, "Woman in Suspected 'Honor Killing' Dies," *Arizona Republic*, November 2, 2009, http://www.azcentral.com/12news/news/articles/2009/11/02/20091102noor1102-CR-CP.htm (accessed August 26, 2012).

54. John M. Annesse, "New Brighton Wife Tried to Kill Husband over Muslim Principles, Police Allege," *Staten Island Live*, October 29, 2009, http://www.silive.com/northshore/index.ssf/2009/10/new_brighton_wife_tried_to_kil.html (accessed August 26, 2012).

55. Steve Barnes and James Dao, "Gunman Kills Soldier outside Recruiting Station," *New York Times*, June 1, 2009; "The Little Rock, Arkansas Recruiting Station Shooting," NEFA Foundation, Report 18, June 2009, http://www.nefafoundation.org/miscellaneous/FeaturedDocs/NEFA_littlerockrecruitingshooting.pdf (accessed August 26, 2012).

56. Doug Hagmann, "Beheading in Buffalo—at Muslim TV Station," *Canada Free Press*, February 14, 2009, http://www.canadafreepress.com/index.php/article/8463 (accessed August 26, 2012).

57. Phyllis Chesler, "Are Honor Killings Simply Domestic Violence?" *Middle East Quarterly*, Spring 2009, http://www.meforum.org/2067/are-honor-killings-simply-domestic-violence (accessed August 26, 2012).

58. "Father Charged with Murder after Daughter Was Unhappy with an Arranged Marriage," CNN, July 9, 2008, http://www.wluml.org/node/4720 (accessed August 26, 2012).

59. "Muslim Teen Goes on Shooting Spree at the Mall," *Big Story*, Fox News, February 9, 2008, http://www.youtube.com/watch?v=IyFyM25-tm0 (accessed August 26, 2012).

60. Jason Riley, "Judge Rules Biyad Guilty of Killing His Four Children," *Daily News Journal* (Murfreesboro, TN), April 22, 2011, http://www.limitstogrowth.org/articles/2011/04/23/somali-found-guilty-of-murdering-his-four-children-in-louisville/ (accessed August 26, 2012).

61. Michelle Malkin, "San Fran Car Rampage Ends at Jewish Community Center," michellemalkin.com, August 29, 2006, http://michellemalkin.com/2006/08/29/san-fran-car-rampage-ends-at-jewish-community-center/ (accessed August 27, 2012).

62. "Hatred Hits Home: 6 Shot at Jewish Office," *Seattle Times*, July 29, 2006, http://seattletimes.nwsource.com/html/localnews/2003160605_shooting29m1.html (accessed August 27, 2012).

63. "Suspect, Victims Identified in Safeway Shooting Rampage," Denver News 7 (ABC), June 26, 2006.

64. Daniel Pipes, "More on the North Carolina Jihadi," *Daniel Pipes Blog*, March 14, 2006, http://www.danielpipes.org/blog/2006/03/more-on-the-north-carolina-jihadi-mohammed (accessed August 27, 2012).

65. Andrew Tilghman, "Muslim Pleads Guilty to Killing Jewish Man," *Houston Chronicle*, January 13, 2004, http://www.chron.com/news/houston-texas/article/Muslim-pleads-guilty-to-killing-Jewish-man-1603906.php (accessed August 27, 2012).

66. Daniel Pipes, "The Beltway Snipers' Motives," *Daniel Pipes Blog*, August 19, 2003, http://www.danielpipes.org/blog/2003/08/the-beltway-snipers-motives (accessed August 27, 2012).

67. Michelle Malkin, "Lee Malvo, Muslim Hatemonger," Townhall, December 10, 2003, http://townhall.com/columnists/michellemalkin/page/2003 (accessed August 27, 2012).

68. Charles Feldman, "Federal Investigators: L.A. Airport Shooting a Terrorist Act," CNN, September 4, 2002, http://articles.cnn.com/2002-09-04/us/lax.shooting_1_federal-investigators-terrorist-group-lone-gunman?_s=PM:US (accessed August 27, 2012).

69. Liz Glazier, "Lost Lives Remembered during 9/11 Ceremony," *Rocket*, September 11, 2008, http://www.theonlinerocket.com/news/lost-lives-remembered-during-9-11-ceremony-1.2333384 (accessed August 27, 2012).

CHAPTER 21. CHRISLAM

1. George W. Bush, "President Bush Addresses the Nation," *Washington Post*, September 20, 2001, http://www.washingtonpost.com/wp-srv/nation/specials/attacked/transcripts/bushaddress_092001.html (accessed August 27, 2012).

2. Michael Foust, "Christians, Muslims Worship Same God, Bush Tells

Reporters," *Baptist Press,* November 20, 2003, http://www.sbcbaptistpress.org/bpnews.asp?id=17133 (accessed August 27, 2012).

3. William J. Federer, *What Every American Needs to Know about the Quran: A History of Islam and the United States* (St. Louis: Amerisearch, 2008), p. 205.

4. Agha Saeed, quoted in Paul Sperry, *Infiltration: How Muslim Spies and Subversives Have Penetrated Washington* (New York: Nelson Current, 2005), p. 12.

5. Mohammed al-Hanooti, quoted in Sperry, *Infiltration,* p. 12.

6. Transcript of remarks by Secretary of State Colin Powell, *Charlie Rose Show,* PBS, September 22, 2003.

7. Janet Levy, "State House Proselytism," Front Page Magazine, February 1, 2008, http://frontpagemag.com/Articles/Printable.aspx?GUID=D96619B1-E105-43F2-9505-AE84B9213187 (accessed August 27, 2012).

8. Robert Spencer, quoted in Levy, "State House Proselytism."

9. Ibid.

10. Robert Spencer, "Islamic Supremacy at the DNC," Front Page Magazine, February 6, 2007, http://archive.frontpagemag.com/readArticle.aspx?ARTID=278 (accessed August 27, 2012).

11. Ibid.

12. Federer, *What Every American Needs to Know,* p. 205.

13. Jeff Zeliny, "Obama Says U.S. Could Be Seen as a Muslim Country, Too," *New York Times,* June 2, 2009.

14. Katelyn Sabochik, "President Obama Celebrates Ramadan at White House Iftar Dinner," *White House Blog,* http://www.whitehouse.gov/blog/2010/08/14/president-obama-celebrates-ramadan-white-house-iftar-dinner (accessed August 27, 2012).

15. Jim Hinch, "Rick Warren Builds Bridge to Muslims," *Orange County Register,* February 23, 2012, http://www.ocregister.com/articles/muslims-341669-warren-saddleback.html?utm_source=feedburner&utm_medium=feed&utm_campaign=Feed%3A+delicious%2Fgqlf+%28Christian+Headlines+Top+Headlines%2 (accessed August 27, 2012).

16. Faith Shared, http://www.faithshared.org/index.html (accessed August 27, 2012).

17. Interfaith Alliance, "Participating Congregations," Faith Shared, http://www.faithshared.org/participating.html (accessed August 27, 2012).

18. Stefanie Schartel, "Chrislam Rising," *Charisma Magazine,* November 22, 2011, http://www.charismanews.com/world/32349-chrislam-rising (accessed August 27, 2012).

19. Ibid.

EPILOGUE

1. Rob Stein, "U.S. Birth Rate Falls Again: A Possible Effect of Economic Downturn," *Washington Post,* August 27, 2010.

2. Pew Research Group, "A Demographic Portrait of American Muslims," Pew Research Center, August 30, 2011, http://www.people-press.org/2011/08/30/section-1-a-demographic-portrait-of-muslim-americans/ (accessed August 27, 2012).

3. Ibid.

4. Jim Kouri, "Almost Half of Illegal Aliens Entered U.S. Legally, but Overstayed Visas, Senators Say," *Family Security Matters,* May 20, 2011, http://www.familysecuritymatters.org/publications/id.9562/pub_detail.asp (accessed August 27, 2012).

5. Ibid.

6. "Presidential Memorandum—Refugee Admissions," White House, press release, October 8, 2010, http://www.whitehouse.gov/the-press-office/2010/10/08/presidential-memorandum-refugee-admissions (accessed August 27, 2012).

7. "The Fastest Growing Religion in America Is Islam," Pew Forum on Religion and Public Life, May 6, 2012, http://www.pewforum.org/Press-Room/Pew-Forum-in-the-News/The-fastest-growing-religion-in-America-is-Islam.aspx (accessed October 24, 2012).

8. Bernard Lewis, *The Political Language of Islam* (Chicago: University of Chicago Press, 1988), p. 73.

9. Daniel Pipes, *Militant Islam Reaches America* (New York: W. W. Norton, 2003), p. 113.

10. Ibid.

INDEX